WORKBOOK

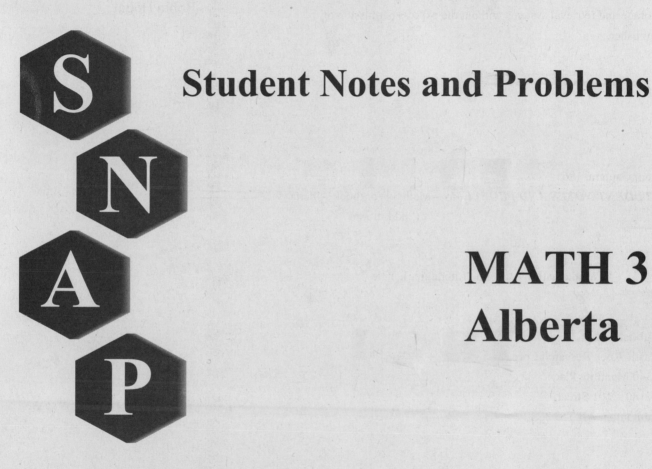

S
N
A
P

Student Notes and Problems

MATH 3
Alberta

CASTLE ROCK
RESEARCH CORP

Rao, Gautam, 1961 –
STUDENT NOTES AND PROBLEMS – Math 3 Workbook Alberta
(2nd Edition)

1. Mathematics – Juvenile Literature. I. Title

Published by
Castle Rock Research Corp.
2340 Manulife Place
10180 – 101 Street
Edmonton, AB T5J 3S4

2 3 4 FP 13 12 11

Publisher
Gautam Rao

Contributors
Robin Hobal

Dedicated to the memory of Dr. V. S. Rao

STUDENT NOTES AND PROBLEMS WORKBOOKS

Student Notes and Problems (SNAP) workbooks are a series of support resources in mathematics for students in grades 3 to 12 and in science for students in grades 9 to 12. SNAP workbooks are 100% aligned with curriculum. The resources are designed to support classroom instructions and provide students with additional examples, practice exercises, and tests. SNAP workbooks are ideal for use all year long at school and at home.

The following is a summary of the key features of all SNAP workbooks.

UNIT OPENER PAGE

- summarizes the curriculum outcomes addressed in the unit in age-appropriate language
- identifies the lessons by title
- lists the prerequisite knowledge and skills the student should know prior to beginning the unit

LESSONS

- provide essential teaching pieces and explanations of the concepts
- include example problems and questions with complete, detailed solutions that demonstrate the problem-solving process

NOTES BARS

- contain key definitions, formulas, reminders, and important steps or procedures
- provide space for students to add their own notes and helpful reminders

PRACTICE EXERCISES

- include questions that relate to each of the curriculum outcomes for the unit
- provide practice in applying the lesson concepts

REVIEW SUMMARY

- provides a succinct review of the key concepts in the unit

PRACTICE TEST

- assesses student learning of the unit concepts

ANSWERS AND SOLUTIONS

- demonstrate the step-by-step process or problem-solving method used to arrive at the correct answer

Answers and solutions for the odd-numbered questions are provided in each student workbook. A *SNAP Solutions Manual* that contains answers and complete solutions for all questions is also available.

CONTENTS

Counting

Representing Numbers

Place Value

Sorting

Estimation

Addition and Subtraction

Mental Math Strategies

Fractions

Multiplication and Division

Solving Equations

Patterns

Time

Length and Perimeter

Mass

3-D Objects

Statistics and Probability

Answers and Solutions

COUNTING

When you are finished this unit, you will be able to…

- count forward and backward by 5s, 10s, and 100s to 1 000, starting at different numbers
- count forward and backward by 3s, 4s, and 25s to 1 000, starting at multiples of that number
- identify errors in a skip counting sequence
- identify a skip counting pattern for a given number sequence
- skip count using money amounts

Lesson	Page	Completed on
1 Skip Counting up to 1 000	2	
2 Skip Counting Backward	9	
3 Skip Counting with Money	16	
Review Summary	22	
Practice Test	23	
Answers and Solutions	at the back of the book	

PREREQUISITE SKILLS AND KNOWLEDGE

Prior to starting this unit, you should be able to…

- skip count
- identify coin values (penny, nickel, dime, quarter, loonie)

Lesson 1   SKIP COUNTING UP TO 1 000

Perhaps you have heard the cheer "two, four, six, eight, who do we appreciate?" This cheer is a perfect example of skip counting by twos. To skip count forward, choose a number as a starting point, choose a number to count by, and then count forward. Begin at your starting point, and add the number you are counting by. You can skip count by any number, and you can start at any number.

When you skip count by fives, add five to each step or count. If you start at 50, you get 50, 55 (50 + 5), 60 (55 + 5), 65 (60 + 5), and so on.

✳ Example

Start from 112, and skip count forward by fives.

112, _____, _____, _____, _____, _____

Solution

112, 117, 122, 127, 132, 137
The ones digits all end in a 2 or a 7.

🦋 Time to Try 1

Start from 244, and skip count forward by fives.

244, _____, _____, _____, _____, _____

When you skip count by 10s, add 10 to each step. If you start at 13, you get 13, 23 (13 + 10), 33 (23 + 10), 43 (33 + 10), and so on.

✳ Example

Start from 426, and skip count forward by 10s.

426, _____, _____, _____, _____, _____

Solution

426, 436, 446, 456, 466, 476
When you count by 10 in this number sequence, only the number in the tens position changes. It goes up by one. The numbers in the hundreds and ones position remain the same.

🦋 Time to Try 2

Start from 233, and skip count forward by 10s.

233, _____, _____, _____, _____, _____

When you skip count by 100s, add 100 to each count. You get 100, 200, 300, 400, and so on. The digits in the ones and tens places stay the same. The digit in the hundreds place goes up by 1 each count.

✳ Example

Start from 34, and skip count forward by 100s.

34, _____, _____, _____, _____, _____

Solution

34, 134, 234, 334, 434, 534

As you skip count forward by 100, you add 100 to the number that comes before. The digits in the tens and ones places stay the same. The digit in the hundreds place goes up by 1.

🦋 Time to Try 3

Start from 238, and skip count forward by 100s.

238, _____, _____, _____, _____, _____

Patterns are helpful when skip counting by 25s. Divide the starting number into equal groups of 25. Look at the following number sequence table. See if you can find the pattern.

25	50	75	100
125	150	175	200
225	250	275	300

If you said that the digits 25, 50, 75, and 00 repeat, you are correct. As long as the starting number can be divided into equal groups of 25, this pattern continues. As you skip count forward, the digits 25, 50, 75, and 00 appear again and again.

NOTES

✳✳ **Example**

Skip count forward by 25s from 100.

100, _____, _____, _____, _____, _____

Solution
100, 125, 150, 175, 200, 225
The two end numbers always follow the same order of 25, 50, 75, and 00.

🐝 **Time to Try 4**

Skip count forward by 25s from 425.

425, _____, _____, _____, _____, _____

COUNTING BY THREES

A grid may be helpful for skip counting by threes. Use a coloured pencil to shade in the squares that you land on as you skip count. The first three have been done for you.

As you skip count, you should stop on the following numbers: 3, 6, 9, 12, 15, 18, 21, 24, 27, 30, 33, 36, 39, 42, 45, 48, 51, 54, 57, 60, 63, 66, 69, 72, 75, 78, 81, 84, 87, 90, 93, 96, and 99.

1	2	3	4	5	6	7	8	9	10
11	12	13	14	15	16	17	18	19	20
21	22	23	24	25	26	27	28	29	30
31	32	33	34	35	36	37	38	39	40
41	42	43	44	45	46	47	48	49	50
51	52	53	54	55	56	57	58	59	60
61	62	63	64	65	66	67	68	69	70
71	72	73	74	75	76	77	78	79	80
81	82	83	84	85	86	87	88	89	90
91	92	93	94	95	96	97	98	99	100

When you skip count by threes, add three to each step or count. Skip counting by threes is like multiplying by three because the numbers are increasing by three each time.

✳ Example

Starting at 6, skip count forward by threes.

6, ____, ____, ____, ____, ____,

Solution

6, 9, 12, 15, 18, 21
Start counting at six, and add three for each count. Each number is a multiple of three, which means it is a number that is multiplied by three. The numbers are increasing by three each count. You get 6 + 3 = 9, 9 + 3 = 12, 12 + 3 = 15, 15 + 3 = 18, and 18 + 3 = 21.

Time to Try 5

Start at 24, and skip count forward by threes.

24, ____, ____, ____, ____, ____, ____

COUNTING BY FOURS

A grid can also help you skip count by fours. Starting from zero, add four for each step.

1	2	3	4	5	6	7	8	9	10
11	12	13	14	15	16	17	18	19	20
21	22	23	24	25	26	27	28	29	30
31	32	33	34	35	36	37	38	39	40
41	42	43	44	45	46	47	48	49	50
51	52	53	54	55	56	57	58	59	60
61	62	63	64	65	66	67	68	69	70
71	72	73	74	75	76	77	78	79	80
81	82	83	84	85	86	87	88	89	90
91	92	93	94	95	96	97	98	99	100

When you skip count by fours, you add four to each count. Skip counting by fours is like multiplying by four because four is added each time. Since four is an even number, when you start at 0, all the numbers in the skip counting sequence will end in 0, 2, 4, 6, or 8.

NOTES

 Example

The numbers 323, 328, 333, 338, and 343 form a sequence. What number is the sequence growing by?

Solution

Find the number the skip counting sequence is growing by. Count from the first number to the second number. You get 323, 324, 325, 326, 327, and 328. That is five counts. Now count from the second number to the third number. You get 328, 329, 330, 331, 332, and 333. That is also five counts. This skip counting sequence is growing by fives.

 Time to Try 6

The numbers 125, 150, 175, 200, 225 form a sequence. What number is the sequence growing by?

6

PRACTICE EXERCISES

1. Starting from 632, skip forward by fives.

    632, _____, _____, _____, _____, _____

2. Start at 167, and skip forward by 100s.

    167, _____, _____, _____, _____, _____

3. Starting at 24, skip forward by fours.

    24, _____, _____, _____, _____, _____

4. The numbers 575, 600, 625, 650, 675 form a sequence. What number is the sequence growing by?

5. From 150, skip count forward by 25s.

    150, _____, _____, _____, _____, _____

6. Starting at 27, skip count by threes.

    27, _____, _____, _____, _____, _____

7. Start from 735, and skip count by 10s.

    735, _____, _____, _____, _____, _____

8. Starting at 9, skip count by threes.

9, _____, _____, _____, _____, _____

9. Start from 44, and skip forward by 100s.

44, _____, _____, _____, _____, _____

10. Skip forward by 25s from 325.

325, _____, _____, _____, _____, _____

11. What number is the sequence of numbers 444, 449, 454, 459, 464 growing by?

12. Starting from 8, skip forward by fours.

8, _____, _____, _____, _____, _____

Lesson 2   SKIP COUNTING BACKWARD

Skip counting means you choose a number as a starting point, choose a number to count by, and then count. To skip count backward, subtract the same number over and over.

When you skip count by fives, subtract five for each step or count. If you start with 90, you get 90, 85 (90 − 5), 80 (85 − 5), 75 (70 − 5), and so on.

Example

Starting from 93, skip count backward by fives.

93, _____, _____, _____, _____, _____

Solution

93, 88, 83, 78, 73, 68
When counting backward by five, the ones digit makes a pattern that ends in a 3 or an 8.

Time to Try 1

Starting from 374, skip count backward by fives.

374, _____, _____, _____, _____, _____

When you skip count backward by 10s, subtract 10 for each step or count. If you start with 90, you get 90, 80 (90 – 10), 70 (80 – 10), 60 (70 – 10), and so on.

✳ Example

From 940, skip count backward by 10s.

940, _____, _____, _____, _____, _____

Solution
940, 930, 920, 910, 900, 890
When you subtract 10, the digit in the tens place will change and the digit in the ones place will remain the same. The ones digit will always end in 0. The tens digits go down by 1 each time.

When you subtract 10 from a number ending in 00 such as 900, the digit in the ones position remains the same, but the digits in the hundreds position and the tens position both change.
900 – 10 = 890

🐝 Time to Try 2

Skip count backward by 10s from 478.

478, _____, _____, _____, _____, _____

When you skip count backward by 100s, subtract 100 for each step or count. If you start at 400, you get 400, 300 (400 – 100), 200 (300 – 100), 100 (200 – 100), and so on.

✳ Example

Starting from 932, skip count backward by 100s.

932, _____, _____, _____, _____, _____

Solution
932, 832, 732, 632, 532, 432
The ones and tens digits both stay the same.
The hundreds digits go down by one each time.

🐝 Time to Try 3

Starting from 784, skip count backward by 100s.

784, _____, _____, _____, _____, _____

Skip counting backward is just like skip counting forward. When you skip count backward by 25, the numbers end in 25, 50, 75, or 00. The digits in the tens and ones places will always end in one of those numbers. The digit in the hundreds place will change when the hundreds place value changes.

✳ Example

From 425, skip count backward by 25s.

425, _____, _____, _____, _____, _____

Solution
425, 400, 375, 350, 325, 300
As you skip count backward, the digits 75, 50, 25 and 00 repeat as the number in the hundreds place decreases.

🐝 Time to Try 4

Skip count backward by 25s from 975.

975, _____, _____, _____, _____, _____

Skip counting backward by threes and fours is repeated subtraction or division.

To skip count backward by threes, subtract three for each step or count. If you start at 18, you get 18, 15 (18 − 3 = 15), 12 (15 − 3 = 12), 9 (12 − 3 = 9), and so on.

🐝 Time to Try 5

Starting at 42, skip count backward by threes.

42, _____, _____, _____, _____, _____

NOTES

To skip count backward by fours, subtract four for each step or count. If you start at 24, you get 24, 20 (24 – 4 = 20), 16 (20 – 4 = 16), 12 (16 – 4 = 12), and so on.

 Time to Try 6

Starting at 48, skip count backward by fours.

48, _____, _____, _____, _____, _____

When you can skip forward and backward, you are able to see patterns and find mistakes.

 Example

The numbers 886, 786, 686, 586, and 576 show an incorrect skip counting sequence of counting by 100s. Find the mistake in the sequence.

Solution

To find the mistake, start with the first number. Then, subtract 100 for each count.
886 – 100 = 786, 786 – 100 = 686, 686 – 100 = 586, 586 – 100 = 486

You can see that the last number is not 486. The last number is 576, which is 10 less than the number before it, not 100 less.

 Time to Try 7

The numbers 394, 384, 374, 364, 363 form a skip counting sequence of counting backward by 10s. What is the mistake in the sequence?

12

You can also fill in missing numbers in the middle of a skip counting sequence, not just at the end.

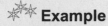 Example

In the sequence 30, 27, 24, ___, 18, 15, what is the missing number?

Solution

To determine the missing number, find the number that the sequence is counting by. Subtract the second number from the first number (30 – 27 = 3). Then subtract the third number from the second number (27 – 24 = 3). This sequence shows skip counting by threes.

Subtract 3 from the number in front of the blank.
24 – 3 = 21

The missing number is 21.

Time to Try 8

In the skip counting sequence 44, 40, 36, 32, ___, 24, what number is missing?

PRACTICE EXERCISES

1. From the number 873, skip count backward by fives.

   873, _____, _____, _____, _____, _____

2. Starting from 475, skip count backward by 25s.

   475, _____, _____, _____, _____, _____

3. Starting at 243, skip count back by 10s.

   243, _____, _____, _____, _____, _____

4. The number sequence 424, 414, 404, 394, 374 show a mistake when backward skip counting by 10s. What is the mistake in the sequence?

5. Starting at 36, skip count back by fours.

   36, _____, _____, _____, _____, _____

6. What number is missing from the skip counting sequence?

   161, 156, _____, 146, 141

7. Starting from 782, skip count backward by 100s.

   782, _____, _____, _____, _____, _____

8. Starting from 361, skip count backward by 10s.

   361, _____, _____, _____, _____, _____

9. What number is missing from the skip counting sequence?

   _____, 42, 39, 36, 33, 30

10. In the skip counting sequence 225, 200, 175, 150, 125, 110, what number is a mistake?

Lesson 3   SKIP COUNTING WITH MONEY

NOTES

Another way to skip count is to use money.

SKIP COUNT BY 5S USING NICKELS (5¢)

Counting 5¢, 10¢, 15¢, and 20¢ is an example of counting forward by nickels.

- One nickel is equal to 5¢.
- Two nickels are equal to 10¢.
- Three nickels are equal to 15¢.
- Four nickels are equal to 20¢.

Counting 20¢, 15¢, 10¢, 5¢ is an example of counting backward by nickels.

SKIP COUNT BY 10S USING DIMES (10¢)

Counting 10¢, 20¢, 30¢, and 40¢ is an example of counting forward by dimes.

- One dime is equal to 10¢.
- Two dimes are equal to 20¢.
- Three dimes are equal to 30¢.
- Four dimes are equal to 40¢.

Counting 40¢, 30¢, 20¢, 10¢ is an example of counting backward by dimes.

SKIP COUNT BY 25S USING QUARTERS (25¢)

Counting 25¢, 50¢, 75¢, and 100¢ is an example of counting forward by quarters.

• One quarter is equal to 25¢.

• Two quarters are equal to 50¢.

• Three quarters are equal to 75¢.

• Four quarters are equal to 100¢ or $1.00.

Counting 100¢, 75¢, 50¢, and 25¢ is an example of counting backward by quarters.

SKIP COUNT BY 100S USING LOONIES (100¢) AND TOONIES (200¢)

Counting $1.00, $2.00, $3.00, and $4.00 is an example of counting forward by loonies.

• One loonie is equal to 100¢ or $1.00.

• Two loonies are equal to 200¢ or $2.00.

• Three loonies are equal to 300¢ or $3.00.

• Four loonies are equal to 400¢ or $4.00, and so on.

Counting $2.00, $4.00, $6.00, and $8.00 is an example of counting forward by toonies.

• One toonie is equal to 200¢ or $2.00.

• Two toonies are equal to 400¢ or $4.00.

• Three toonies are equal to 600¢ or $6.00.

• Four toonies are equal to 800¢ or $8.00, and so on.

NOTES

 Example

Skip count by quarters to determine the total value of the coins.

Solution

A quarter is worth 25 cents. When you skip count by quarters, you will add 25 to each count.
25, 50, 75, 100, 125, 150

The value of the quarters is 150¢ or $1.50.

 Time to Try 1

Skip count by dimes to determine the total value of the coins.

✳ Example

Starting at 75, skip count backward by nickels.

75, ___, ___, ___, ___

Solution

A nickel is worth five cents. Skip count backward by nickels by subtracting 5 from each count.
75, 70 (75 − 5 = 70), 65 (70 − 5 = 65), 60 (65 − 5 = 60), 55 (60 − 5 = 55)

 Time to Try 2

Skip count forward by dimes from 10.

10, ___, ___, ___, ___

PRACTICE EXERCISES

Use the following diagram to answer the next four questions.

1. Skip count to find the total value of the dimes.

2. Skip count to find the total value of the quarters.

3. Skip count to find the total value of the nickels.

4. Skip count to find the total value of the toonies.

Answer the following questions using skip counting.

5. Start at 75¢, and skip count forward by quarters.

    75¢, _____, _____, _____, _____, _____

6. Start at 55¢, and skip count forward by nickels.

    55¢, _____, _____, _____, _____, _____

7. Start at 80¢, and skip count backward by dimes.

    80¢, _____, _____, _____, _____, _____

8. The skip counting sequence $5.50, $5.25, $5.00, _____, $4.50 is counting by quarters. What is the missing number in the sequence?

9. Start at $9.00, and skip count backward by dollars.

    $9.00, _____, _____, _____, _____, _____

REVIEW SUMMARY

- To count forward, choose a number as a starting point, choose a number to count by, and add the same number over and over. Look for patterns that can help you.
  - To count forward by fives, add 5 to each number.
  - To count forward by 10s, add 10 to each number.
  - To count forward by 100s, add 100 to each number.
  - To count forward by threes, add 3 to each number.
  - To count forward by fours, add 4 to each number.
  - To count forward by 25s, add 25 to each number.
- To count backward, choose a number as a starting point, choose a number to count by, and subtract (take away) the same number over and over. Look for patterns that can help you.
  - To count backward by fives, subtract 5 from each number.
  - To count backward by 10s, subtract 10 from each number.
  - To count backward by 100s, subtract 100 from each number.
  - To count backward by threes, subtract 3 from each number.
  - To count backward by fours, subtract 4 from each number.
  - To count backward by 25s, subtract 25 from each number.
- To skip count money, and the same value over and over.
  - When skip counting with nickels, add 5¢ to each number.
  - When skip counting with dimes, add 10¢ to each number.
  - When skip counting with quarters, add 25¢ to each number.
  - When skip counting with loonies, add 100¢ to each number.

PRACTICE TEST

1. Starting from 527, skip count forward by fives.

    527, _____, _____, _____, _____, _____

2. Starting from 289, skip backward by 10s.

    289, _____, _____, _____, _____, _____

3. From 822, skip count backward by fives.

    822, _____, _____, _____, _____, _____

4. From $1.25, skip count forward by quarters.

    $1.25, _____, _____, _____, _____, _____

5. Starting at 32, count backward by fours.

    32, _____, _____, _____, _____, _____

6. Starting at 36, count forward by threes.

    36, _____, _____, _____, _____, _____

7. Start at 625, and count backward by 25s.

    625, _____, _____, _____, _____, _____

8. Starting at 120¢, skip count backward by nickels.

    120¢, _____, _____, _____, _____, _____

9. From $2.75, skip count backward by quarters.

    $2.75, _____, _____, _____, _____, _____

10. Starting at $7.20, skip count backward by dimes.

    $7.20, _____, _____, _____, _____, _____

11. Starting from 504, skip count backward by threes.

    504, _____, _____, _____, _____, _____

12. Starting from 136, skip count forward by fours.

    136, _____, _____, _____, _____, _____

13. From $2.75, skip count backward by quarters.

    $2.75, _____, _____, _____, _____, _____

14. Starting at 199, skip count forward by 10s.

    199, _____, _____, _____, _____, _____

15. Start at 225, and skip count backward by 10s.

    225, _____, _____, _____, _____, _____

16. From 36, skip count forward by fours.

    36, _____, _____, _____, _____, _____

REPRESENTING NUMBERS

When you are finished this unit, you will be able to…
• read and write numbers to 1 000
• read and write number words to 1 000
• show and explain numbers up to 1 000 using base ten blocks and money
• show numbers to 1 000 as number sentences or expressions

Lesson	Page	Completed on
1 Reading and Writing Numbers to 1 000	26	
2 Representing Numbers in Other Ways	31	
Review Summary	43	
Practice Test	44	
Answers and Solutions	at the back of the book	

PREREQUISITE SKILLS AND KNOWLEDGE

Prior to starting this unit, you should be able to…
• read and write number words up to 100
• read and write numbers up to 100
• understand money amounts
• add and subtract numbers

Lesson 1 READING AND WRITING NUMBERS TO 1 000

When you read and write numbers, start from the left and move to the right. This means you move from the greatest place value position to the lowest place value position. Watch the spacing of digits for numerals greater than 999. A number in the thousands position is separated by a space from the numbers in the hundreds, tens, and ones positions. For example, one thousand is written as 1 000.

Pay attention to zeros. A zero is just as important as any other number. Zeros keep all the other numbers in their proper place value positions. Without the zero, the number 405 would be incorrectly written as 45.

Look at the following chart. It shows the numerals from 1 to 100 and how they are written in words.

1	one	11	eleven	30	thirty
2	two	12	twelve	40	forty
3	three	13	thirteen	50	fifty
4	four	14	fourteen	60	sixty
5	five	15	fifteen	70	seventy
6	six	16	sixteen	80	eighty
7	seven	17	seventeen	90	ninety
8	eight	18	eighteen	100	one hundred
9	nine	19	nineteen		
10	ten	20	twenty		

Any number word up to 1 000 can be written by using the numbers in the chart.

Write a number word the same way you read it out loud. Do not say *and* when you read numerals or write number words. To read a number in words, start from the left digit with the greatest place value. Move toward the right to the digit with the lowest place value.

 Example

Read the number 445 in words.

Solution

The number 445 in words is four hundred forty-five. Begin by saying the first number word grouped with the word hundred. Then say the tens and ones together. Do not say the word *and* between the numbers.

 Example

Write the number 300 using words.

Solution

To write the number 300 using words, look at the digit in the hundreds place. The digit is three. Add the word *hundred* after the word *three*.

The number 300 in words is three hundred.

 Time to Try 1

Write the number 800 in words.

NOTES

Use a hyphen when you write any two-digit number between 21 and 99 that does not end in a zero. The hyphen separates the word for the value in the tens place from the value in the ones place. For example, 763 is written as seven hundred sixty-three.

 Example

The teacher asked Maya to record the number of books stored in the library computer system. Maya discovered there were 727.

Write the number 727 in words.

Solution

To write the number 727 in words, start from the left and move to the right. Write the name for the digit in the hundreds place, and add the word *hundred* after it. You get seven hundred. Next, write the tens and the ones places together. Do not forget to write the hyphen between the numbers. You get twenty-seven. The number 727 is written in words as seven hundred twenty-seven.

 Time to Try 2

Mitch wondered how many chocolate chips were in a package. He counted them and found there were 243. Write the number 243 in words.

PRACTICE EXERCISES

1. Match the numbers in written form with their numeric form. Draw a line from the written word to the numeral. Read carefully.

seven hundred eight	99
ninety-nine	780
twenty-eight	992
nine hundred ninety-two	28
seven hundred eighty	708

2. Ian has read one hundred sixty-four library books this year. Write the number of books as a numeral.

3. Sonja has 632 marbles. Write the number of marbles in words.

4. Jerry has four hundred seventy-six building blocks. Write the number of building blocks as a numeral.

5. Ahmir has 806 pennies. Write the number of pennies in words.

6. Yesterday Miguel walked seven hundred ninety-two metres. Write the distance he walked as a number.

7. Rochelle owns 53 dolls. Write the number of dolls in words.

8. Match the numbers in written form with their numeric form. Draw a line from the numeral to the written word. Read carefully.

117	two hundred forty-two
173	four hundred twenty
420	one hundred seventeen
242	four hundred two
402	one hundred seventy-three

Use the following information to answer the next question.

Dermot likes to play hockey. Last week he took 250 shots on goal.

9. Write the number of shots in words.

10. Juan has 409 comic books in his collection. Write the number of comic books in words.

Use the following information to answer the next question.

Louise collects Barbie dolls. She has forty-seven dolls.

11. Write the number of dolls as a numeral.

Use the following information to answer the next question.

Dakota likes to drink milk. During the summer holidays, he drank two hundred two glasses of milk.

12. Write how much milk he drank as a number.

Lesson 2 *REPRESENTING NUMBERS IN OTHER WAYS*

Objects such as counting beads, beans, and sticks can be used to stand for numbers. Objects that stand for or represent numbers are called manipulatives. Manipulatives can help you build a number or solve a problem. Number sentences and expressions can also be used to represent numbers. Another way to represent numbers is to use money.

REPRESENTING NUMBERS USING BASE TEN BLOCKS

Base ten blocks are manipulatives you can use to build numbers. Units, ten rods, hundred flats, and thousand cubes are used to build any number from 1 to 1 000.

A **unit** has a value of 1.

A **ten rod** is made up of 10 units and has a value of 10.

1 + 1 + 1 + 1 + 1 + 1 + 1 + 1 + 1 + 1 = 10

A **hundred flat** is made up of 10 ten rods or 100 units and has a value of 100.

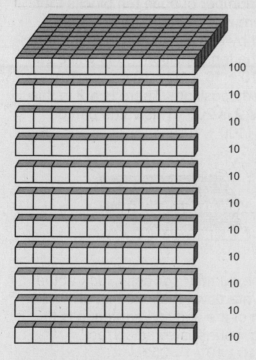

100
10
10
10
10
10
10
10
10
10

10 + 10 + 10 + 10 + 10 + 10 + 10 + 10 + 10 + 10 = 100

NOTES

A **thousand cube** is made up of 10 hundred flats and has a value of 1 000. It could also be made up of 100 ten rods or 1 000 units.

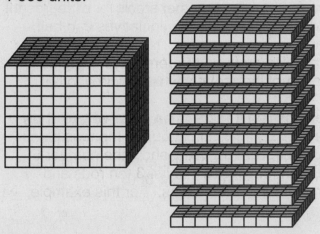

100 + 100 + 100 + 100 + 100 + 100 + 100 + 100 + 100 + 100 = 1 000

✷✷✷ **Example**

Build the number 251 using the fewest possible base ten blocks.

Solution

To build the number 251, look at the digit in each place value position. Draw the number of base ten blocks that represent each digit. There is a 1 in the ones position. The 1 can be represented by unit block. Move to the tens position. There is a 5 in the tens position. This value can be shown by 5 ten rods (10 + 10 + 10 + 10 + 10 = 50). Finally, look at the hundreds position. There is a 2 in this position. The value of this 2 is 200. This value can be shown by 2 hundred flats (100 + 100).

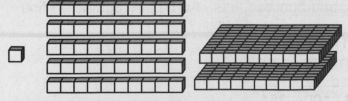

Check your work.
To see if you have built the number correctly, look at the blocks you have used. Write down their values, and add them together. If the sum of the addition sentence is the number you were building, your answer is correct.

$$100 + 100 + 10 + 10 + 10 + 10 + 10 + 1 = 251$$
$$200 + 50 + 1 = 251$$

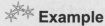 **Example**

Build the number 251 using a different combination of base ten blocks than shown in the previous example.

Solution

A number can be built in many different ways using base ten blocks because of their relationship to one another.

Start in the ones position. There is no other way to show a value of 1 other than using 1 unit. Look at the tens place. The 5 has a value of 50. You could show the number 50 using 50 units, 4 ten rods and 10 units, 3 ten rods and 20 units, or many other combinations. For this example, use 4 ten rods and 10 units.

There is a 2 in the hundreds place with a value of 200. There were 2 hundred flats used in the first example. There are many ways to show the value 200. You could show it using a hundred flat and ten rods. If you use 1 hundred flat, 10 ten rods would be needed to equal the total value of 200.

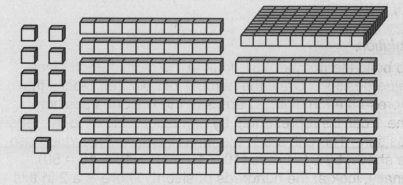

Check your work.
Look at the base ten blocks. Write the value of the units, ten rods, and hundred flats. Add them together to find the sum.

$$11 \text{ units} = 11$$
$$14 \text{ ten rods} = 140$$
$$1 \text{ hundred flat} = 100$$
$$11 + 140 + 100 = 251$$

The sum of the addition sentence equals the number you are building, so your answer is correct.

Time to Try 1

Using the fewest base ten blocks, build the number 437.

 Example

What number is represented by the base ten blocks shown here?

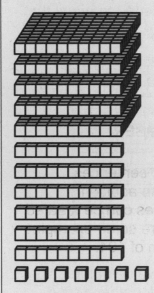

Solution

567

There are 5 flats (500), 6 rods (60), and 7 units (7).

The number shown by the base ten blocks is 567.

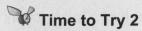 Time to Try 2

This picture shows base ten blocks.

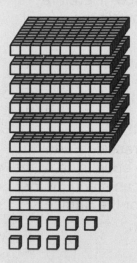

What number do the base ten blocks in the picture represent?

REPRESENTING NUMBERS USING NUMBER SENTENCES AND EXPRESSIONS

Numbers are often represented by number sentences. Any number can be shown as the sum of an addition sentence. Many different addition sentences can be created to show the same number or sum. Here are some examples of addition sentences representing the sum of 104.

$$
\begin{array}{r}
100 + 4 = 104 \\
50 + 50 + 4 = 104 \\
25 + 25 + 25 + 25 + 2 + 2 = 104
\end{array}
$$

NOTES

A number can also be shown as the difference of a subtraction sentence. Again, there are many subtraction sentences you can write to represent a number as a difference. Here are some examples of subtraction sentences showing the difference of 104.

$$105 - 1 = 104$$
$$200 - 96 = 104$$
$$1\,000 - 896 = 104$$

Numbers can also be represented using expressions. An expression is a number sentence without the equal side or the answer. For example, the expression 2 + 2 can stand for the number 4. The expression 4 − 2 can stand for the number 2.

 Example

The number 57 can be shown by the expressions 23 + 34 and 16 + 41. It can also be expressed as 100 − 43 and 99 − 42.

Think of more ways to show the number 57 as an expression.

Solution
Other possible ways to show the number 57 as an expression are:
$$56 + 1$$
$$20 + 37$$
$$60 - 3$$
$$77 - 20$$

REPRESENT NUMBERS USING MONEY

Another way you can represent a number is by using money. Here is a review of the value in cents of the following coins and bills:

penny	one cent
nickel	five cents
dime	ten cents
quarter	twenty-five cents
one dollar (loonie)	one hundred cents
two dollars (toonie)	two hundred cents
five-dollar bill	five hundred cents
ten-dollar bill	one thousand cents
twenty-dollar bill	two thousand cents

36

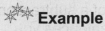 **Example**

How could you use money to represent the number 748?

Solution

You need 1 five-dollar bill, 2 loonies, 4 dimes, and 8 pennies.

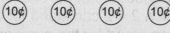

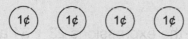

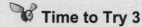

Another way to show the number 748 is with 7 loonies, 4 dimes, 1 nickel, and 3 pennies.

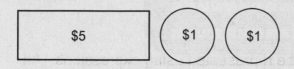 **Time to Try 3**

Use money to represent the number 626.

PRACTICE EXERCISES

Use the following information to answer the next question.

The picture shows base ten blocks.

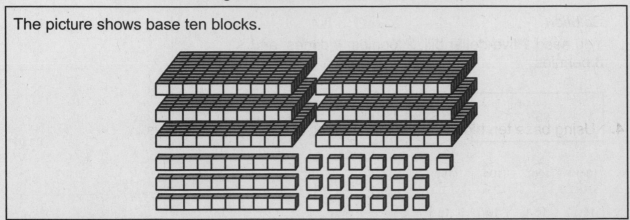

1.   What is the value of the base ten blocks shown?

Use the following information to answer the next question.

Here is a picture of base ten blocks.

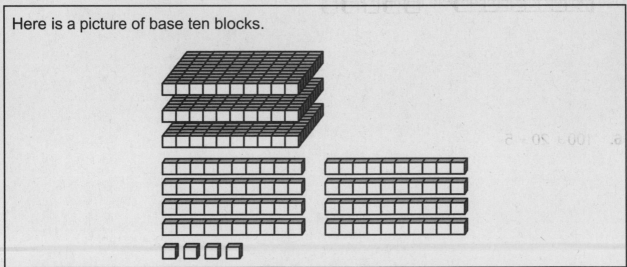

2.   What is the value of the base ten blocks in the picture?

3. Using the fewest possible base ten blocks, build the number 297.

4. Using base ten blocks, build the number 356 in 2 different ways.

The next seven questions show different ways of representing the number 125. Determine if each question is correct or incorrect, and explain your answer.

5.

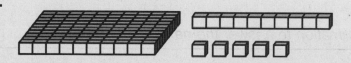

6. 100 + 20 + 5

7. 150 − 25

8.

H	T	O
1	2	5

9. One hundred twenty-five

10. 1 loonie and 20 pennies

11.

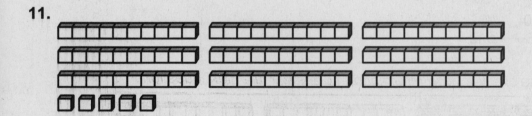

12. Use the fewest possible base ten blocks to represent the number 243.

Use the following information to answer the next question.

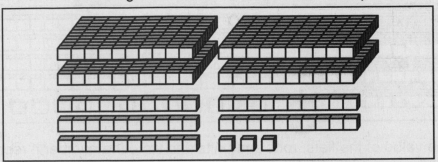

13. Identify the value of the flats, rods and units and write the number it represents.

14. Insert a √ on every line that represents the number 697 as an expression.

    ___   352 + 345
    ___   941 − 244
    ___   804 − 107
    ___   469 + 238

Use the following information to answer the next question.

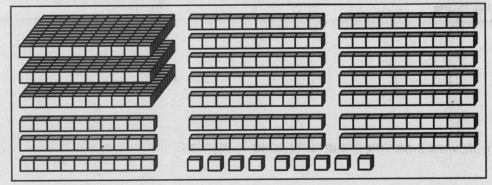

15. Identify the value of the flats, rods and units and write the number it represents.

Use the following information to answer the next question.

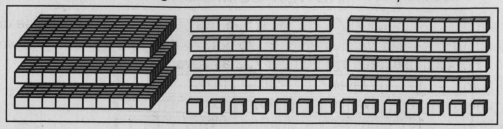

16. Identify the value of the flats, rods and units and write the number it represents.

17. Insert a √ on every line that represents the number 868 using money.

___ 8 loonies, 5 dimes, 1 nickel, 3 pennies
___ one 5 dollar bill, 3 loonies, 6 dimes, 8 pennies
___ one five dollar bill, 2 loonies, 4 quarters, 5 dimes, 3 nickels, 3 pennies
___ 8 loonies, 1 quarter, 4 dimes, 3 pennies

18. A number can be represented in many different ways. Insert a √ on every line next to the addition or subtraction sentence if it correctly shows 573.

___ 300 + 273
___ 935 − 368
___ 652 − 79
___ 126 + 447

42

REVIEW SUMMARY

- Whole numbers are the digits 0, 1, 2, 3, 4, 5, 6, 7, 8, 9, and any mix of these digits.
- When reading three-digit whole numbers, do not say the word *and* after the word *hundred*. For example, read the number 732 as seven hundred thirty-two.

0	zero	11	eleven	30	thirty
1	one	12	twelve	40	forty
2	two	13	thirteen	50	fifty
3	three	14	fourteen	60	sixty
4	four	15	fifteen	70	seventy
5	five	16	sixteen	80	eighty
6	six	17	seventeen	90	ninety
7	seven	18	eighteen	100	one hundred
8	eight	19	nineteen		
9	nine	20	twenty		
10	ten				

- All numbers up to 999 can be written using the above number words.
- The number 1 000 can be written as one thousand.
- When writing three-digit numerals, start with the number of hundreds, then the tens, and then the ones. Use a hyphen between any two-digit numbers between 21 and 99 that do not end in zero. Do not write the word *and* after the word *hundred*.
- Base ten blocks can be used to represent numbers. The base ten blocks are called units, ten rods, and hundred flats.
  - A unit has a value of 1.

  - A ten rod has a value of 10. It is made up of 10 units.

  - A hundred flat has a value of 100. It is made up of 10 ten rods or 100 units.

- Equations, sometimes called number sentences, can be used to represent numbers.
- Money can be used to represent numbers as well. Money is similar to base ten blocks. It can be expressed as 1 penny = 1 unit, 1 dime = 1 ten rod, 1 dollar = 1 hundred flat, and 1 ten-dollar bill = 1 thousand cube. For example, the number 121 can be represented using 1 loonie, 2 dimes, and 1 penny.

PRACTICE TEST

1. Match the numbers with their written from. Draw a line from the numeral to the written form.

    479   four hundred forty-four
    408   four hundred seventy-nine
    460   four hundred eight
    444   four hundred sixty

2. Match the numbers in written form with their numerical form. Draw a line from the written word to the numeral.

    six hundred ninety   699
    six hundred nine   690
    six hundred ninety-nine   619
    six hundred nineteen   609

3. Using words, write the number 818.

4. Write three hundred thirty-three as a number.

5. Write seven hundred seven as a numeral.

6. Write the number 206 in words.

Use the following information to answer the next question.

This picture shows a group of base ten blocks.

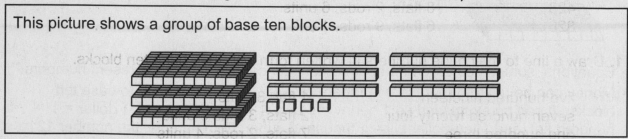

7. What number do the base ten blocks in the picture represent?

44

Use the following information to answer the next question.

Here is a picture showing base ten blocks.

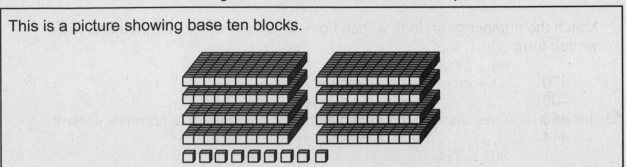

8. What number do the base ten blocks shown represent?

Use the following information to answer the next question.

Here is a picture of base ten blocks.

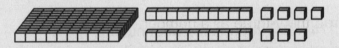

9. What number do the base ten blocks in the picture represent?

10. Match the numbers with their base ten blocks.

347	4 flats, 2 rods, 3 units
691	3 flats, 4 rods, 7 units
423	8 flats, 2 rods, 6 units
826	6 flats, 9 rods, 1 unit

11. Draw a line to match the numbers in written form with their base ten blocks.

five hundred nineteen	1 flat, 3 units
seven hundred twenty-four	2 flats, 3 rods 3 units
one hundred three	7 flats, 2 rods, 4 units
two hundred thirty-three	5 flats, 1 rod, 9 units

12. Insert a √ on the line next to every addition sentence with a sum of 471.

_____ 255 + 216
_____ 309 + 162
_____ 84 + 386
_____ 67 + 404

13. Insert a √ on the line next to every subtraction sentence that correctly show 87.

_____ 301 – 214
_____ 657 – 570
_____ 928 – 841
_____ 114 – 17

14. The addition sentence 25 + 95 represents what number?

15. The subtraction sentence 864 – 397 represents what number?

16. The expression 174 + 241 represents what number?

17. The expression 715 – 140 represents what number?

18. Insert a √ on the line next to every money amount that correctly shows 385.

_____ 3 loonies, 8 dimes, 5 pennies
_____ 2 loonies, 6 quarters, 3 dimes, 5 pennies
_____ 3 loonies, 2 quarters, 1 dime, 5 nickels
_____ 2 loonies, 7 quarters, 2 nickels,

19. What number is represented by 7 loonies, 3 dimes, and 5 pennies?

20. What number is represented by 2 loonies, 2 quarters, 3 dimes, and 4 pennies?

PLACE VALUE

When you are finished this unit, you will be able to…
- understand and show place value of numbers up to 1 000
- build, compare, and put in order numbers 0 to 1 000
- identify errors in numbers placed in ordered sequence

PREREQUISITE SKILLS AND KNOWLEDGE

Prior to starting this unit, you should be able to…
- understand that each digit has a value depending on its place in a number
- identify whether a number is greater than, less than, or equal to another number

Lesson 1   VALUE OF A DIGIT

Some numbers have only one digit while other numbers are made up of many digits. A digit is worth different amounts depending on which position it has in a number. The position of a digit in a number is called place value. The value of a digit increases as it moves from the ones to the tens to the hundreds to the thousands place value positions.

The value of a digit in the ones place value position is how many ones are in that number. The value of the 2 in 76<u>2</u> is 2. The ones position is the first column on the right.

 Example

For the number 786, underline the digit in the ones position, and then express the value of the underlined digit.

Solution

78<u>6</u>

The value of the digit in the ones column is 6.

 Time to Try 1

For the number 428, underline the digit in the ones position, and then express the value of the underlined digit.

428

The value of a digit in the tens place value position is how many tens are in that number. The value of the 6 in number 7<u>6</u>2 is 60. The tens position is the second column from the right.

 Example

For the number 943, underline the digit in the tens place value position, and then express the value of the underlined digit.

Solution

9<u>4</u>3

The value of the digit in the tens column is 40.

Time to Try 2

For the number 554, underline the number in the tens place value position, and then express the value of the underlined digit.

554

The value of a digit in the hundreds place value position is how many hundreds there are in a number. The 7 in the number **7**62 is in the hundreds place. The hundreds position is the third column from the right.

 Example

For the number 738, underline the digit in the tens place value position, and then express the value of the underlined digit.

Solution

<u>7</u>38
The value of the digit in the hundreds column is 700.

 Time to Try 3

For the number 321, underline the digit in the hundreds place value position, and then express the value of the underlined digit.

321

In the number 333, all the digits are the same. However, the 3 in each number has a different value based on where it stands. The first 3 in the ones place value position has a value of 3. The next 3 in the tens place has a value of 30. The 3 in the hundreds place has a value of 300.

333
ones
tens
hundreds

NOTES

 Example

What is the value of the digit 5 in the numbers 568, 453, and 125?

Solution

Remember the value of a digit in the hundreds place is how many hundreds there are, the value of a digit in the tens place is how many tens there are, and the value of the digit in the ones place is how many ones there are. Now, look at the numbers.

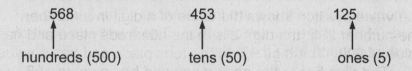

- In the number 568, the digit 5 is in the hundreds place and has a value of 500.
- In the number 453, the digit 5 is in the tens place and has a value of 50.
- In the number 125, the digit 5 is in the ones place and has a value of 5.

 Time to Try 4

What is the value of the digit 4 in the numbers 481, 842, and 274?

PLACE VALUE CHART

A place value chart shows the value of the digits in a number. Each place value position is 10 times greater than the position to its right. For example, the tens place has a value that is 10 times greater than the value of the ones place.

Thousands	Hundreds	Tens	Ones

The headings for the place value columns may be shortened to Th, H, T, and O.

In the number 9 999, the digit 9 appears in the ones, tens, hundreds, and thousands place value positions. The value of 9 in each position is shown in the right-hand column.

Th	H	T	O	Value
			9	9
		9		90
	9			900
9				9 000

Place value position shows the value of a digit in a number. In the number 295, the digit 2 is in the hundreds place and has a value of 200. The digit 9 is in the tens place and has a value of 90. The digit 5 is in the ones place and has a value of 5. Here is the number 295 written in a place value chart.

H	T	O
2	9	5

✳ Example

Insert 843 into the place value table to correctly show its value.

Solution

H	T	O
8	4	3

There are 8 hundreds in the number 843. The value of the 8 is 800 so write the 8 in the hundreds column. There are 4 tens in the number 843. The value of the 4 is 40 so write the 4 in the tens columns. There are 3 ones in the number 843. The value of the 3 is 3 so write the 3 in the ones column.

Time to Try 5

Insert 679 into the place value table to correctly show its value.

H	T	O

PRACTICE EXERCISES

1. Write a √ on the line next to each table that correctly shows 467.

Hundreds	Tens	Ones
400	60	7

Hundreds	Tens	Ones
4	6	7

Hundreds	Tens	Ones
		467

Hundreds	Tens	Ones
400	6	7

Look at the numbers below.
- *Circle the digit in the tens position.*
- *Underline the digit in the hundreds position.*
- *Write the value of the digit in the tens position on the line next to the number.*

2. 846 ___

3. 251 ___

4. Write the total value of each number shown in the table.

H	T	O	Value
7	9	6	
	12		
3	8	11	

For the next three questions, read the clue, then write the correct digit in the proper place value position.

5. This digit's value in the ones position is 6.

   54___

6. This digit's value in the tens position is 70.

   9___4

7. This digit's value in the hundreds position is 600.

   ___23

8. What is the value of the digit 6 in the numbers 326, 465, and 671?

Look at the two numbers below.
- *Circle the digit in the ones position.*
- *Underline the digit in the hundreds position.*
- *Write the value of the digit in the tens position on the line next to the number.*

9. 318 ___   **10.** 262 ___

Lesson 2   PLACE VALUE WITH BASE TEN BLOCKS

NOTES

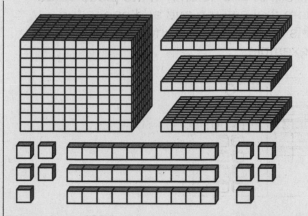

You have already used these materials to represent and build numbers. Now, you will learn to use base ten blocks with a place value chart. The position of the blocks in the chart shows the value of the number.

What do you see in the chart?

H	T	O
		▢▢ ▢▢ ▢▢

You see 6 units in the ones place value position.
This represents a value of 6.

What do you see now?

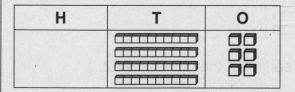

You see 4 rods in the tens place and 6 units in the ones place. The 4 tens and the 6 ones represent a value of 46.

When you use a place value chart, it is important to remember that each place value position in the chart tells something about the digit in that position.

In this last example, the tens place shows that there are four groups of ten. You could also draw 40 units in the ones place. However, 40 units are harder to read and count.

REGROUPING

Once there are 10 or more in one column in the place value chart, take away 10 from that column and add one to the column on the left. This is called regrouping or trading. Look at the following example.

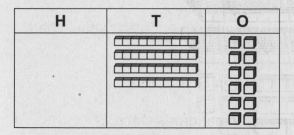

What number is represented in the chart? There are 4 rods in the tens place and 12 units in the ones place. If you regroup the ones by taking away 10 units and adding 1 rod, the number becomes easier to read.

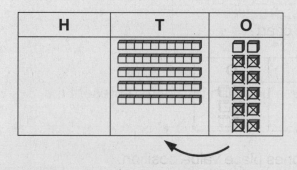

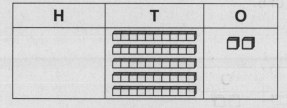

Now the chart shows clearly that the number is 52.

You can use base ten blocks to show the value of each digit when all the digits in a number are the same.

NOTES

 Example

Use base ten blocks in a place value chart to represent the number 222.

Solution

First, look at the digit in the ones place.
Draw 2 units in the ones column of your place value chart.

Next, look at the digit in the tens place.
Draw 2 rods in the tens column of your chart.

Finally, look at the digit in the hundreds place.
Draw 2 flats in the hundreds column.
This value chart represents the number 222.

H	T	O

 Time to Try 1

In a place value chart, use base ten blocks to represent the number 444.

 Example

Use base ten blocks to represent the number 357 in a place value chart.

Solution

First, look at the digit in the ones place (7).
Draw 7 units in the ones column of your place value chart.

Next, look at the digit in the tens place (5).
Draw 5 rods in the tens column.

Finally, look at the digit in the hundreds place (3).
Draw 3 flats in the hundreds column.

The following place value chart represents the number 357.

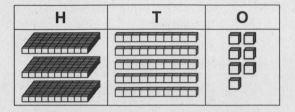

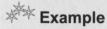 **Example**

What new number will you have if you add five units in the ones place value position?

Solution

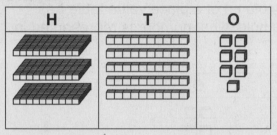

In the first example of 357, you had 3 flats, 5 rods, and 7 units. When you add 5 units to the ones place you get 3 flats, 5 rods, and 12 units.

Regroup the ones by taking away 10 units from the ones column and adding 1 rod to the tens column. Now you have 3 flats, 6 rods, and 2 units, as shown here.

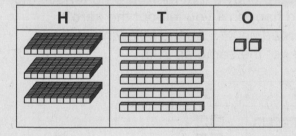

NOTES

 Time to Try 2

Using the fewest possible base ten blocks, show the number 452 in a place value chart.

THE ZERO PLACE HOLDER

What happens if one column of a place value table has nothing in it? For example, what number is represented in this table?

H	T	O
▦▦		▫▫ ▫▫

Since there are 2 flats, no rods, and 4 units, the number is two hundred four. How can you express this as a number? You write 204.

When there is nothing in a certain place value position, put a zero in that place value. The zero is used as a place holder. In this example, the zero shows that there are no tens in the number. What would happen if you left out the zero? Your number would read as 24. As the following charts show, 24 is certainly not the same as 204.

H	T	O
	▭▭	▫▫ ▫▫

24

H	T	O
▦▦		▫▫ ▫▫

204

PRACTICE EXERCISES

Use the following information to answer the next question.

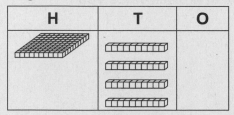

1. Write the number that is shown by the base ten blocks in the place value chart.

Use the following information to answer the next question.

H	T	O

2. Write the number that is shown by the base ten blocks in the place value chart.

3. Draw base ten blocks in a place value chart to show the number 345.

4. Draw base ten blocks in a place value chart to show the number 423.

5. Draw base ten blocks in a place value chart to show the number 196.

6. Use base ten blocks in a place value chart to represent the number 333.

Use the following information to answer the next question.

H	T	O

7. Write the number is represented by the base ten blocks shown in the place value chart.

60

Lesson 3 COMPARING AND ORDERING

COMPARING NUMBERS

Place value can be used to compare numbers. Look at the digits on the left first. They are the digits at the greatest place value position. If they are the same, move on to the next place value position.

Follow this order when you are comparing numbers:
- Compare the digits in the hundreds place.
- Compare the digits in the tens place.
- Compare the digits in the ones place.

Try it with the numbers 246 and 237 to see which number is greater.

	Hundreds	Tens	Ones
246			
237			

Step 1

Start at the left, and compare the digits in the hundreds place. There are 2 hundreds in 246 and 2 hundreds in 237. This means you need to compare the digits in the tens place to see which number is greater.

Step 2

Compare the digits in the tens place. There are 4 tens in 246 and 3 tens in 237. Since 4 is greater than 3, the number 246 is greater than 237.

You do not need to compare the digits in the ones place for these numbers because you already know which number is greater.

Numbers can also be compared using symbols. Symbols are simply marks that stand for something. Use a *greater than* sign (>), a *less than* sign (<), or an *equal* sign (=) as symbols to compare two numbers.

For example, to compare the numbers 3 and 7, you can write either 3 < 7 or 7 > 3. The smaller number has the closed part of the arrow facing it. The larger number has the open part of the arrow facing it. If the two numbers are equal, use the equal sign.
3 = 3

To compare numbers with more than one digit, look at the digits in the greatest place value position. If the digits are different from one another, you can see which number is greater or smaller. The number with the greater digit is a greater number. It will have the open end of the arrow facing it (>). The number with the smaller digit is smaller. It will have the closed part of the arrow facing it (<).

If the digit in the greatest place value position is the same for both numbers, move on to compare the digit in the next place value to the right. If these digits are also the same, continue to move to the right. If the two numbers have all digits the same in all place value positions, they are equal.

To remember which symbol to use, think of an alligator. The alligator will always eat the larger number. Let the alligator's head help you compare the numbers 23 and 32. Start with the greatest place value position. You see that 2 is less than 3. Therefore, 23 is less than 32, and the alligator will open its mouth to eat the 32. The open end of the arrow faces the larger number.

23   32

23 < 32

This number sentence tells you that 23 is less than 32. The arrow used to compare these two numbers is a *less than* sign.

A comparison is always read from left to right. In this example, the number sentence 32 > 23 tells you that 32 is greater than 23. The arrow used to show this comparison is called a *greater than* sign.

62

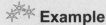 **Example**

Insert the sign >, <, or = to make the comparison true.

a) 456 ___ 526

Solution

To compare these numbers, figure out if 456 is greater or less than 526. Look at the first digit of each number in the hundreds place value position. The 4 (400) is worth less than the 5 (500), so draw a *less than* (<) arrow (closed part toward 456).
456 < 526

b) 237 ___ 319

Solution

To compare these numbers, determine if 237 is greater or less than 319. Look at the first digit of each number in the hundreds place value position. The 2 (200) is worth less than the 3 (300), so draw a *less than* (<) arrow (closed part toward 237).
237 < 319

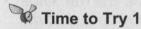 **Time to Try 1**

Insert >, <, or = to make the comparison true.

a) 958 ___ 938   **b)** 434 ___ 434

ORDERING NUMBERS USING A HUNDRED CHART

You can use a hundred chart to help you put numbers in order. A hundred chart is easy to read and shows the order of numbers from least to greatest. Here is a hundred chart for you to look at. Notice where the numbers are located.

1	2	3	4	5	6	7	8	9	10
11	12	13	14	15	16	17	18	19	20
21	22	23	24	25	26	27	28	29	30
31	32	33	34	35	36	37	38	39	40
41	42	43	44	45	46	47	48	49	50
51	52	53	54	55	56	57	58	59	60
61	62	63	64	65	66	67	68	69	70
71	72	73	74	75	76	77	78	79	80
81	82	83	84	85	86	87	88	89	90
91	92	93	94	95	96	97	98	99	100

✳✳ Example

Three numbers are missing in the following hundreds chart. Can you figure out what the missing numbers are?

1	2	3	4	5	6	7	8	9	10
11	12	13	14	15	16	17	18	19	20
21	22	23	24	25	26	27	28	29	30
31	32		34	35	36	37	38	39	40
41	42	43	44	45	46	47	48	49	50
51	52	53	54	55		57	58	59	60
61	62	63	64	65	66	67	68	69	70
71	72	73	74	75	76	77	78	79	80
81	82	83		85	86	87	88	89	90
91	92	93	94	95	96	97	98	99	100

Solution

Look at the spaces to determine which numbers are missing. Each row (going across) has a place value determined by the tens place except for the first row since it is counting up to ten. Each column (going up and down) is determined by the ones place value. There is a blank space in the fourth row down and the third column over. That is the 3 tens place and 3 ones place. The number in that square should be 33. You can also count each square to find out which number is missing, or count along the row.

Count along the fifth row down. The numbers are 51, 52, 53, 54, and 55. The missing number must be 56.

Finally, the last blank square is in the eighth row, which is the 80s place value. Count across the numbers 81, 82, 83, 84. The number 84 belongs in the last blank square.

64

Time to Try 2

Here is a hundreds chart with three numbers missing.

1	2	3	4	5	6	7	8	9	10
11	12	13	14	15	16	17	18	19	20
21	22	23	24	25	26	27		29	30
31	32	33	34	35	36	37	38	39	40
41	42	43	44	45	46	47	48	49	50
51	52	53	54	55	56	57	58	59	60
61	62	63	64	65	66	67	68	69	70
71	72	73	74	75		77	78	79	80
81	82	83	84	85	86	87	88	89	90
91		93	94	95	96	97	98	99	100

Which three numbers are missing from the chart?

_____, _____, _____

ORDERING LARGE NUMBERS

When you place numbers in order from the greatest value to the least value, each number will be less than the number before it. This is called **descending order**. These numbers are written in descending order: 890, 776, 345.

When you place numbers in order from the least value to the greatest value, each number will be greater in value than the number before it. This is called **ascending order**.
These numbers are written in ascending order: 345, 776, 890.

Use these steps to compare and order numbers.

1. Write the numbers down on a piece of paper.
2. Place one number below the other number, and line up the place values.
3. Start with the greatest place value, and compare the digits.
4. Move to the place value to the right, and compare the digits
5. Keep moving to the place value to the right until the digits in each place value have been compared.

NOTES

 Example

Write the numbers 856, 869, and 798 in ascending order (from least to greatest).

Solution

Step 1
Look at the digits in the hundreds position to put the numbers **8**56, **8**69, and **7**98 in order from least to greatest. You can compare them by writing them one below the other and lining up the place values.
856
869
798

Step 2
Look for the digit with the least value. The value of 7 is 700, while the value of 8 is 800. The number 798 should be first because it has the least value.

Step 3
Both of the other numbers have the same value in the hundreds position, so move to the tens position.
The number 8**5**6 has a 5 in the tens position. The number 8**6**9 has a 6 in the tens position. Choose the digit whose value is less. The number 856 is less, so it should be second. The number 869 is the greatest number, so it comes last.

Step 4
Write the numbers written in ascending order:
798, 856, and 869.

 Time to Try 3

Write the numbers 1 000, 929, 839, 818, and 955 in descending order (from greatest to least).

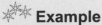 **Example**

Create 6 different 3-digit numbers using the numerals 2, 7, and 5. Then, put them in order from least to greatest.

Solution

First, create 6 different 3-digit numbers. Use a chart to help. Start by using each digit in each of the place value positions.

> 275
> 257
> 725
> 752
> 527
> 572

You can make 6 numbers.

Next, to put them in order from smallest to largest, look at the digits in the hundreds place.

- 2 is the smallest number so compare 275 and 257. Look at the tens place. 5 is smaller than 7 so 257 would be first, followed by 275.
- 5 is the next smallest number, so compare 527 and 572. Look at the tens place. 2 is smaller than 7 so 527 would come third and 572 would be fourth.
- 7 is the largest number. Look at the digits in the tens place. 2 is smaller than 5 so 725 would be the next number in sequence and 752 would be the largest number.

Placed in sequence from smallest to largest:
257, 275, 527, 572, 725, 752.

 Time to Try 4

Create as many 3-digit numbers as you can using the numerals 3, 4, and 8. Then, put them in order from least to greatest.

3   4   8

NOTES

 Example

Are the following numbers correctly ordered from smallest to largest?

549, 562, 558.

Solution

Starting with the hundreds place, all of the numbers have a 5 and the same value of 500.

Next, look at the tens place. The number 549 has a 4, 562 has a 6, and 558 has a 5. The digit with the smallest value is the 4, so it should be first. The next smallest digit is the 5, so it should be second.

You can see that the numbers are not in the correct order because the number with the 6 is second.

The correct order from smallest to largest is 549, 558, and 562.

PRACTICE EXERCISES

*For the next four questions, write >, <, or = in the blank between the numbers to make the comparison **true**.*

1. 555 ___ 667

2. 752 ___ 715

3. 213 ___ 213

4. 320 ___ 430

Use the following information to answer the next question.

Marble collections are very popular at Windsor Elementary School. There are five students in the Grade 3 class that have more than 100 marbles in their collections.
- Taneisha has 319 marbles.
- Jason has 167 marbles.
- Gillian has 328 marbles.
- Craig has 287 marbles.
- Rebecca has 276 marbles.

5. Listed from least to greatest, what is the order for the number of marbles in the students' collections?

_____, _____, _____,

_____, _____

6. Order the numbers 89, 96, 86 from greatest to least.

7. Order the numbers 871, 867, 887 from greatest to least.

8. Order the numbers 743, 782, and 675 from least to greatest.

Use the following information to answer the next question.

Some numbers are missing in the following hundreds chart.

1	2	3	4	5	6	7	8	9	10
11	12	13		15	16	17	18	19	20
21	22	23	24	25	26	27	28	29	
31	32	33	34	35	36	37	38	39	40
41	42	43		45	46	47	48	49	50
51	52	53	54	55	56	57	58	59	60
61	62	63	64	65	66		68	69	70
71	72	73	74	75	76	77	78	79	80
81	82	83	84	85	86	87	88	89	90
91	92	93	94		96	97	98	99	100

9. What numbers are missing from the chart?

REVIEW SUMMARY

- A digit is any of the numbers 0, 1, 2, 3, 4, 5, 6, 7, 8, or 9. Some numbers have one digit only while other numbers are made up of many digits.
- A place value chart shows the position of a digit in a number.
- This chart shows the place values for the number 948.

H	T	O	Number
9	4	8	948

- A place value chart also shows the value of the digits in a number.
  This chart shows the value of the digit 1 in four different positions.

Th	H	T	O	Value of Digit 1
			1	1
		1		10
	1			100
1				1 000

- A place value chart can show value with base ten blocks.
- Zero acts as a place holder. When the digit in the place value position has no value, a zero is used to hold the position.
- Begin with the greatest place value position and work toward the least place value to compare numbers. The number with the greatest digit in the greatest place value position is the greatest number.
- Look at place value in numbers to put numbers in order. Descending order means greatest to least. Ascending order means least to greatest.

PRACTICE TEST

1. Insert the number 951 into the place value table to show its value.

H	T	O

2. The digit in the ones position in the number 845 is ___.

3. For the number 346, the value of the digit in the tens position is ___.

4. In the number 782, what is the value of the digit in the hundreds position?

5. Read the clue next to the number and write the correct number into the hundreds place value position.

   ___21   This number's value in the hundreds position is 400.

6. What is the value of the digit 2 in the numbers 296, 327, and 452?

Use the following information to answer the next question.

H	T	O

7. What number is shown by the base ten blocks?

Use the following information to answer the next question.

H	T	O

8. What number is shown by the base ten blocks?

9. Draw base ten blocks in a place value chart to represent the number 231.

10. Using the fewest possible base ten blocks, show the number 444 in a place value chart.

11. When comparing numbers, what symbol must be placed in the space to make 243 ___ 327 true?

12. To make the number sentence 543 ___ 543 true, what symbol must be placed in the space?

13. Order the numbers 582, 536, and 425 from least to greatest.

14. Order the numbers 382, 485, 386 from greatest to least.

15. Using the digits 4, 2, and 6, create six different 3-digit numbers. Then put the numbers you created in order from least to greatest.

Use the following information to answer the next question.

Some numbers are missing in the following hundreds chart.

1	2	3	4	5	6	7	8	9	10
11	12	13	14	15	16	17	18	19	20
21	22		24	25	26	27	28	29	30
31	32	33	34	35	36	37	38	39	40
41		43	44	45	46	47	48	49	50
51	52	53	54	55		57	58	59	60
61	62	63	64	65	66	67	68	69	70
71	72	73	74	75	76	77	78		80
81	82	83	84	85	86	87	88	89	90
91		93	94	95	96	97	98	99	100

16. What are the missing numbers?

NOTES

SORTING

When you are finished this unit, you will be able to…
• sort objects and numbers into groups using two attributes
• explain sorting rules
• compare and sort objects using a Venn diagram
• identify and sort polygons by the number of sides

Lesson	Page	Completed on
1. Sorting Numbers	78	
2. Sorting Objects	86	
3. Polygons	96	
Review Summary	103	
Practice Test	104	
Answers and Solutions	at the back of the book	

PREREQUISITE SKILLS AND KNOWLEDGE

Prior to starting this unit, you should be able to…
• define odd and even numbers, fractions and whole numbers
• sort shapes using one feature
• name common polygons

Lesson 1 SORTING NUMBERS

Numbers can be sorted in many ways. They can be sorted into groups of odd numbers or even numbers, fractions or whole numbers, or even by how many digits they have. Sometimes, numbers are sorted using more than one of these features. A feature that helps you identify something is called an attribute. Sorting numbers means using attributes and following rules. The rules tell you what group to put the numbers in. The attributes help you identify the numbers.

SORTING WITH ONE ATTRIBUTE

Numbers can be sorted by the number of digits they have. Numbers from 0 to 9 have 1 digit. Numbers from 10 to 99 have 2 digits. Numbers from 100 to 999 have 3 digits.

 Example

Here is a list of numbers.

     2, 5, 14, 6, 97, 0, 26, 34

Sort the numbers into groups of 1-digit numbers or 2-digit numbers.

Solution

These numbers are sorted by the number of digits they have. The numbers that have 1 digit are less than 10. The numbers that have 2 digits are 10 or greater.

The 1-digit numbers are 2, 5, 6, and 0.
The 2-digit numbers are 14, 97, 26, and 34.

 Time to Try 1

Here is a list of numbers.

     1, 3, 19, 7, 45, 63, 4

Sort the numbers into groups of 1-digit numbers or 2-digit numbers.

Numbers can also be sorted into groups of odd or even numbers. An even number ends in 0, 2, 4, 6, or 8. It can be divided evenly into groups of 2. An odd number ends in 1, 3, 5, 7, or 9. It cannot be evenly divided into 2 groups.

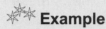 **Example**

Sort the numbers into groups of even or odd numbers.
    8, 14, 23, 35, 47, 56, 69, 81, 92

Solution

Remember that even numbers end in 0, 2, 4, 6, 8 and can be divided evenly into groups of 2. Odd numbers end in 1, 3, 5, 7, 9 and cannot be evenly divided into 2 groups.

The even numbers are 8, 14, 56, and 92.
The odd numbers are 23, 35, 47, 69, and 81.

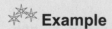 **Time to Try 2**

Sort the numbers into groups of even or odd numbers.
    7, 15, 20, 34, 23, 58, 76, 39, 67

Another way to sort numbers is as fractions or whole numbers. Remember that fractions are numbers that are parts of a whole. Fractions are shown as one number above the other, as in $\frac{1}{2}$. Fractions have a numerator (top number) and a denominator (bottom number) to show they are part of a whole number.

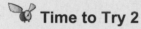 **Example**

Sort the following numbers as fractions or whole numbers.
    $\frac{1}{2}$, 1, $\frac{1}{3}$, 2, 14, $\frac{5}{10}$

Solution

Fractions have a numerator and a denominator to show they are part of a whole number.

The fractions are $\frac{1}{2}$, $\frac{1}{3}$, and $\frac{5}{10}$.

The whole numbers are 1, 2, and 14.

Time to Try 3

Sort the numbers as fractions or whole numbers.

$$26, \frac{2}{3}, \frac{1}{4}, 1, \frac{1}{5}, 12$$

SORTING WITH MORE THAN ONE ATTRIBUTE

Numbers can be sorted using more than one feature or attribute. You can use a table to help you sort numbers using more than one attribute.

 Example

Sort the numbers by whether they are less than 10 or 10 and greater and whether they are even or odd.

1, 2, 3, 4, 7, 8, 9, 11, 13, 14, 16, 17, 18

	Even	Odd
Less than 10		
Greater than 10		

Solution

When you are sorting numbers using more than one feature, think about the rules you are given. The first rule is even or odd. The second rule is less than 10 or greater than 10.

Start by going through the numbers in the box one by one. Ask yourself if 1 is an even or an odd number. The number 1 cannot be divided into two equal groups, so it is an odd number. Next, ask yourself if 1 is greater or less than 10. It is less than 10, so place it in the box for numbers that are odd and less than 10.

The number 2 can be divided into two equal groups of 1, so it is an even number. It is also less than 10. Place it in the box for numbers that are even and less than 10.

Continue with the other numbers until all of the numbers are placed in the correct box in the table.

This table shows all the numbers placed correctly.

	Even	Odd
Less than 10	2, 4, 8	1, 3, 7, 9
Greater than 10	14, 16, 18	11, 13, 17

Another way to show the column with the sorting rules less than and greater than is by using symbols.

- The less than symbols looks like <
- The greater than symbol looks like >

	Even	Odd
< 10	2, 4, 8	1, 3, 7, 9
> 10	14, 16, 18	11, 13, 17

 Time to Try 4

Sort the numbers by whether they are less than 12 or greater than 12 and whether they are even or odd.

2, 5, 6, 9, 15, 16, 19, 20, 21, 24, 25

	Even	Odd
Less than 12		
Greater than 12		

You have been using rules to sort numbers into different groups. You can also find the rule being used when you are given a set of numbers already divided into groups.

 Example

Find the sorting rules used to group the numbers in the table.

2, 14, 18, 24	28, 32, 40, 44, 46, 50
7, 21	25, 29, 35, 37, 41, 43, 49

Solution

Start by looking at the top box of numbers on the left. The numbers 2, 14, 18, and 24 are all even numbers. The bottom box has the numbers 7 and 21. They are odd numbers. The rule that divided those two boxes was even or odd numbers.

Next, look at the top box on the right. The numbers are all even, but they are numbers starting at 28. The bottom box on the right has all odd numbers ranging from 25 to 49. Since the number 24 is in the left-hand column of numbers and the 25 is on the right-hand side, the column on the left has numbers 24 and less. The column on the right has numbers 25 and greater.

The numbers were sorted by the rules of even or odd numbers and then by numbers 24 and less or 25 and greater.

	24 or less than 24	25 or greater than 25
Even	2, 14, 18, 24	28, 32, 40, 44, 46, 50
Odd	7, 21	25, 29, 35, 37, 41, 43, 49

 Time to Try 5

Find the sorting rules used to group this table of numbers.

1, 3, 5, 7	11, 13, 15, 17
2, 4, 6, 8	10, 12, 14, 16, 18

PRACTICE EXERCISES

Use the following information to answer the next question.

$$15, \frac{1}{8}, \frac{2}{5}, 4, \frac{4}{6}, 10, \frac{1}{2}$$

1. Sort the numbers as fractions or whole numbers.

Use the following information to answer the next question.

4, 6, 75, 74, 61, 36, 47, 33, 58

2. Sort the given set of numbers as even or odd.

Use the following information to answer the next question.

34, 16, 63, 15, 45, 5, 31, 13, 56

3. Sort this set of numbers as greater than or less than 20.

Use the following information to answer the next question.

2, 7, 14, 18, 21, 24, 25, 28, 29, 32,
35, 37, 40, 41, 43, 44, 46, 49, 50

4. Sort the numbers in the box below according to whether they are less than 25 or 25 and greater and according to whether they are even or odd.

	<25	25 and >25
Even		
Odd		

Use the following information to answer the next question.

1, 6, 14, 16, 18, 3, 20,11, 21, 22, 23,7, 24, 25

5. Sort the numbers by whether they are greater than or less than 13 and whether they are even or odd.

Use the following information to answer the next question.

5, 24, 27, 8, 12, 15, 17, 18, 19, 20, 23, 28, 30, 31, 9, 10

6. Sort the numbers by whether they are greater than or less than 21 and whether they are odd or even.

Use the following information to answer the next question.

9, 11, 12, 2, 15, 8, 16, 5, 17, 19, 21, 3, 6, 22, 26, 4, 59

7. Sort the numbers in the box by whether they are 16 and less or greater than 16 and whether they are even or odd.

Determine the sorting rules used to group the numbers in the following tables.

8.

2, 6, 10, 12	14, 18, 24, 26, 28
1, 7, 9,11	13, 15, 19, 21, 25, 29, 31

9.

3, 5, 13, 15	17, 19, 21, 27, 29, 33, 41
4, 6, 12, 14	18, 20, 22, 26, 28, 30, 36

10.

6, 8, 10, 18	22, 26, 28, 30, 34, 36
5, 9, 13, 17, 19	21, 23, 25, 27, 29, 31, 39

Lesson 2 SORTING OBJECTS

The world is full of objects of all different shapes, sizes, and colours. Some objects are alike, and some are different. Look closely at the objects around you. The similarities and differences can be used to sort and organize them. Objects can be sorted by features such as colour, shape, size, and number.

✳✳ Example

Sort the following shapes into two groups according to size.

Solution

The shapes can be sorted into groups of small shapes and large shapes. Draw the three small shapes close to each other to show that they form one group. Then, draw the three large shapes close to each other to form another group.

The small shapes are sorted into one group. The large shapes are sorted into another group.

Just like numbers, you can sort objects using two or more attributes at the same time. Sometimes, the attributes are expressed as rules. For example, a sorting problem could be worded like this:

Sort these objects using the following rules:
• Rule 1 is large or small.
• Rule 2 is squares or circles.

 Time to Try 1

Sort these shapes into two groups according to size.

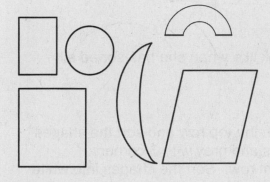

Sometimes shapes need to be sorted according to two different features. It can be helpful to use a table to sort the shapes or numbers. When objects are sorted by more than one similarity or difference, it is important to understand how they are grouped. Objects are sorted or grouped according to rules.

NOTES

 Example

Anna sorts these six shapes using the following rules:

• Rule 1 is 4 corners or 3 corners.

• Rule 2 is grey or white.

She uses this table to help her.

	4 Corners	3 Corners
Grey		
White		

What will Anna's chart look like when she has sorted all the shapes?

Solution

Remember to start with the top row and sort the shapes into grey with 4 corners and grey with 3 corners.
Next, look at the bottom row. Sort the shapes into white with 4 corners and white with 3 corners.

	4 Corners	3 Corners
Grey	▬ ▬	▲
White	▢	◺ △

Time to Try 2

Sort the following shapes according to size and number of sides.

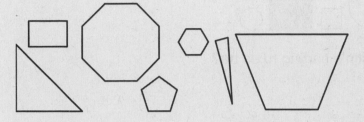

	Large Shape	**Small Shape**
3 sides		
4 or more sides		

Example

Sally sorts these buttons into the chart. Determine how the objects are sorted, and explain the sorting rule used.

Solution

Rule 1 is large or small.
Rule 2 is 2 holes or 4 holes.

	Large Buttons	**Small Buttons**
2 holes	⦿	⦿
4 holes	⦿	⦿

The buttons are sorted using two rules. First, they are placed into two different boxes because of their different sizes. Then, they are placed in two different boxes because of the number of holes.

NOTES

Time to Try 3

Justin wants to sort these six shapes using two rules.

What will Justin's sorting rules be?

VENN DIAGRAM

A Venn diagram is made up of two or more overlapping circles. It is used to show relationships between sets. The overlapping part of the circles shows the features that the sets have in common.

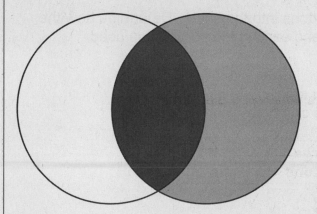

Venn diagrams are useful when you are comparing the features of two or more objects, shapes, or groups of numbers. Any feature that is located in the overlapping area of the circles is a feature that is shared. Using a Venn diagram allows you to easily recognize patterns (similarities and differences) in a problem because you have a picture to look at.

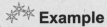 **Example**

Look at these objects, and sort them into the Venn diagram.

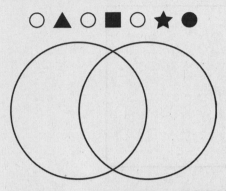

To solve this problem, decide how the shapes are the same and how they are different. Venn diagrams must have at least one thing in common. You can see that there are circles and some other shapes. Also, there are some white shapes and some dark shapes. The rule for the first circle is circles. The rule for the second circle is dark shapes. The dark circle goes in the overlapping space.

Solution

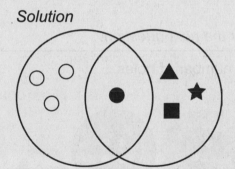

Time to Try 4

Sort these shapes using a Venn diagram.

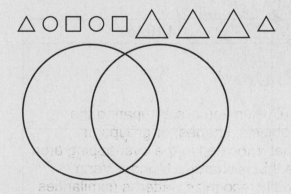

PRACTICE EXERCISES

Use the following information to answer the next question.

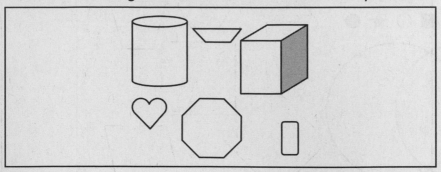

1. Sort the shapes in the box into two groups according to size.

Use the following information to answer the next question.

The buttons in the box need to be sorted by size and number of holes.

2. Sort the buttons according to the features listed in the table by drawing each button in the proper box.

	2 Holes	4 Holes
Small buttons		
Large buttons		

Use the following information to answer the next question.

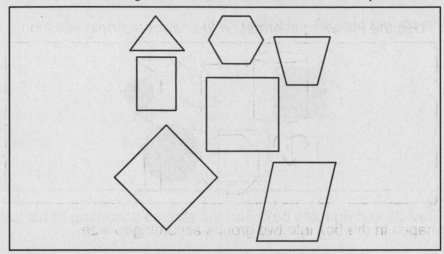

3. Sort the shapes according to size and number of sides.

	Large Shape	**Small Shape**
3 sides		
4 or more sides		

Use the following information to answer the next question.

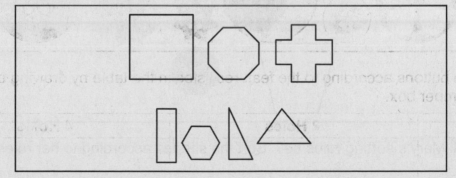

4. Mrs. Avery drew these shapes on the whiteboard. She wanted the class to sort them using two rules. What rules can the class use to sort them?

Use the following information to answer the next question.

David wants to sort six shapes using two rules.

5. What will David's sorting rules be? Sort the shapes according to his rules.

Use the following information to answer the next question.

Mary wants to sort these six shapes using two rules.

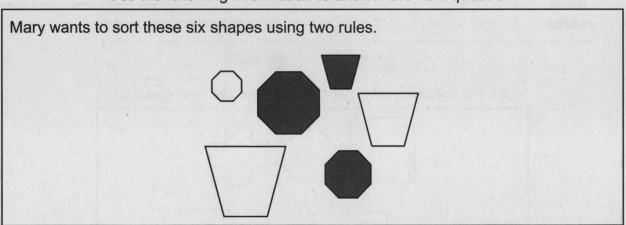

6. What will Mary's sorting rules be? Sort the shapes according to her rules.

Use the following information to answer the next question.

These seven shapes need to be placed in the Venn diagram shown.

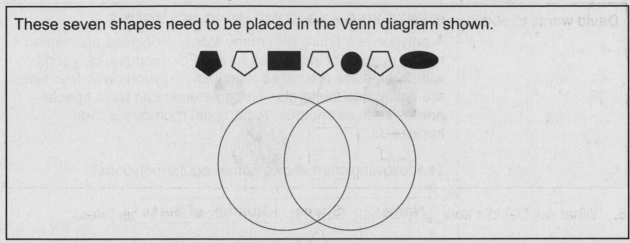

7. Sort the shapes into the Venn diagram.

Use the following information to answer the next question.

These seven shapes need to be placed in the Venn diagram shown.

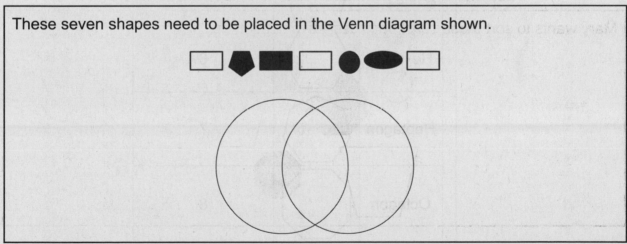

8. Sort the shapes using the Venn diagram shown.

Lesson 3   POLYGONS

NOTES

IDENTIFYING AND COMPARING POLYGONS

A polygon is a figure with many sides. Polygons are named by the number of sides they have. For example, polygons with three sides are called triangles. Polygons with four sides are called quadrilaterals. Quadrilaterals can have special names such as squares, rectangles, rhombuses, and trapezoids.

The following chart shows some regular polygons.

Name	Shape	Number of Sides
Triangle	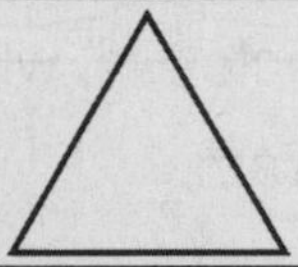	3
Square		4
Pentagon	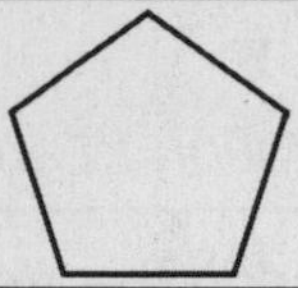	5
Hexagon	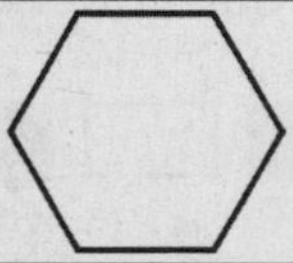	6
Heptagon	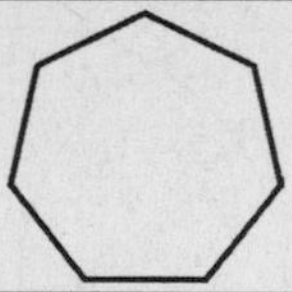	7
Octagon	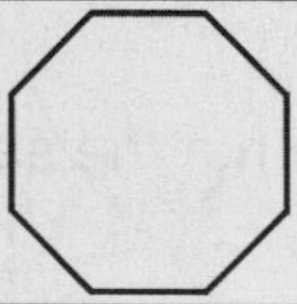	8

Example

What is the name of this polygon?

Solution

To answer this question, remember that a polygon is named by the number of sides it has. This figure has 8 sides. The name for an 8-sided figure is an octagon.

To help you remember, think of an octopus, which has 8 legs. The prefix *octo*- means 8.

 Time to Try 1

What is the name of this polygon?

In a regular polygon, all the sides are the same length. These shapes are regular polygons.

In an irregular polygon, all the sides are not the same length. These shapes are irregular polygons.

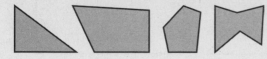

NOTES

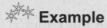 **Example**

Is this shape a regular or an irregular polygon?

Solution

It is a regular polygon.
All of the sides of the shape are the same length.
They are all equal. Irregular polygons have sides that
are different lengths.

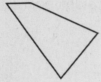 **Time to Try 2**

Is this shape a regular or an irregular polygon? Explain
your answer.

You can sort polygons by the number of sides the shape has.

Example

Sort these shapes based on the number of sides each
shape has.

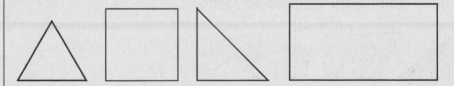

Solution

For this problem, you are comparing two different kinds of
polygons. You are comparing triangles and quadrilaterals.

Count the number of sides each polygon has.
The triangles have 3 sides. The rectangle and the square
each have 4 sides.

3 sides	4 sides
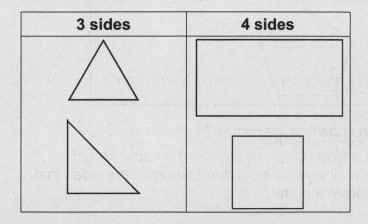	

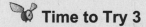 **Time to Try 3**

Sort the following shapes according to how many sides each
shape has.

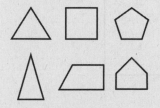

PRACTICE EXERCISES

Use the following information to answer the next question.

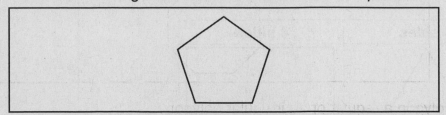

1. What is the name of the polygon shown in the picture?

Use the following information to answer the next question.

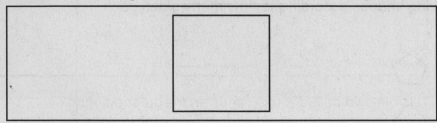

2. What is the name of this polygon?

Use the following information to answer the next question.

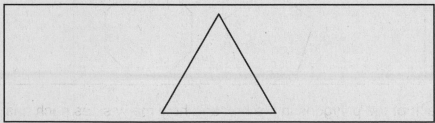

3. What is the name of the polygon shown here?

The shape shown here is a polygon.

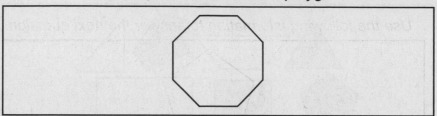

4. Is the polygon a regular or an irregular polygon?

The shape shown here is a polygon.

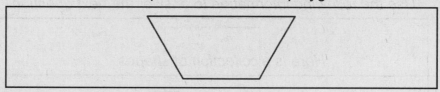

5. Is the polygon shown called a regular or an irregular polygon?

The shapes shown here is are polygons. .

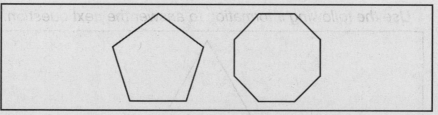

6. Name each of the polygons in the box and how many sides each has.

Here is a collection of shapes.

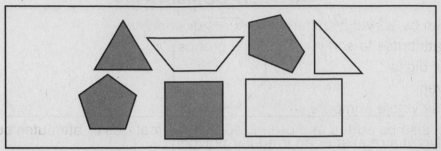

7. Sort the shapes according to how many sides each shape has.

Here is a collection of shapes.

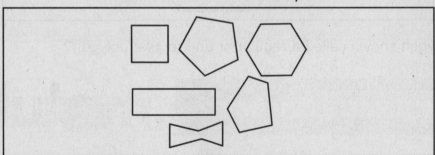

8. Sort the shapes in the picture according to the number of sides each shape has.

REVIEW SUMMARY

- Numbers can be sorted by different features or attributes.
- Use these attributes to sort numbers into groups:
  - Number of digits
  - Odd or even
  - Fractions or whole numbers
- Objects can also be sorted and organized by their features or attributes such as:
  - Shape
  - Size
  - Number
- Venn diagrams are used to show relationships between sets. They organize groups of shapes that are different but have a characteristic that is shared by both groups.
- Rules are used to sort objects or numbers into groups or sets.
- Polygons are many-sided figures. They are named according to the number of sides they have.
  - Regular polygons have equal side lengths and equal angles.
  - Irregular polygons have sides that are not equal and angles that are not equal.

PRACTICE TEST

Use the following information to answer the next question.

> 21, 28, 12, 34, 37,11, 41, 43, 9, 44, 45, 19, 16

1. Sort the numbers in the box according to whether they are less than or greater than 23 and whether they are even or odd.

Use the following information to answer the next question.

> 7, 10, 8,11, 12, 6, 3, 13, 14, 15, 16, 2, 5, 17, 18, 4

2. Sort the numbers in the box according to whether they are less than or greater than 9 and whether they are odd or even.

Use the following information to answer the next question.

> 3, 45, 6, 9, 42, 12, 39, 15, 36, 18, 33, 30, 21, 24, 27

3. Sort the numbers in the box given according to whether they are 27 or less or greater 27, and whether they are even or odd.

Use the following information to answer the next question.

4, 6, 8, 12	18, 20, 22, 24, 26
1, 3, 5, 7	13, 15, 17, 19, 21

4. Name the sorting rules used to group the numbers in the box.

Use the following information to answer the next question.

1, 3, 5, 7, 9, 11	13, 15, 17, 19, 21
2, 4, 6, 8, 10	12, 14, 16, 18, 20

5.   Name the sorting rules used to group the numbers in the box.

Use the following information to answer the next question.

2, 6, 12, 18	20, 28, 30, 34, 38
1, 3, 7, 9, 17	19, 27, 29, 33, 35, 41

6.   Name the sorting rules used to group the numbers in the box.

Use the following information to answer the next question.

$$1, \frac{1}{6}, \frac{9}{11}, 7, \frac{2}{3}, 2, \frac{1}{9}$$

7.   Sort the given numbers as fractions or whole numbers.

Sort the given shapes *into two groups according to size.*

8.

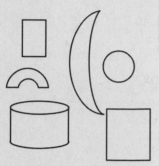

9.

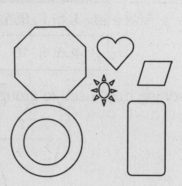

Use the following information to answer the next question.

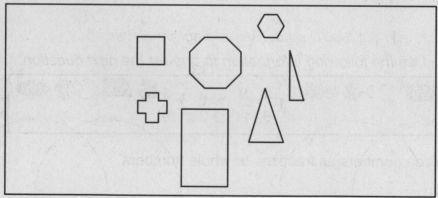

10. Sort the given shapes according to size and number of sides.

	Large Shape	**Small Shape**
3 sides		
4 or more sides		

Use the following information to answer the next question.

Jackson wants to sort these eight shapes using two rules.

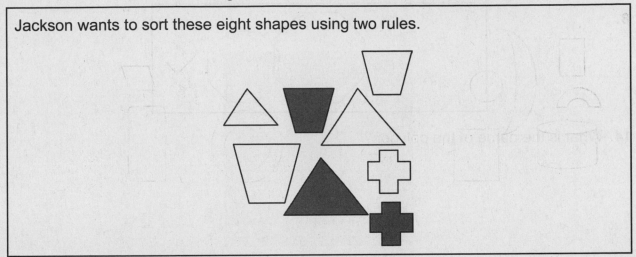

11. What sorting rules will Jackson use to sort the shapes?

Sort the shapes, and put them into the Venn diagram shown.

12.

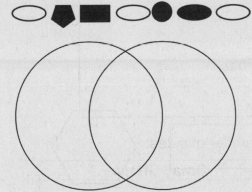

13.

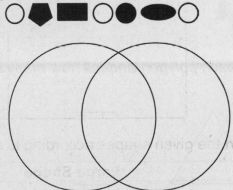

The shape shown here is a polygon.

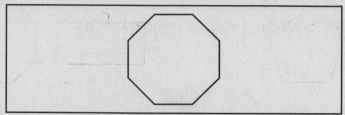

14. What is the name of the polygon?

The shape shown here is a polygon.

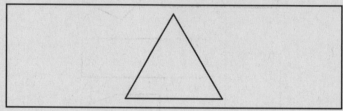

15. Is the polygon regular or irregular?

Name each polygon and tell how many sides each has.

16.

17.

18.

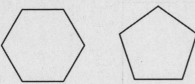

19.

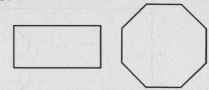

Use the following collection of shapes to answer the next question.

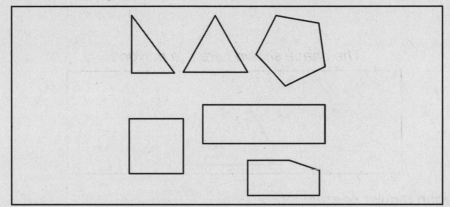

20. Sort the shapes according to how many sides each shape has.

NOTES

ESTIMATION

When you are finished this unit, you will be able to…
• estimate a given quantity using 10 as a referent
• estimate a given quantity using 100 as a referent
• estimate and count the number of objects in a group, then compare the estimated number with the actual number
• round numbers to the hundreds place value position

Lesson	Page	Completed on
1. Estimate, Count, and Compare	112	
2. Rounding Numbers	120	
Review Summary	124	
Practice Test	125	
Answers and Solutions	at the back of the book	

PREREQUISITE SKILLS AND KNOWLEDGE

Prior to starting this unit, you should be able to…
• estimate an answer
• round numbers to the tens place value position

Lesson 1 ESTIMATE, COUNT, AND COMPARE

NOTES

Questions about large numbers of objects can take a long time to answer. It would take a long time to count the number of pennies in a huge container or the number of cookies in a large jar. Making an estimate is an easier way to answer such questions.

An **estimate** is an answer that tells about how many. An estimate does not give the exact number. When you estimate an answer, you give your best guess, not the actual number. There are many different ways to make estimates.

One way to make an estimate is to use a referent. A referent can be a small group with a particular number of objects in it. This referent can be used to estimate a larger group of objects.

For example, break up a large group of objects into groups of about the same size. Count one group of objects to find an exact number. Then, use that exact number as a referent to estimate the total number of objects in the large group. Using numbers like 10 or 100 as equal groups makes it easier to count.

✳ Example

Estimate how many stars there are in this picture by counting out equal groups of 10.

112

Solution

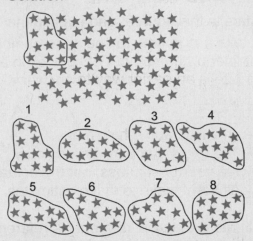

To estimate how many stars there are, count out one group of 10. Draw a circle around it. Next, break up the large group into smaller groups that look about the same size as your grouping of 10. Draw circles around those groups also. There will be about 8 equal smaller groups with about 10 stars in each group. To estimate the number of stars, count by 10 or add the number of groups together.
$10 + 10 + 10 + 10 + 10 + 10 + 10 + 10 = 80$

There are about 80 stars.

You can see if your estimate is close to the actual number of stars by counting the actual amount of stars in each group. Then, add the number of stars together.

The estimated number of stars is 80. The actual number of stars is 89. Use subtraction to find the difference between the actual number and the estimate.

$$\begin{array}{r} 89 \\ -80 \\ \hline 9 \end{array}$$

The estimate is close to the actual number. There are nine more stars than the estimated number of stars.

NOTES

 Time to Try 1

Estimate the number of stars in this square, and explain the strategy used.

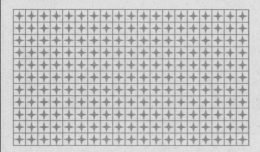

Another way to estimate a large number of objects is to compare the number of objects to 100. Count out 100 of the objects. See what that number of objects looks like. Then, estimate how many groups of that size could be in the original large group. You can count by 100s. The number you come up with is your estimate.

NOTES

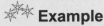 **Example**

Estimate the number of pennies in the jar if there are 100 pennies in the hand shown below.

Solution

Look at the 100 pennies in the small group.
Compare them to the number of pennies in the jar.
Think of how many groups of 100 pennies there are in the jar. It looks like about 4 groups of 100 pennies.

Add $100 + 100 + 100 + 100 = 400$.

The estimated number of pennies in the jar is 400.

 Time to Try 2

Estimate the number of pages in the math textbook shown below. There are 100 pieces of paper in a stack next to the textbook shown below. Use this information to estimate how many pages are in the textbook.

I estimate that there are _____ pages in the textbook

because _____.

Sometimes an exact answer is needed after an estimate has been made. For example, if the person who estimates the number of pennies correctly wins the container of pennies, an exact answer must be known. In a case like this, you must count the objects one by one and compare the exact number with the estimated number.

PRACTICE EXERCISES

This picture shows a collection of stars.

1. Explain how you would estimate the number of stars in the picture using 10 as a referent.

Here is a design of flower shapes.

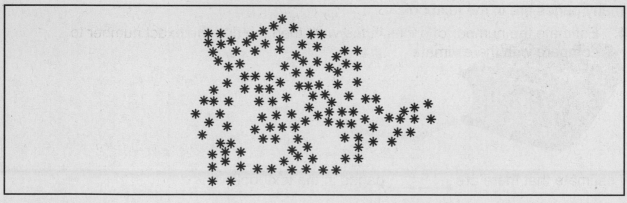

2. Using equal groups, estimate how many flower shapes are in the picture.

The following picture is a group of small squares.

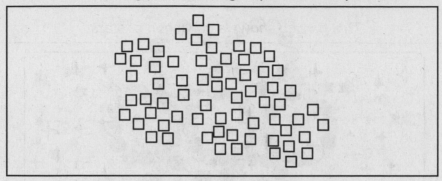

3. Using equal groups, estimate the number of squares there are in the picture.

Use the following picture of bricks to answer the next question.

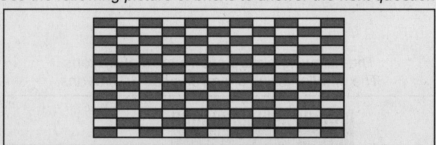

4. Estimate the number of bricks in the wall, then the find the exact number to compare with the estimate.

This picture shows a set of bangles made up of beads.

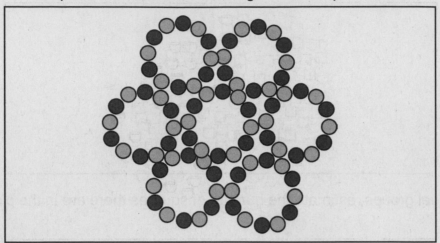

5. Estimate how many beads are used to make the set of bangles, and then find the exact number of beads.

The following picture shows rows of crayons.
The smaller group of crayons has 10 crayons.

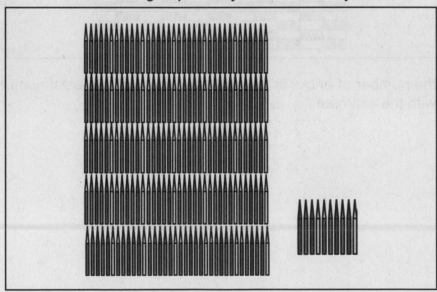

6. Using equal grouping, estimate how many crayons are shown in the picture.

Use the following diagram to answer the next question.

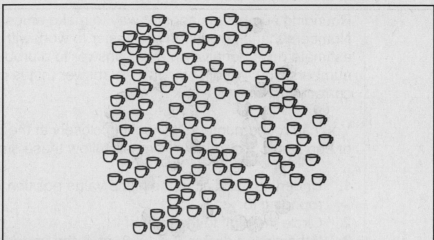

7. Austin estimates that there are about 100 cups in this picture. Using the strategy of counting out groups of 10, explain if his estimate is reasonable.

Lesson 2   ROUNDING NUMBERS

NOTES

Rounding numbers is another way to make an estimate. Numbers that are rounded are easier to work with. Since an estimate does not give an exact answer to a problem, rounded numbers work well. They give an answer that is close to the correct answer.

You can round numbers by looking closely at the place value of each digit. To round a number, follow these steps.

1. Underline the digit in the place value position that you are rounding to.
2. Circle the digit to the right of it.
3. If the circled digit is 0, 1, 2, 3, or 4, the underlined digit stays the same. The digits to the right of the underlined digit become zeros.
4. If the circled digit is 5, 6, 7, 8, or 9, the underlined digit goes up by 1. The digits to the right of the underlined digit become zeros.

Example

Round the following numbers to the nearest ten.

a) 38

Solution

3⑧
The number is being rounded to the nearest ten.
Underline the digit 3 because it is in the tens place.
Circle the 8 in the ones position. Since 8 is greater than 5, the 3 goes up by 1 to become 4. The digit to the right becomes zero. The number 38 is rounded up to 40.

b) 74

Solution

7④
Underline the digit 7 because it is in the tens place and the number is being rounded to the nearest ten. Circle the 4 in the ones place. The digit 4 is less than 5, so the 7 stays the same. The number to the right becomes zero.
The number 74 is rounded down to 70.

NOTES

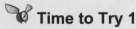 **Time to Try 1**

Round the following numbers to the nearest ten.

a) 92   **b)** 15

Numbers can also be rounded to the hundreds place value position. Follow the same steps that you have been using. Underline the digit in the hundreds position, and circle the digit to the right of it.

Example

Round the number 864 to the nearest hundred.
8⑥4

Solution

900
The number is being rounded to the nearest hundred.
Underline the 8 because it is in the hundreds position.
Circle the 6 in the tens position. Since 6 is greater than 5, the 8 changes. The 8 becomes 1 greater, which is 9.
All the other numbers to the right become zeros.
Rounded to the nearest hundred, the number 864 is 900.
This is called rounding up because the rounded number is greater than the original number.

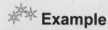 **Time to Try 2**

Round the number 455 to the nearest hundred.

PRACTICE EXERCISES

1. Round the number 24 to the nearest ten.

2. Round the number 67 to the nearest ten.

3. Round the number 419 to the nearest hundred.

4. Round the number 562 to the nearest hundred.

Use the following information to answer the next three questions.

Nigel is doing a report on the number of students in his school who play sports. The table shows the information that he has gathered.

Sport	Number of Students
Soccer	105
Hockey	82
Baseball	65
Gymnastics	43
Swimming	36

5. Rounded to the nearest ten, about how many students at Nigel's school play a sport?

6. Exactly how many students at Nigel's school play a sport?

7. How far away from the exact amount was your estimate? Circle one.

   A. < 5
   B. 5 to 10
   C. >10
   D. 15 to 20

REVIEW SUMMARY

- An estimate is an answer that tells about how many, not the exact number. It is your best guess, not the actual answer.
- One way to make an estimate for a large number of objects is to break up the objects into groups of about the same size.
  - Count the objects in one of the groups. Use this number to estimate the total number of objects.
  - Use numbers like 10 and 100 for your equal groups to make it easier to count.
- Another way to make an estimate is to round numbers. Rounding numbers can help you predict the answers to math problems. Numbers that are rounded are easier to work with.
  - Round up (increase by 1) if the digit to the right of your place value position is 5 or more.
  - Round down (leave the number the same) if the digit to the right of your place value position is 4 or less.
- Number lines are another way to round numbers. Number lines help you see which ten or hundred a number is closer to.
- You can compare your estimate to the exact number to see how close your estimate is.

PRACTICE TEST

Here is a design of flower shapes.

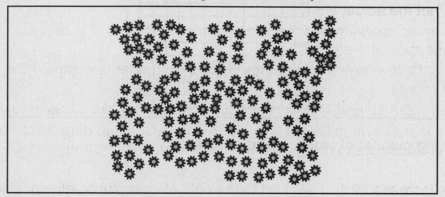

1. Using a group of 10 as a referent, estimate how many flowers there are in the picture.

Here is a design of heart shapes.

2. Use a group of 10 as a referent, and estimate how many hearts there are in this picture.

Here is a design of square blocks.

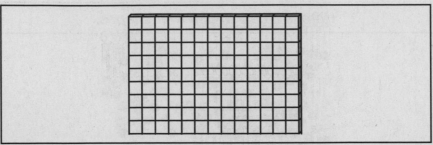

3. Estimate the number of blocks in this picture.

The star in this picture is filled with bubbles.

4. The number of bubbles shown in the small group is 100. Estimate the number of bubbles in the star.

Use the following diagram to answer the next question.

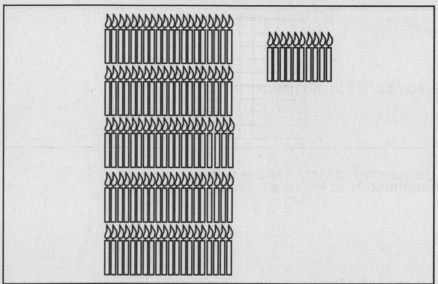

5. If the referent group is 10 candles, estimate the number of candles shown in the figure.

Here is a design of hexagon shapes

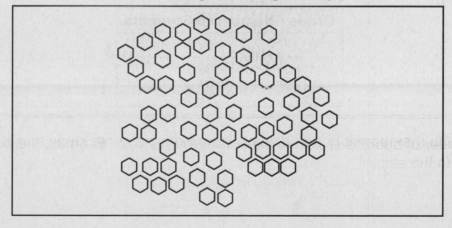

6. Jordan uses equal groups of 10 to estimate the number of hexagons to be 60. Is Jordan's estimate reasonable?

7. Round the number 86 to the nearest ten.

8. Round the number 73 to the nearest ten.

9. Round the number 17 to the nearest ten.

10. Round the number 637 to the nearest hundred.

Use the following information to answer the next two questions.

Susan is doing a report on the number of students in her school who study music. She looks at different grades. The table shows the information that she gathered.

Grade	Number of Students
3	274
4	196
5	231

11. Rounded to the nearest hundred, about how many students study music in Grade 3?

12. Rounded to the nearest hundred, how many students study music in all the grades shown?

ADDITION AND SUBTRACTION

When you are finished this unit, you will be able to...

• use objects and pictures to show how to add and subtract up to 1 000 with and without regrouping

• recognize key words to solve addition or subtraction problems

• estimate the solution to an addition or subtraction problem using rounding

Lesson	Page	Completed on
1. Addition with and without Regrouping	130	
2. Subtraction with and without Regrouping	141	
3. Solving Problems with Addition, Subtraction, and Estimation	149	
Review Summary	158	
Practice Test	159	
Answers and Solutions	at the back of the book	

PREREQUISITE SKILLS AND KNOWLEDGE

Prior to starting this unit, you should be able to...

• add and subtract two-digit numbers without regrouping

• round numbers to the nearest tens and hundreds places

Lesson 1 ADDITION WITH AND WITHOUT REGROUPING

Every day you are faced with the task of adding numbers, at home, at school, even when you are playing with your friends. To add number together, first line up the numbers by matching their place value positions. Then, work from the right to the left. Knowing your basic math facts will make two-digit and three-digit addition problems easier.

BASIC MATH FACTS

You can use basic math facts to help you add other numbers as well. For example, you know that $2 + 3 = 5$. This basic fact can help you solve other expressions such as $20 + 30$ and $200 + 300$.

Since $2 + 3 = 5$, then $20 + 30 = 50$, and $200 + 300 = 500$.

Keep the place value chart in mind when you are adding and subtracting numbers.

Hundreds	Tens	Ones
H	T	O

Be sure to line up the place value positions of the digits in the numbers.

247
+32
279

You can also organize information in a place value chart. This will help you see what is actually happening when you add numbers in your head.

For example, what is the sum of $30 + 40$?

H	T	O
	3	0
	4	0

Both numbers have a zero in the ones place, so you only need to add the numbers in the tens place.
$3 + 4 = 7$

The answer is 7 tens. You can write 7 tens as 70.

H	T	O
	3	0
	4	0
	7	0

To add a three-digit number, line up the place value positions in the same way.

 Example

Add the numbers 257 and 32.

2	5	7
+	3	2

Solution

Step 1
Start on the right, and work to the left. Add the ones column.
$7 + 2 = 9$

Write a 9 in the ones place under the line.
$$\begin{array}{r} 257 \\ + \ 32 \\ \hline 9 \end{array}$$

Step 2
Move to the left. Add the tens column.
$5 + 3 = 8$

Write an 8 in the tens place under the line.
$$\begin{array}{r} 257 \\ + \ 32 \\ \hline 89 \end{array}$$

Step 3
Move to the left. Add the hundreds column.

There is no number to add to the top number in the hundreds place, so write the top number under the line in the hundreds place (2).

2	5	7
+	3	2
2	8	9

NOTES

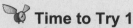 **Time to Try 1**

What is the sum of 482 and 117?

```
  482
+ 117
```

ADDING WITH BASE TEN BLOCKS

You can use base ten blocks to help you solve addition questions.

To show the addition problem 152 + 24 with base ten blocks, decide which blocks to use.
The number 152 can be shown with 1 flat, 5 rods, and 2 units.

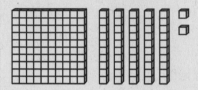

The number 24 can be shown with 2 rods and 4 units.

Line the base ten blocks up as you would the numbers.
This is how the addition problem 152 + 24 looks with base ten blocks.

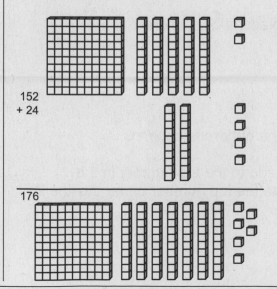

```
152
+ 24
```

```
176
```

132

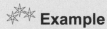 **Example**

Using base ten blocks, show the addition problem 231 + 642, and then solve it.

Solution

To show this addition problem, decide which blocks to use.

- The number 231 can be shown using 2 flats, 3 rods, and 1 unit.
- The number 642 can be shown using 6 flats, 4 rods, and 2 units.

Line up the blocks to add them.

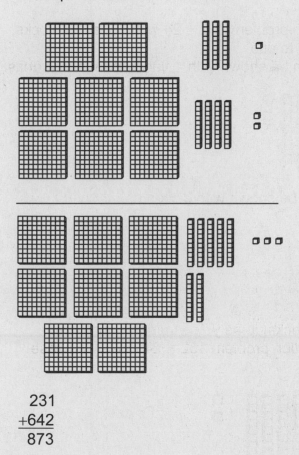

231
+642
873

NOTES

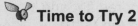 **Time to Try 2**

Show the addition problem 846 + 143 using base ten blocks, and then solve.

ADDITION WITH REGROUPING

Some addition problems cannot be done without regrouping. Regrouping is when you exchange amounts of an equal value to rename a number. For example, 11 units can be regrouped into 1 ten rod and 1 unit. Both base ten blocks equal 11.

NOTES

As well, 11 rods can be regrouped into 1 hundred flat and 1 ten rod. Both equal the number one hundred ten (110).

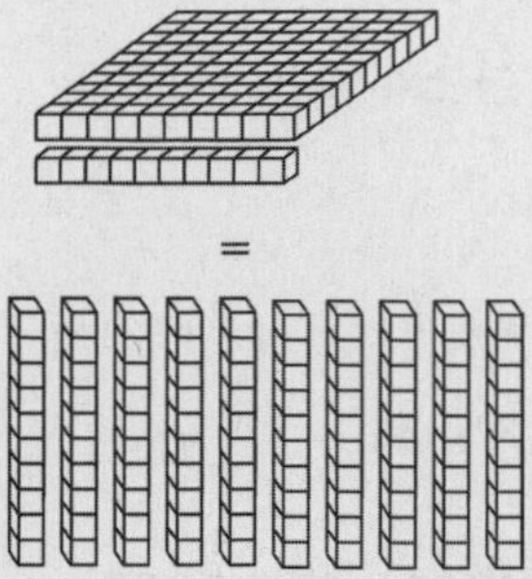

Only one digit is allowed in each place value position. Regroup the base ten materials whenever the sum is a two-digit number.

Example

Use regrouping when adding 37 and 54 with base ten blocks.

Solution

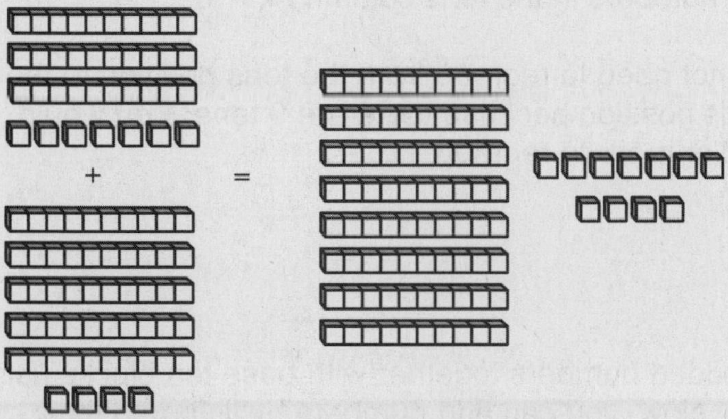

There are 11 units.

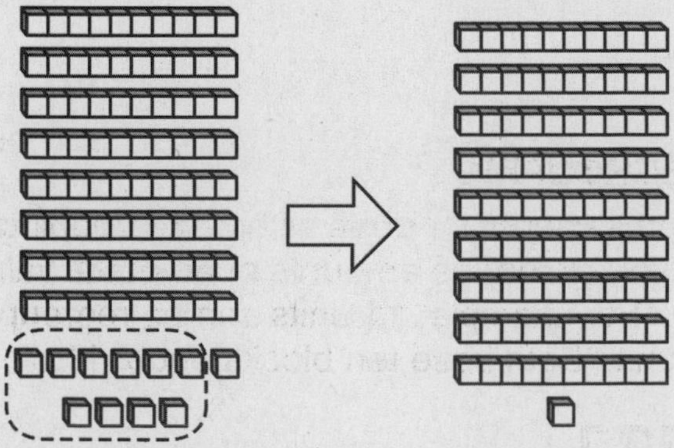

Regroup the units.
10 units = 1 tens rod
$10+10+10+10+10+10+10+10+10+1=91$

NOTES

You can also regroup using pencil and paper.

 Example

Use regrouping in the addition problem 37 + 54 with pencil and paper.

Solution

Step 1

Add the numbers in the ones column (7 + 4).

The sum is 11, which is a two-digit number. The ones column can only hold one digit, so the number needs to be regrouped. Regroup the 11 ones into 1 ten and 1 one.

Keep the 1 unit in the ones place, and add 1 ten to the top of the tens place value column. Now you have 4 tens in the tens place.

Step 2

Add the numbers in the tens column (4 + 5).

You do not need to regroup from the tens position to the hundreds position because there are 9 tens. You would need 10 or more to regroup.

$$
\begin{array}{r}
{}^{1} \\
37 \\
+\,54 \\
\hline
91
\end{array}
$$

You have added numbers together with base ten blocks using regrouping. Now, you can add numbers by lining up their place value positions.

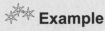 **Example**

Use base ten blocks to show the addition problem 268 + 524, and then solve.

Solution

Step 1
Set up the addition problem.

Start by choosing the base ten blocks to represent the numbers 268 and 524.

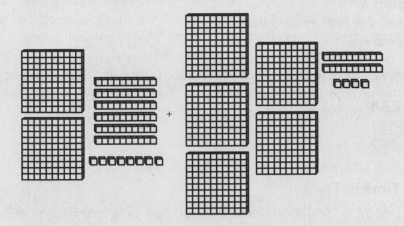

Next, line up the place value positions. Write the numbers one above the other so you can add them together.

268
+524

Step 2
Add the ones column.
$8 + 4 = 12$

Only 1 digit is allowed in a place value position, so you need to regroup the 12. The 12 ones regroup into 1 ten and 2 ones.

Write a 2 in the ones place under the line. Put a small 1 above the tens column.

$\overset{1}{2}68$
+524
2

NOTES

Step 3
Add the tens column.
$1 + 6 + 2 = 9$

It is important to remember to add the 1.
Write a 9 in the tens place under the line.

$$
\begin{array}{r}
^{1} \\
268 \\
+524 \\
\hline
92 \\
\end{array}
$$

Step 4
Add the hundreds column.
$2 + 5 = 7$

Write a 7 in the hundreds place under the line.

$$
\begin{array}{r}
^{1} \\
268 \\
+524 \\
\hline
792 \\
\end{array}
$$

 Time to Try 3

Use base ten blocks to show the addition problem 615 + 369, and then solve.

PRACTICE EXERCISES

1.   644
    +231

2.   287
    +455

3.   367
    +285

4.   470
    +204

5.   609
    +246

6. Using base ten blocks, show the addition problem 862 + 125, and then solve.

7. 467
   +216

8. 284
   +468

9. 229
   +597

10. Using base ten blocks, show the addition problem 464 + 387, and then solve.

Lesson 2 SUBTRACTION WITH AND WITHOUT REGROUPING

You can also use basic math facts to help you subtract numbers. For example, you could use math facts to answer the number sentence 12 – 4.
12 – 4 = 8

However, if you had to subtract 120 – 40 your knowledge of basic facts could help you solve this question.

Ignore the zeros for a moment, and simply subtract 4 from 12. You get 8. Since both 120 and 40 end with a zero, a zero needs to be added to your solution of 8 to get the number 80.
120 – 40 = 80

H	T	O
1	2	0
	4	0
	8	0

To subtract a three-digit number, line up the place value positions. Subtract the smaller number (on the bottom) from the bigger number (on the top).

 Example

  369
–145

Solution

Step 1
Start on the right, and work to the left. Subtract the bottom number in the ones column from the top number in the ones columns.
9 – 5 = 4

Write the 4 under the line in the ones place.
  369
–145
    4

NOTES

Step 2
Next, subtract the bottom number in the tens column from the top number in the tens column.
$6 - 4 = 2$

Write the 2 under the line in the tens place.

```
  369
 −145
   24
```

Step 3
Finally, subtract the bottom number in the hundreds column from the top number in the hundreds column
$3 - 1 = 2$

Write the 2 under the line in the hundreds place.

```
  369
 −145
  224
```

 Time to Try 1
Solve the subtraction problem 743 − 21.

```
 743
− 21
```

SUBTRACTING WITH BASE TEN BLOCKS
Base ten blocks can be used to help solve subtraction problems. In each place value position, look at the digits carefully. If the digit being taken away is smaller than the digit it is being taken away from, you do not need to regroup. Here is a good example.

```
 78
−32
 46
```

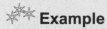 **Example**

Using base ten blocks, show the subtraction problem
179 – 64, and then solve.

Solution

To show the subtraction problem 179 – 64 with base ten
blocks, decide which blocks represent which place value.
The number 179 can be shown with 1 flat, 7 rods, and 9
units.

The number 64 can be shown with 6 rods and 4 units.

Line up the base ten blocks as you would the numbers.
Flats are hundreds, rods are tens, and units are ones.
These base ten blocks show the subtraction problem
179 – 64.

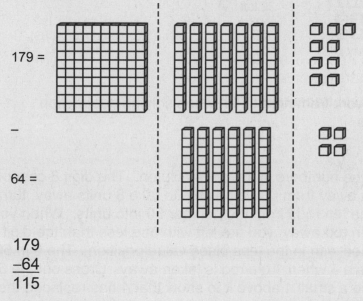

179 =

–

64 =

$$\begin{array}{r} 179 \\ -\ 64 \\ \hline 115 \end{array}$$

Time to Try 2

Using base ten blocks, show the subtraction problem
687 – 254 , and then solve.

NOTES

SUBTRACTION WITH REGROUPING

Often you will need to regroup in a subtraction question. If the digit that is being taken away is larger than the digit it is being taken away from, you must regroup. For example, the subtraction problem 50 – 28 requires regrouping.

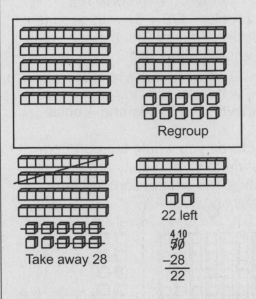

Always work from right to left when solving subtraction problems.

Step 1

Look at the numbers in the ones column. The digit 8 cannot be taken away from 0. To be able to take 8 units away, turn one of the ten rods from the number 50 into units. When you take a ten rod away, you are left with one less than the digit you started with in the tens place value position. The 5 in 50 becomes a 4 when 1 ten rod is taken away. Cross out the 5, and place a small 4 above it to show that 4 has replaced the 5.

Step 2

To bring the ten rod into the ones place value position, it needs to be broken into units. The 10 units equal 1 ten rod. Now that you have 10 units in the ones position, continue working on the subtraction problem. Take away the 8 units from the 10 units. This leaves 2 units in the ones place value position. Move to the left to complete the problem. The 2 ten rods are taken away from the 4 ten rods. That leaves 2 ten rods. The answer to this problem is 22.

You can easily solve subtraction questions using pencil and paper after you build the question with base ten blocks.

 Example

Use base ten blocks to show $731 - 413$, then solve the number sentence.

Solution

Subtract 413 from 731. Be sure to line up the numbers. Remember to subtract the bottom digit from the top digit.

$$\begin{array}{r} {\scriptstyle 212} \\ 7\cancel{3}1 \\ -413 \\ \hline 318 \end{array}$$

The number 731 can be shown using 7 flats, 3 rods, and 1 unit. The number 413 can be shown using 4 flats, 1 rod, and 3 units.

Step 1

There is only 1 unit in the ones place value position for the top number. You cannot take away 3 units from 1 unit. Therefore, you need to borrow 1 ten rod and regroup.

The 3 tens rods can be regrouped into 2 tens rods and 10 units. Cross out the 3 tens, and write a small 2 above the 3.

Add the 10 units to the 1 unit. You now have 11 units. Cross out the 2, and write a small 12 above the 2.

Now, subtract the units.
$11 - 3 = 8$

Step 2
Subtract the rods.
$2 - 1 = 1$

NOTES

Step 3
Subtract the flats.

7 − 4 = 3

The following base ten blocks show the subtraction problem 731 − 413 and the answer.

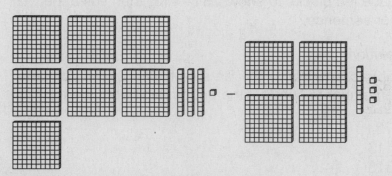

 Time to Try 3

Use base ten blocks to show 578 − 49, then solve the problem using regrouping.

578
−49

146

PRACTICE EXERCISES

1. 187
   −42

2. 789
   −356

3. 827
   −614

4. Using base ten blocks, show the subtraction problem 574 – 342, and then solve.

5. Using base ten blocks, show the subtraction problem 698 – 453, and then solve.

6. Use base ten blocks to show 662 – 247, and then solve the question.

7. Using base ten blocks, show the subtraction problem 843 – 216, and then solve.

8. Using base ten blocks, show the subtraction problem 425 – 367, and then solve.

9. Using base ten blocks, show the subtraction problem 321 – 165, and then solve.

10. Using base ten blocks, show the subtraction problem 536 – 274, and then solve.

Lesson 3 SOLVING PROBLEMS WITH ADDITION, SUBTRACTION, AND ESTIMATION

Now that you know how to regroup, addition and subtraction with bigger numbers becomes simpler. Solving addition and subtraction word problems is easier because you can focus on the problem-solving steps, strategies, and key words. You do not have to worry about how to do the adding and subtracting anymore.

Problem-Solving Steps
- Figure out what the question is asking.
- Find the important information.
- Choose a strategy.
- Solve the problem.
- Check the answer using inverse operations.
- Write the answer in a complete sentence

ADDITION PROBLEMS

A problem is usually an addition problem if it contains such key words as:

- add
- sum
- total
- plus
- altogether
- in all

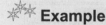 **Example**

Underline the key word or words in the word problem.
Then, solve the problem.

A school bus stops four times on the way to school. At the first stop, the bus picks up 7 children. It picks up 6 children at the second stop, 9 children at the third stop, and 12 children at the last stop. How many children are picked up by the school bus altogether?

Solution

Step 1
There is a lot of information in this word problem.
The first step in solving the problem is to find out what the question is asking. The question is asking you how many children the bus picks up. The key word *altogether* tells you that you are going to add to find the answer to this problem. Did you underline the word *altogether*?

NOTES

Step 2
The second step is to find the important information.
The important information is the number of children picked up at each stop.
- First stop: 7
- Second stop: 6
- Third stop: 9
- Fourth stop: 12

Some helpful problem-solving strategies are:
- Draw a picture.
- Make an organized list.
- Use a table.
- Look for a pattern.
- Work backward.
- Guess and check.

Step 3
You could use a number of different strategies to solve this problem. Choose the strategy that works best for you.
Try drawing a picture to solve this problem.

First Stop

Second Stop

Third Stop

Fourth Stop

Step 4
To solve the problem, add the number of children from each bus stop.
7 + 6 + 9 + 12 = 34

or

$$\begin{array}{r} {\scriptstyle 2} \\ 7 \\ 6 \\ 9 \\ +12 \\ \hline 34 \end{array}$$

Be sure to line up the place value positions.

Step 5
To check the answer, use the inverse operation or a calculator.

You have added numbers to solve this problem. To use the inverse operation, start with 34 children. Then, subtract the number of children at each stop.
34 − 12 − 9 − 6 − 7 = 0

Step 6
Write the answer in a complete sentence.

Altogether, 34 children are picked up by the school bus.

NOTES

 Time to Try 1

Alaina's school was collecting food for the food bank. Alaina's mom put 34 food items in a bag. Then, Alaina's grandpa gave her a bag with 16 food items. How many food items did Alaina collect in all?

SUBTRACTION PROBLEMS

A problem is usually a subtraction problem if it contains such key words as

- Subtract
- Less
- Difference
- How many more
- Minus
- How much more
- Remains
- How many left

 Example

Carrie baked 26 muffins for her family and her friends. She gave 4 muffins to her friend Teiya. Her brother Ted ate 6 muffins, and then the family ate 4 for dessert. How many muffins does Carrie have left?

Solution

The words *how many…left* tell you that this problem is a subtraction problem. Subtract each amount that was given away or eaten from the total number that Carrie baked.
$26 - 4 = 22$
$22 - 6 = 16$
$16 - 4 = 12$
Check your answer.
$12 + 4 + 6 + 4 = 26$

Carrie has 12 muffins left.

or

Add up the number of muffins that were given away or eaten. Then subtract this sum from the total number of muffins Carrie baked.
$4 + 6 + 4 = 14$
$26 - 14 = 12$
Check your answer.
$12 + 14 = 26$

Carrie has 12 muffins left.

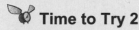 **Time to Try 2**

Matteo took 153 hockey cards to school. When he got home, he had 138 left. How many more hockey cards did Matteo take to school than he brought home?

ESTIMATION

You can also use estimation to find the sum or difference in problems. The key words *approximately* and *about* tell you to estimate. To find *approximately how much* or *about how many*, estimate the answer by rounding the numbers in the problem. When an exact amount is asked for, do not use estimation.

ESTIMATION USING THE FIRST DIGIT

One way to estimate numbers is to use the first digit of the number and replace all the digits to the right with zeros.

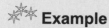 **Example**

Noah has 73 marbles in his red bag and 28 marbles in his blue bag. Approximately how many marbles does Noah have altogether?

Solution

The word *approximately* lets you know that you are looking for an estimated answer, not an exact answer.

Estimate the numbers using the first digit of the number. Replace the digit in the ones with a zero. Find the sum by adding the numbers together.

73 → 70   70
28 → 20   +20
                    90

Noah has approximately 90 marbles.

NOTES

 Time to Try 3

Jonah collects hockey cards and baseball cards. He has 86 baseball cards and 31 hockey cards. About how many more hockey cards than baseball cards does Jonah have?

ESTIMATION BY ROUNDING

A more accurate way to estimate is by rounding numbers. Follow these steps to round numbers:

• Underline the number in the place value position that you are rounding to. When you are rounding to the greatest place value position, underline the number in the position farthest to the left.

• Circle the number to the right of it.

• If the circled number is 0, 1, 2, 3, or 4, the underlined number remains the same. The numbers to the right of the underlined number become zeros.

• If the circled number is 5, 6, 7, 8, or 9, the underlined number goes up by one. The numbers to the right of the underlined number become zeros.

 Example

Try to answer the following problem using estimation.

Rhonda is keeping track of the number of vehicles that her family passes on the way to Lethbridge. So far, she has counted 46 cars and 32 trucks. Approximately how many vehicles has her family passed?

Solution

The word *approximately* lets you know that you are looking for an estimated answer, not an exact answer. Round the numbers to the nearest ten, and then find the sum.

46 → 50
32 → 30
      30

Rhonda's family has passed approximately 80 vehicles.

Time to Try 4

Treva has two different collections. One collection is rocks, and the other is stamps. Her rock collection has 96 rocks. She has 25 stamps in her stamp collection. About how many more rocks than stamps does she have?

PRACTICE EXERCISES

1. Marnie has 621 marbles. She plays a game of marbles and wins 192 more.
    How many marbles in total does Marnie have now?

2. Abby bakes 33 cookies. She eats 3 and gives 4 each to her friends Mona, Trista,
    and Babs. Then, she gives 2 cookies to her brother and 1 to her grandmother.
    How many cookies does Abby have left?

3. Roggie is collecting money to donate to a charity. He donates $5 himself.
    His mother gives him $7, his father gives $10, his grandfather gives $15, his
    grandmother gives $8, and his sister gives $3. What is the total amount of money
    Roggie collects to donate to the charity?

4. Forrest is putting pictures into his album. He has already put 56 pictures in the
    album, but he has 127 pictures in his collection. How many more pictures does he
    have to put in his album?

5. Sammy has 784 acorns. Bob has 916 acorns. How many more acorns does Bob
    have than Sammy?

6. Mary has 47 pennies, Alice has 137 pennies, and Jeff has 249 pennies. How many pennies do the children have altogether?

7. Keith has 24 baseball cards. Kelly has 37 baseball cards. If you round to the nearest ten, approximately how many cards do they have altogether?

8. Bolun is reading a book that has 92 pages. Brenna's book has 27 pages. About how many more pages does Bolun's book have than Brenna's book?

9. Morris saved $157. Bonnie saved $343 more than Morris. How much money did they save altogether?

10. A skateboard costs $130. A hockey stick costs $50 less than a skateboard. If Ashis gives the cashier $100 to buy a hockey stick, how much change will he get?

REVIEW SUMMARY

- Use basic facts for two-digit and three-digit addition and subtraction.
- Line up the numbers in their correct place value positions when you add and subtract.
  - Only one digit is allowed in each place value position.
- Regroup to exchange amounts of equal value to rename a number.
- Use base ten blocks to help you solve problems.
- Check the answer using a calculator, estimation, or inverse operations.
  - An inverse operation is an opposite operation. Addition is used to check the answer to a subtraction problem. Subtraction is used to check the answer to an addition problem.
- An addition problem usually uses one or more of the following key words: add, sum, total, plus, altogether, in all.
- A subtraction problem usually uses one or more of the following key words: subtract, difference, minus, remains, how many more, how much more, how much less.
- You can also use estimation to find the sum or difference in problems.
  - One way to estimate numbers is to use the first digit of the number and replace all the digits to the right with zeros.
  - A more accurate way to estimate is by rounding numbers

PRACTICE TEST

1.   240
       +255

2.   324
       +265

3.   699
       −527

4.   319
       −216

5.   239
       +109

6.   799
       +107

7.   381
       −224

8.   906
       −860

9. Estimate the sum of $\begin{array}{r} 72 \\ +86 \end{array}$ by rounding to the nearest ten.

10. Estimate the sum of $\begin{array}{r} 18 \\ +31 \end{array}$ by rounding to the nearest ten.

11. 194
    −96

12. 962
    −108

13. Abrar, Angela and Nimesha went bowling. Abrar bowled 127, Angela bowled 94, and Nimesha bowled 138. What is the sum of their scores?

14. Matt, Danielle, and Timothy were collecting seashells. Matt collected 214, Danielle collected 197, and Timothy collected 64. How many seashells did all three friends collect?

15. The Calgary Stampeders played the Edmonton Eskimos in a football game. The Stampeders scored 42 points. The Eskimos scored 27 points. How many more points did the Stampeders score than the Eskimos?

16. Jayden and Kayla each have a bag of candy. Jayden's bag has 142 candies, and Kayla's bag has 67 candies. How many more candies does Jayden have than Kayla?

17. Christian needs to collect 73 stickers to win a prize. He has collected 28 so far. Estimate using the first digit of each number to find about how many more stickers he needs to collect?

18. Ayesha, Portia, and Yestina each buy a bag of peppermints. Ayesha's bag has 92 peppermints, Portia's bag has 37, and Yestina's bag has 53. Estimate using the first digit of each number to find approximately how many peppermints they have altogether?

19. You buy a toy drum that costs $6 and a doll that costs $8. You hand the cashier $20. If there is no tax on the items, how much change will you receive?

20. A toy robot costs $8, and a beach ball costs $2. You buy 2 robots and 4 beach balls. You hand the cashier two twenty-dollar bills. What will your change be?

NOTES

MENTAL MATH STRATEGIES

When you are finished this unit, you will be able to…
• add and subtract basic facts to 18
• explain the strategy you use to solve addition or subtraction problems
• tell why the strategy you choose for an addition or subtraction problem is best

Lesson	Page	Completed on
1. Basic Facts	164	
2. Metal Math Addition Strategies	174	
3. Metal Math Subtraction Strategies	179	
Review Summary	183	
Practice Test	184	
Answers and Solutions	at the back of the book	

PREREQUISITE SKILLS AND KNOWLEDGE

Prior to starting this unit, you should be able to…
• use addition and subtraction facts to 10
• count up or down by different amounts

Lesson 1 BASIC FACTS

Practice, practice, and more practice will help you become quicker at recalling basic math facts. The best way to recall basic math facts is to memorize them. There are also some strategies you can learn and use to help you recall various math facts. A strategy is simply a plan that helps you solve problems. **Doubles**, **doubles-plus-one**, and **make-a-ten** are some of the strategies you can use. However, there is not a strategy for every math fact. You must memorize your math facts to make the strategies easier to use. Use an addition grid to help you find the answer to an addition or subtraction fact if you cannot remember it.

DOUBLES

Knowing your doubles is a helpful strategy. Learn these doubles to help you recall math facts quickly.

Addition Doubles	Subtraction
$1+1=2$	$2-1=1$
$2+2=4$	$4-2=2$
$3+3=6$	$6-3=3$
$4+4=8$	$8-4=4$
$5+5=10$	$10-5=5$
$6+6=12$	$12-6=6$
$7+7=14$	$14-7=7$
$8+8=16$	$16-8=8$
$9+9=18$	$18-9=9$

Notice that the sums for the doubles from one to nine go up by two for each step.

Addition and subtraction are related. Because of this, doubles can help solve subtraction problems as well. Since $4 + 4 = 8$, you know that $8 - 4 = 4$.

You can think of $12 - 6$ as 12 take away 6 equals what number. If you are not as comfortable with subtraction, think of this subtraction problem in a different way. Think, 6 plus what number equals 12? You are searching for the same number either way.

164

Example

Use your knowledge of doubles to complete the following math facts.

a) $5 + 5 =$

Solution
$5 + 5 = 10$

b) $18 - 9 =$

Solution
$18 - 9 = 9$

c) $14 - 7 =$

Solution
$14 - 7 = 7$

d) $6 + 6 =$

Solution
$6 + 6 = 12$

 Time to Try 1

Use your knowledge of doubles to complete the following math facts.

a) $6 - 3 =$ **b)** $2 + 2 =$

c) $10 - 5 =$ **d)** $8 + 8 =$

DOUBLES PLUS ONE

Now you can use what you already know about doubles with a strategy called doubles plus one. Doubles plus one is used for addition problems. To solve an addition problem using doubles plus one, double the lesser number and add one.

NOTES

 Example

Solve the basic fact 6 + 7 using the doubles-plus-one strategy.

Solution

To write the sum for 6 + 7, double the lesser number (6 + 6). Then, add 1 to find the total for 6 + 7.

$$6 + 7 = \underbrace{6 + 6}_{12} + 1$$
$$= 13$$

So, 12 + 1 = 13.

 Time to Try 2

Fill in the table using your knowledge of doubles plus one.

Addition Problem	Double the Lower Number	Sum of the Double + 1	Answer to Problem
8 + 7	7 + 7	14 + 1	15
4 + 5			
9 + 8			
6 + 5			
3 + 2			

DOUBLES MINUS ONE

You can also use your knowledge of doubles with a strategy called doubles take away one or doubles minus one. To solve an addition problem using doubles minus one, double the greater number and subtract one.

 Example

Solve the basic fact 7 + 8 using the doubles-minus-one strategy.

Solution

To write the sum for 7 + 8, double the greater number (8 + 8). Then, take away 1 to find the total for 7 + 8.

$$7 + 8 = \underbrace{8 + 8}_{16} - 1$$
$$= 15$$

So, 16 – 1 = 15

Time to Try 3

Fill in the tables using your knowledge of doubles minus one.

Addition Problem	Double the Greater Number	Sum of Double − 1	Answer to Problem
7 + 8	8 + 8	16 − 1	15
5 + 6			
3 + 4			

DOUBLES PLUS TWO

Now that you have had practice with doubles, doubles plus one, and doubles minus one, you can also use doubles plus two and doubles minus two. For the doubles-plus-two strategy, double the lower number and add two.

 Example

Solve the basic fact 6 + 8 using the doubles-plus-two strategy.

Solution

To write the sum for 6 + 8, double the lower number (6 + 6). Then, add 2 to find the sum.

$$6 + 8 = \underbrace{6 + 6}_{12} + 2$$
$$= 14$$

So, 12 + 2 = 14

 Time to Try 4

Show how you would use the doubles-plus-two strategy in the addition fact 7 + 9.

DOUBLES MINUS TWO

For the strategy of doubles minus two, you double the greater number and subtract two.

NOTES

 Example

Solve the basic fact 6 + 8 using the doubles-minus-two strategy.

Solution

To write the sum for 6 + 8, double the 8 (8 + 8).
Take away 2 to find the total.

$$6 + 8 = \underbrace{8 + 8}_{16} - 2$$
$$= 14$$

So, 16 − 2 = 14

 Time to Try 5

Show how you would use doubles-minus-two to solve the addition fact 5 + 7.

MAKE A TEN

Make a ten is another strategy that can be used for addition facts. This strategy is used to find the sum of numbers when one of the numbers is close to ten. This strategy makes addition facts with a 9 easier.

 Example

Solve the basic fact 9 + 4 using the make-a-ten strategy.

Solution

The basic fact 9 + 4 can be made easier. Make a ten by taking 1 away from the 4 and adding it to the 9. This makes the 9 a 10. The 4 becomes a 3 because 1 was borrowed from it. Find the answer by adding 3 to 10.

$$\underset{(+1)}{9} + \underset{(-1)}{4} \;\Rightarrow\; 10 + 3 = 13$$

or
10 + 4 = 14
14 − 1 = 13

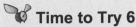 **Time to Try 6**

Find the sum for the following number problems using the make-a-ten strategy.

a) 6 + 9 =

b) 8 + 5 =

c) 9 + 7 =

USING A GRID

You can use an addition grid to find the answers for basic math facts up to 18. Find one number in the side column on the left of the grid, and place your finger on it. Find the other number in the top row, and place a finger from the other hand on it. Run one finger across the row from left to right and the other finger down the column from the top toward the bottom. Keep going until your fingers meet. The sum of the math fact is the number in that box.

Example

Use the addition grid shown here to find the answer to 8 + 4.

Addition Grid

+	0	1	2	3	4	5	6	7	8	9
0	0	1	2	3	4	5	6	7	8	9
1	1	2	3	4	5	6	7	8	9	10
2	2	3	4	5	6	7	8	9	10	11
3	3	4	5	6	7	8	9	10	11	12
4	4	5	6	7	8	9	10	11	12	13
5	5	6	7	8	9	10	11	12	13	14
6	6	7	8	9	10	11	12	13	14	15
7	7	8	9	10	11	12	13	14	15	16
8	8	9	10	11	12	13	14	15	16	17
9	9	10	11	12	13	14	15	16	17	18

Solution

Go down the first column on the left to find the number 8.
Go across the row at the top to find the number 4.
Follow the row and the column to the point where they
meet. The number 12 is in the box.

The answer to 8 + 4 is 12.

Try this again by finding the 4 in the column on the side
and the 8 in the row at the top. You will find that the
answer is the same both ways.

Time to Try 7

Find the sum for the following addition equations using an
addition grid.

+	0	1	2	3	4	5	6	7	8	9
0	0	1	2	3	4	5	6	7	8	9
1	1	2	3	4	5	6	7	8	9	10
2	2	3	4	5	6	7	8	9	10	11
3	3	4	5	6	7	8	9	10	11	12
4	4	5	6	7	8	9	10	11	12	13
5	5	6	7	8	9	10	11	12	13	14
6	6	7	8	9	10	11	12	13	14	15
7	7	8	9	10	11	12	13	14	15	16
8	8	9	10	11	12	13	14	15	16	17
9	9	10	11	12	13	14	15	16	17	18

a) 5 + 4 =   b) 8 + 7 =

c) 4 + 4 =   d) 6 + 9 =

An addition grid can also be used to help answer basic subtraction problems. On the side column, find the number that is being taken away. Place your finger on this number. Run your finger from the left side of the grid toward the right until you find the first number in the problem. Stop. Run your finger up the column to the very top of the grid. The number that your finger lands on at the top of the grid is the answer to the problem.

 Example

Use the addition grid to find the answer to 12 – 8.

Solution

+	0	1	2	3	4	5	6	7	8	9
0	0	1	2	3	4	5	6	7	8	9
1	1	2	3	4	5	6	7	8	9	10
2	2	3	4	5	6	7	8	9	10	11
3	3	4	5	6	7	8	9	10	11	12
4	4	5	6	7	8	9	10	11	12	13
5	5	6	7	8	9	10	11	12	13	14
6	6	7	8	9	10	11	12	13	14	15
7	7	8	9	10	11	12	13	14	15	16
8	8	9	10	11	12	13	14	15	16	17
9	9	10	11	12	13	14	15	16	17	18

Find the 8 in the side column of the grid. Move your finger to the right until you find the 12. Stop. Run your finger all the way to the top of the grid. You end up on 4. The difference between 12 and 8 is 4 (12 – 8 = 4).

 Time to Try 8

Using the addition grid, find the difference for the following subtraction sentences.

a) 13 – 4 =

b) 14 – 7 =

c) 7 – 3 =

d) 11 – 9 =

PRACTICE EXERCISES

Use addition doubles to solve the following number equations.

1. $8 + 8 =$ [ ]

2. $10 - 5 =$ [ ]

Use the doubles-plus-one strategy to solve the following number equations.

3. $9 + 8 =$ [ ]

4. $6 + 7 =$ [ ]

Use the doubles-minus-one strategy to solve the following number equations.

5. $6 + 7 =$ [ ]

6. $4 + 5 =$ [ ]

Use the strategy of doubles plus two to solve the following number equations.

7. $7 + 9 =$ [ ]

8. $6 + 8 =$ [ ]

Use the doubles-minus-two strategy to solve the following number equations.

9. $5 + 7 =$ [ ]

10. $9 + 11 =$ [ ]

Using the make-a-ten strategy, find the sum of the following number equations.

11. $5 + 8 =$ [ ]

12. $7 + 11 =$ [ ]

Use this addition grid to answer the next four questions.

+	0	1	2	3	4	5	6	7	8	9
0	0	1	2	3	4	5	6	7	8	9
1	1	2	3	4	5	6	7	8	9	10
2	2	3	4	5	6	7	8	9	10	11
3	3	4	5	6	7	8	9	10	11	12
4	4	5	6	7	8	9	10	11	12	13
5	5	6	7	8	9	10	11	12	13	14
6	6	7	8	9	10	11	12	13	14	15
7	7	8	9	10	11	12	13	14	15	16
8	8	9	10	11	12	13	14	15	16	17
9	9	10	11	12	13	14	15	16	17	18

13. $9 + 7 =$ ☐

14. $8 + 5 =$ ☐

15. $15 - 7 =$ ☐

16. $13 - 8 =$ ☐

Lesson 2 MENTAL MATH ADDITION STRATEGIES

A mental strategy is a plan that can help you add or subtract numbers quickly in your head. You do not have to use paper and pencil or a calculator.

Solving problems is easier when you break numbers down into simpler numbers and do the calculations in your head.

ADDING FROM LEFT TO RIGHT

The first strategy is to use place value and add from left to right. For this strategy, start at the left, and add the digits in the same place value position. With practice, you will be able to do this in your head.

Add 31 and 26 in your head using the place-value strategy.

Step 1
There are 3 tens in 31 (30) and 2 tens in 26 (20).
In your head, add 30 + 20.
30 + 20 = 50

Step 2
There is 1 ones in 31 (1) and 6 ones in 26 (6).
In your head, add 1 + 6.
1 + 6 = 7

Step 3
Now, add the two sums together.
50 + 7 = 57
This means that 31 + 26 = 57.

 Example

Add the numbers 46 and 14 in your head using place value.
46 + 14 = ?

Solution
Think 46 = 40 + 6. Think 14 = 10 + 4.

Add the tens.
40 + 10 = 50
Add the ones.
6 + 4 = 10
Add the tens and ones.
50 + 10 = 60
46 + 14 = 60

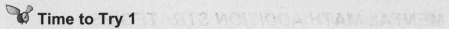 **Time to Try 1**

Using place value and working from left to right, add the numbers 23 + 36 in your head.

MAKING A ZERO

Another strategy for adding 2 two-digit numbers is to start by making one of the numbers end in a zero, which is a multiple of 10.

Follow these steps to make a zero:
1. Start with the number that is closest to a multiple of 10.
2. Make that number end in zero.
3. Add the two numbers.
4. Whatever number you added or subtracted to make the number end in zero, do the opposite after you add the two numbers.

For example, 18 + 15 can be solved using this strategy.
Add 2 to 18 to make it 20. Now, the number sentence is
20 + 15 = 35. Take away 2 from the 35. You get 33.
So, 18 + 15 = 33.

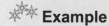 **Example**

Solve the problem 28 + 47 using the make a zero strategy.

Solution

Think 30 instead of 28 because it is an easier number to add. If you add 2 to 28, the problem becomes
30 + 47 = 77. Now, take away the 2 that was added.
77 − 2 = 75

The solution to the problem 28 + 47 is 75.

Another way to solve this problem is to think 50 instead of 47 (47 + 3 = 50).
50 + 28 = 78

Next, take away the 3 that was added.
78 − 3 = 75

The solution is 28 + 47 = 75.

NOTES

 Time to Try 2

Solve the problem 49 + 25 using the make a zero strategy.

You can also make both numbers end in zeros so that the numbers are easier to add. Once you add the numbers together, you must remember to subtract the same number you added to get your final answer.

Example

Solve the problem 19 + 29.

Solution

Step 1
Add 1 to 19 and 1 to 29 so you get 20 + 30.

Step 2
In your head, add 20 + 30.
20 + 30 = 50

Step 3
Now, subtract 2 (1 + 1) from 50 to get your final answer.
This means that 19 + 29 = 49.

DOUBLES

Finally, another strategy to help you add two-digit numbers is using doubles. You practised using doubles with basic facts. The same idea applies to numbers with two digits.

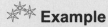 **Example**

Solve the problem 24 + 26 using the strategy of doubles.

Solution

Think to yourself that 24 + 26 is the same as 25 + 25.
25 + 25 = 50

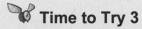 **Time to Try 3**

Using the doubles strategy, solve the problem 33 + 35.

You can also use the strategy of doubles plus one and doubles minus one with two-digit numbers.

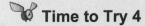 **Time to Try 4**

Using the doubles-plus-one strategy, solve the problem 22 + 23.

Always use the strategy that makes the most sense to you and helps make adding easier and faster.

PRACTICE EXERCISES

Use the adding from left to right strategy to add these number equations.

1. $27+32 =$ ☐

2. $43+15 =$ ☐

3. $12+56 =$ ☐

Use the making a zero strategy to solve these equations.

4. $22+37 =$ ☐

5. $68+24 =$ ☐

6. $39+52 =$ ☐

Using the end-in-zero strategy, solve these number equations.

7. $28+39 =$ ☐

8. $47+36 =$ ☐

9. $54+23 =$ ☐

10. Using the strategy of doubles, solve the equation 44 + 46.

11. Using the doubles-plus-one strategy, solve the equation 42 + 43.

Lesson 3 MENTAL MATH SUBTRACTION STRATEGIES

There are also mental math strategies that can help you solve subtraction problems. You can find the answer to problems by playing with the numbers in your head. There are many strategies, and people use the strategies that make sense to them. Two people may solve the same problem using different strategies. Always use the strategy that works best for you.

DOUBLES

As you did with addition, you can use your knowledge of doubles to help you with subtracting two-digit numbers. Use doubles for subtraction the same way you used doubles for addition.

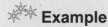 **Example**

Solve the subtraction problem 22 – 11 using the doubles strategy.

Solution

To solve the problem quickly, think of the double, 11 + 11. If 11 + 11 = 22, then 22 – 11 = 11.

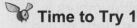 **Time to Try 1**

Using the doubles strategy, solve the subtraction problem 44 – 22.

ADDING ON

Another strategy to help you subtract two-digit numbers quickly in your head is to add on. Adding on means that you take the lesser number (the number being subtracted) and add up in small chunks until you get to the greater number. For example, look at 50 – 43. Start at 43, and count 44, 45, 46, 47, 48, 49, 50. You counted up 7 to get from 43 to 50. The solution to 50 – 43 is 7.

NOTES

 Example

Solve the subtraction problem 62 – 45 using the strategy of adding on.

Solution

To solve this problem, think 45 + 5 = 50. It is easy to add once you have made one number end in a zero. Next, think 50 + 12 = 62.

You have added a total of 17 (5 + 12 = 17) to 45 to get to 62.

So, 62 – 45 = 17.

 Time to Try 2

Using the adding-on strategy, solve the subtraction problem 73 – 59.

MAKING A ZERO

Another strategy to help you subtract two-digit numbers is making a zero (a multiple of 10). Follow these steps to use this strategy:

1. Start with the lesser number (the number being subtracted).
2. Make a zero by making the number into the nearest multiple of 10.
3. Subtract the two numbers.
4. Whatever number you added or subtracted to make the number end in zero, do the same after you subtract the two numbers.

For example, to quickly subtract 39 – 18, make the 18 into a multiple of 10. Add 2 to 18 to get 20. Subtract 39 – 20. Add 2 back again to find the answer.

First 39 – 20 = 19, then 19 + 2 = 21.

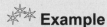 **Example**

Solve the problem 74 – 17 using the making a zero strategy.

Solution

To solve this problem, start by making the lesser number end in a zero. Add 3 to 17 to make 20. Subtract 74 – 20 = 54. Add 3, the 3 you subtracted when making the 17 into a 20, back again.

First 54 + 3 = 57, then 74 – 17 = 57.

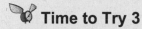 **Time to Try 3**

Use the strategy of making a zero, solve the problem 62 – 19.

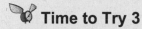 **Time to Try 4**

Using the strategy of making a zero, solve the problem 70 – 22 = ?

PRACTICE EXERCISES

Using the doubles strategy, solve these subtraction equations.

1. $66 - 33 =$ ☐

2. $88 - 44 =$ ☐

Using the adding-on strategy, solve these subtraction equations.

3. $64 - 48 =$ ☐

4. $52 - 24 =$ ☐

5. $59 - 47 =$ ☐

Using the strategy of making a zero, solve these equations.

6. $77 - 38 =$ ☐

7. $64 - 21 =$ ☐

8. $81 - 27 =$ ☐

REVIEW SUMMARY

- A mental strategy is a plan that can help you add or subtract quickly in your head instead of using paper and pencil or a calculator.
- You can use mental strategies to quickly solve basic facts. Some of the strategies are doubles, doubles-plus-one, doubles-minus-one, doubles-plus-two, doubles-minus-two, and make-a-ten.
- Addition and subtraction are related. You can use one to help you find the answer to another. You can also use an addition grid to help you find the answers to addition and subtraction facts to 18.
- Certain mental strategies are useful for addition.
  - Adding from left to right
  - Making a zero
  - Using doubles
- Certain mental strategies are more useful for subtraction.
  - Adding on
  - Making a zero
  - Using doubles

PRACTICE TEST

1. Using the doubles strategy, add 7 + 7.

2. Using the doubles-plus-one strategy, add 25 + 26.

3. Using the doubles-minus-one strategy, add 34 + 35.

4. Use the doubles-plus-two strategy to solve 45 + 47.

5. Use the doubles-minus-two strategy to add 13 + 15.

6. Use the make-a-ten strategy to add 13 + 19.

7. Use the strategy of make-a-ten to add 6 + 9.

Use this addition grid to answer questions 8 and 9.

+	0	1	2	3	4	5	6	7	8	9
0	0	1	2	3	4	5	6	7	8	9
1	1	2	3	4	5	6	7	8	9	10
2	2	3	4	5	6	7	8	9	10	11
3	3	4	5	6	7	8	9	10	11	12
4	4	5	6	7	8	9	10	11	12	13
5	5	6	7	8	9	10	11	12	13	14
6	6	7	8	9	10	11	12	13	14	15
7	7	8	9	10	11	12	13	14	15	16
8	8	9	10	11	12	13	14	15	16	17
9	9	10	11	12	13	14	15	16	17	18

8. 7 + 5

9. 8 + 9

10. Using the place-value strategy, add 26 + 42.

11. Using the place-value strategy, add 71 + 18.

12. Use the strategy of making a zero to solve the problem 46 + 28.

13. Use the making a zero strategy to solve the problem 32 + 56.

14. Use the strategy of make-a-ten to solve the problem 18 + 47.

Use this addition grid to answer questions 15 and 16.

+	0	1	2	3	4	5	6	7	8	9
0	0	1	2	3	4	5	6	7	8	9
1	1	2	3	4	5	6	7	8	9	10
2	2	3	4	5	6	7	8	9	10	11
3	3	4	5	6	7	8	9	10	11	12
4	4	5	6	7	8	9	10	11	12	13
5	5	6	7	8	9	10	11	12	13	14
6	6	7	8	9	10	11	12	13	14	15
7	7	8	9	10	11	12	13	14	15	16
8	8	9	10	11	12	13	14	15	16	17
9	9	10	11	12	13	14	15	16	17	18

15. 16 − 7

16. 14 − 9

17. Using the doubles strategy, solve 88 − 44.

18. Using the adding-on strategy, solve the subtraction problem 52 – 27.

19. Make the number being subtracted a ten and compensate to solve the subtraction problem 64 – 28.

20. Use the strategy of making a ten to solve the subtraction problem 71 – 33.

NOTES

FRACTIONS

When you are finished this unit, you will be able to...
• understand and show how a whole object can be split into equal parts
• represent fractions using objects or pictures
• identify the numerator and denominator
• compare fractions with the same denominator

Lesson	Page	Completed on
1. Introduction to Fractions	190	
2. Parts of a Whole	196	
3. Comparing Fractions	203	
Review Summary	207	
Practice Test	208	
Answers and Solutions		at the back of the book

PREREQUISITE SKILLS AND KNOWLEDGE

Prior to starting this unit, you should be able to...
• understand that an object or group of things can be divided into smaller parts

Lesson 1 *INTRODUCTION TO FRACTIONS*

An object or a group of objects is often divided into smaller parts. A whole orange may divided into sections to share with friends. A group of children may be split up to play a game. Here are some more examples of when you can use fractions during the day.

- Fractions can be used to tell time. Your brother may tell you that lunch is in half $\left(\dfrac{1}{2} \right)$ an hour.

- Fractions can be used when baking. Your mother asks you to add a quarter $\left(\dfrac{1}{4} \right)$ cup of raisins to a cookie recipe.

- Fractions can also be used to group children in the class using different features. If there are 10 girls in your class and 3 of them have red hair, then $\dfrac{3}{10}$ (three-tenths) of the girls in your class have red hair.

Can you think of any others?

A **fraction** is a part of a whole. It is a number that names a part of a group when the group is split into equal parts.
A fraction is made up of two numbers. One number is written above the other number.

$$\dfrac{\text{Numerator}}{\text{Denominator}}$$

- The **numerator** is the top number of a fraction.
  The numerator tells how many parts of the whole you are working with. In the fraction $\dfrac{1}{2}$, the numerator is 1.

- The **denominator** is the bottom number of a fraction.
  The denominator tells you how many parts there are in total. In the fraction $\dfrac{1}{3}$, the denominator is 3.

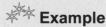 Example

In the fraction $\dfrac{1}{3}$, which number is the numerator?

Solution

The top number of a fraction is called the numerator.
The bottom number is called the denominator.
The numerator in this fraction is 1.

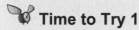 Time to Try 1

In the fraction $\dfrac{3}{5}$, which number is the denominator?

EQUAL PARTS

You can represent a fraction with materials found in your classroom, such as fraction strips or tiles. You can also draw pictures to represent parts of a whole.

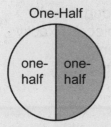

One-Half

This circle is divided into 2 equal parts. Each part is called one-half. The fraction is $\dfrac{1}{2}$.

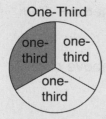

One-Third

This circle is divided into 3 equal parts. Each part is called one-third. The fraction is $\dfrac{1}{3}$.

One-Quarter

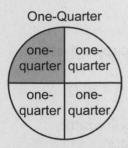

This circle is divided into 4 equal parts. Each part is called one-quarter. The fraction is $\frac{1}{4}$.

One-Fifth

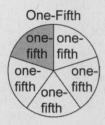

This circle is divided into 5 equal parts. Each part is called one-fifth. The fraction is $\frac{1}{5}$.

UNEQUAL PARTS

Not all shapes that are divided into parts are divided equally. Think about cutting a cake. It is hard to cut the pieces exactly the same. Some pieces may be larger than others. The following shape is not divided into equal parts.

You can see that some parts of the circle are bigger than others.

Fractions can only be made of equal parts. The above circle is not divided into quarters.

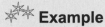 Example

These circles are divided into parts. Sort the circles that represent equal parts from those that do not.

Solution

To sort the shapes into those that represent equal parts and those that do not, look carefully at the shapes in the circles. This table shows the circles sorted correctly.

Equal Parts	Not Equal Parts

Time to Try 2

Sort the circles that represent equal parts into one group and those that do not into another group.

PRACTICE EXERCISES

1. In the fraction $\frac{5}{10}$, which number is the numerator?

2. In the fraction $\frac{1}{8}$, which number is the denominator?

3. Teresa divides an apple into equal parts for her two sons. Draw a picture of a circle showing two equal parts.

Use the following information to answer the next question.

4. Sort the circles that are divided into equal parts into one group and those that are not into another group.

Use the following information to answer the next question.

The pizza in the picture is divided into 4 equal pieces.

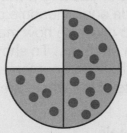

5. Write the fraction that represents the missing part of the pizza.

Use the following information to answer the next question.

The circle in the picture has some of its parts shaded.

6. Write the fraction that tells how many parts are **not** shaded.

Lesson 2   PARTS OF A WHOLE

A fraction describes some of the parts that belong to a whole. For example, you might want to order a pizza with pepperoni on one side and pineapple on the other side. A fraction can be used to describe how many parts of the whole pizza have pepperoni on them. To show how a picture can represent a fraction, shade the numerator. The shaded part will tell how many parts of the whole are represented by the fraction.

 Example

Shade $\frac{1}{5}$ of the circle.

Solution

When a whole is split into 5 equal parts, each part is called a fifth. One fifth, which means one of the five pieces

that make the whole, is shown by the fraction $\frac{1}{5}$.

The numerator (1) represents one piece of the total number of pieces. The denominator (5) tells you that the whole has been split into 5 equal pieces.

This picture shows $\frac{1}{5}$ of the circle shaded.

 Time to Try 1

Shade $\frac{1}{5}$ of the star.

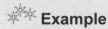 **Example**

a) Shade $\dfrac{4}{5}$ of the circle.

Solution

A fraction with a 5 as a denominator has 5 equal parts.

Each fifth $\left(\dfrac{1}{5}\right)$ represents an equal part of the whole.

The fraction $\dfrac{2}{5}$ represents 2 pieces of the whole.

The fraction $\dfrac{3}{5}$ represents 3 pieces of the whole, and so on.

The fraction $\dfrac{4}{5}$ can also be shown as $\dfrac{1}{5}+\dfrac{1}{5}+\dfrac{1}{5}+\dfrac{1}{5}=\dfrac{4}{5}$.

To shade $\dfrac{4}{5}$ of the circle, colour in 4 of the 5 sections.

b) What fraction of the circle is **not** shaded?

Solution

One of the sections of the circle is not shaded.

The fraction that represents this is $\dfrac{1}{5}$.

Check your answer. The fraction of the shaded part $\left(\dfrac{4}{5}\right)$

added to the fraction of the part that is not shaded $\left(\dfrac{1}{5}\right)$

equals a whole. A whole is shown as the numerator and denominator being the same number.

$\dfrac{1}{5}+\dfrac{4}{5}=\dfrac{5}{5}$

$\dfrac{5}{5}=1\,\text{whole}$

NOTES

🐝 Time to Try 2

a) Shade $\frac{3}{5}$ of the star.

b) What fraction of the star is **not** shaded?

If a whole is divided into 10 equal parts, each part is called a tenth. The denominator for a whole cut into ten parts is $10 \left(\frac{}{10} \right)$. To talk about one section of the ten parts, the fraction $\frac{1}{10}$ is used.

| $\frac{1}{10}$ | $\frac{1}{10}$ | $\frac{1}{10}$ | $\frac{1}{10}$ | $\frac{1}{10}$ | $\frac{1}{10}$ | $\frac{1}{10}$ | $\frac{1}{10}$ | $\frac{1}{10}$ | $\frac{1}{10}$ |

✳ Example

When the numerator is the same as the denominator, the fraction represents one whole. Any fraction whose numerator matches the denominator is equal to 1.

Shade $\frac{10}{10}$ of the rectangle.

Solution

The rectangle is divided into 10 equal pieces, so the denominator is 10. The numerator of the fraction is 10. You need to shade 10 of the sections. This means that you will shade in the entire rectangle, which is one whole.

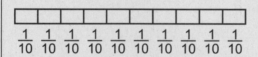

Time to Try 3

Shade $\frac{4}{4}$ of the square.

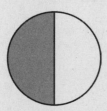

✳ **Example**

Draw a picture to represent the fraction $\frac{1}{2}$ as part of a whole.

Solution

To represent $\frac{1}{2}$ as part of a whole, first draw a whole

object. Divide the object into 2 equal parts. Then, shade
1 part.

🦋 **Time to Try 4**

Draw a picture to represent the fraction $\frac{2}{5}$ as part of a whole.

PRACTICE EXERCISES

Use the following information to answer the next question.

This rectangle is divided into equal parts. Some of the parts are shaded.

1. What fraction does the shaded part of the rectangle represent?

Use the following information to answer the next question.

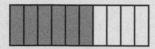

2. Circle all of the pictures or fractions that equal one whole.

3. Shade $\frac{5}{5}$ of the rectangle.

Use the following information to answer the next question.

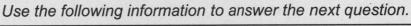

4. What fraction does the shaded part of the picture represent?

Use the following information to answer the next question.

Dana, Cheyenne, Evelyn, and Kendra ordered a large pizza for lunch. A large pizza has 10 equal-sized pieces. Each of the girls eats 2 pieces.

5. Write a fraction to show how much of the pizza is left.

Use the following information to answer the next question.

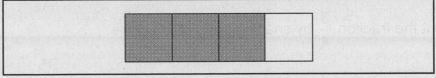

6. What part of the whole does the shaded part represent?

Use the following information to answer the next question.

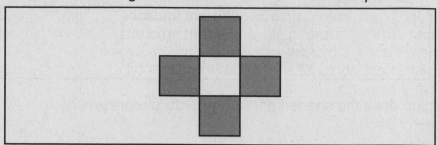

7. What fraction of the figure is shaded?

8. Draw a picture to represent the fraction $\frac{1}{3}$ as part of a whole.

9. Represent the fraction $\frac{3}{4}$ by shading parts of the circle.

Lesson 3   COMPARING FRACTIONS

You can use strips of paper to represent different fractions. Fold the strip into different sizes to show different amounts. You can compare fractions by folding the paper to show each fraction. Follow this activity to help you see how fractions represent different amounts.

Start with a strip of paper.

 1

To show two equal parts, fold the strip in half so the corners are matched up. Press your finger along the fold so the paper lies flat.

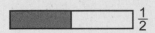 $\frac{1}{2}$

To show four equal parts, fold the piece of paper in half again so the corners are matched up. When you open the paper, the folds divide the paper into 4 equal parts. Each part represents $\frac{1}{4}$ or one quarter.

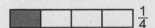 $\frac{1}{4}$

You can fold it in half again so that the edges and corners touch. When you open the paper, the folds divide the paper into eight equal parts. Each part represents $\frac{1}{8}$ or one eighth.

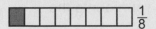 $\frac{1}{8}$

Fold the paper in half again. When you open the paper, the folds divide the paper into 16 equal parts. Each part represents $\frac{1}{16}$ or one sixteenth.

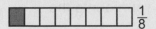 $\frac{1}{16}$

You can fold the piece of paper to make many different fractions. Try folding the strip of paper into thirds, sixths, and twelfths.

NOTES

NOTES

When two fractions represent two different amounts, you can compare and order them. For now, you will compare fractions that have the same denominator. To compare two fractions with the same denominator, look at the numerators. The fraction with the greater numerator is the greater fraction.

 Example

The following pictures show a whole divided into thirds. Each picture represents a different fraction. Which of the fractions shown is greater?

$$\frac{2}{3} \qquad \frac{1}{3}$$

Solution

When you compare fractions that have the same denominator, you can show which fraction is greater. The fraction with the greater numerator is greater.

$$\frac{2}{3} \qquad > \qquad \frac{1}{3}$$

The first picture shows 3 parts with 2 of the 3 parts shaded. The second picture shows 3 parts with only 1 part shaded. The picture that shows 2 shaded parts represents the greater fraction.

 Time to Try 1

The following circles show a whole divided into fifths. Each circle has a fraction of the circle shaded. Which of the fractions shown is greater?

$$\frac{1}{5} \qquad \frac{4}{5}$$

PRACTICE EXERCISES

Use the following information to answer the next question.

Mr. Hubbert writes the fractions $\frac{7}{8}$ and $\frac{1}{8}$ on the whiteboard. He wants Mikka to find which fraction is greater.

1.   Which fraction is should Mikka to say is greater?

Use the following information to answer the next question

The picture shows two circles with some parts shaded.

2.   Write a fraction to represent the shaded parts for each circle, and explain which fraction is greater.

3.   Of the fractions $\frac{2}{4}$ and $\frac{3}{4}$, which fraction is greater?

Use the following information to answer the next question

This picture shows two whole shapes divided into sixths. The shaded parts are represented by the fractions written under the shapes.

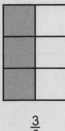
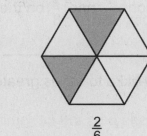

$$\frac{3}{6}$$
$$\frac{2}{6}$$

4. Of the fractions $\frac{3}{6}$ and $\frac{2}{6}$, which fraction is greater?

5. Of the fractions $\frac{5}{6}$ and $\frac{3}{6}$, which fraction is less than the other?

REVIEW SUMMARY

- A fraction is made up of two numbers. One number is written above the other number.
  - The numerator is the top number of a fraction. The numerator tells how many parts of the whole you are working with.
  - The denominator is the bottom number of a fraction. The denominator tells you how many parts there are in total.

  $\dfrac{\text{Numerator}}{\text{Denominator}}$

- When the numerator is the same as the denominator, the fraction represents one whole.

- Sometimes a whole is not divided evenly. A whole can be divided into equal parts or unequal parts.

- You can compare and order fractions that have the same denominator. To compare the fractions, look at the numerators. The fraction with the greater numerator is the greater fraction.

PRACTICE TEST

Use the following information to answer the next question.

This circle is divided into equal parts. Some of the parts are shaded.

1. For the fraction that represents the shaded part of the circle, what is the numerator?

Use the following information to answer the next question.

This rectangle is divided into equal parts. Some of the parts are shaded.

2. For the fraction that shows the shaded part of the rectangle, what is the denominator?

Use the following information to answer the next question.

This rectangle is divided into equal parts.

3. Write a fraction that tells what part of the rectangle is shaded.

Use the following information to answer the next question.

This rectangle is divided into equal parts. Some of the parts are shaded.

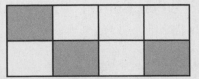

4. Write a fraction that represents the shaded parts of the rectangle.

5. Draw a picture to represent the fraction $\frac{2}{4}$.

Use the following information to answer the next question.

The diagram shows two rectangles divided into sixths. The fractions that represent the shaded parts are written under the rectangles.

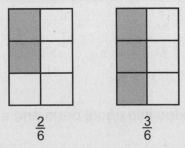

$$\frac{2}{6} \qquad\qquad \frac{3}{6}$$

6. Which of the fractions shown is greater?

7. Of the fractions $\frac{6}{10}$ and $\frac{5}{10}$, which fraction is greater?

Use the following information to answer the next question.

The picture shows two rectangles divided into fourths. The fractions under the rectangles represent the shaded parts.

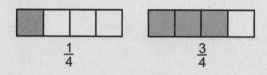

$$\frac{1}{4} \qquad\qquad \frac{3}{4}$$

8. Of the fractions shown, which fraction is greater?

9. Of the fractions $\frac{2}{5}$ and $\frac{4}{5}$, which fraction is less than the other?

10. Draw one shape that is divided into equal parts and another shape that is divided into unequal parts.

MULTIPLICATION AND DIVISION

When you are finished this unit, you will be able to…
- multiply and divide basic facts to 25
- draw pictures and use objects to show how equal groups are used to represent multiplication and division
- show multiplication as repeated addition and division as repeated subtraction
- find the answers to division and multiplication problems using arrays

PREREQUISITE SKILLS AND KNOWLEDGE

Prior to starting this unit, you should be able to…
- skip count
- add and subtract basic facts
- give examples of multiplication and division in everyday life
- understand that multiplication and division can be described using groups

Lesson 1 MULTIPLICATION

NOTES

There are many times in a day when you could use multiplication. For example, you could use multiplication to quickly count the number of desks in your classroom or the number of legs on all the desks.

Multiplication is used to find the total number of items made up of equal-sized groups. It is also used to find the total number of items in a given number of groups. In multiplication, all groups are equal. This means that each group has the same number of items.

A multiplication problem is made up of two numbers. Each number is called a **factor**. The **product** is the answer to a multiplication problem.

EQUAL GROUPS

The following picture shows that there are 2 equal groups of triangles. Each group has 5 triangles. The answer to this problem tells how many triangles there are in all. The answer (product) is 10.

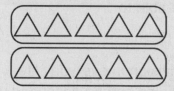

$$2 \times 5 = 10$$

Number of groups	Number in each group	Number in all

There are 10 triangles in the next picture as well. This time, there are 5 equal groups. Each group has 2 triangles. The number of triangles altogether is 10.

$$5 \times 2 = 10$$

Number of groups	Number in each group	Number in all

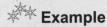 **Example**

Show the multiplication equation $2 \times 4 = 8$ using equal groups.

Solution

Start with how many groups there are (2) and how many there are in each group (4). Draw a picture of 2 groups with 4 in each group. Here is a picture of 2 groups of cookies with 4 cookies in each group. The answer, or product, is that there are 8 cookies altogether.

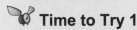 **Time to Try 1**

Using equal groups, show the equation $4 \times 4 = 16$.

REPEATED ADDITION

Multiplication can also be shown as repeated addition. Repeated addition means that you add the numeral to itself a certain number of times. For example, $3 \times 5 = 15$ is the same as adding 5 to itself 3 times.
$5 + 5 + 5 = 15$

You could also show this as adding 3 to itself 5 times.
$3 + 3 + 3 + 3 + 3 = 15$

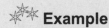 **Example**

How can $3 \times 2 = 6$ be shown as repeated addition?

Solution

Showing $3 \times 2 = 6$ as repeated addition is the same as adding 3 to itself 2 times.
$3 + 3 = 6$

It is also the same as $2 \times 3 = 6$ which is like adding 2 to itself 3 times.
$2 + 2 + 2 = 6$

NOTES

 Time to Try 2

Written as repeated addition, show the multiplication equation $3 \times 4 = 12$.

You can also show a number sentence of repeated addition as multiplication. For example, $1+1+1=3$ is the same as $1 \times 3 = 3$ or $3 \times 1 = 3$. Writing equations as multiplication is faster than writing equations as repeated addition.

 Example

Write the addition equation $2+2+2+2+2 = 10$ as multiplication.

Solution

To write the repeated addition equation as multiplication, count how many times 2 is added to itself. It is added 5 times, so you would write $2 \times 5 = 10$ or $5 \times 2 = 10$.

 Time to Try 3

Write the repeated addition equation $4 + 4 + 4 + 4 + 4 = 20$ as multiplication.

A picture can be drawn to describe a multiplication equation or problem. For example, to draw a picture for a multiplication equation, draw equal groups with equal numbers in each group.

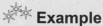 Example

Malia has 3 cans of tennis balls. Each can holds 4 balls. How many tennis balls does she have altogether?
Draw a picture, and write an equation to show and solve the problem.

Solution

To solve this problem, draw 3 groups with 4 balls in each group.

The equations that show and solve the problem are
$4 + 4 + 4 = 12$ or $3 \times 4 = 12$.

To check your answer, count all the tennis balls.

Time to Try 4

Julie sold 5 boxes of chocolates for 3 dollars each.
She wonders how much money she collected altogether.
Draw a picture and write an equation to show and solve
Julie's problem.

MULTIPLYING BY ZERO

When you multiply a number by zero (0), the answer will always be zero. For example, look at the multiplication equation $3 \times 0 = 0$. This equation means that you have 3 groups with nothing in each group.

The multiplication equation $0 \times 3 = 0$ means the same thing. It means that you have 0 groups of 3, which also equals nothing.

PRACTICE EXERCISES

1. Using equal groups, show the multiplication equation $3 \times 5 = 15$.

Use the following information to answer the next question.

Marj has 5 groups of 3 marbles. She wants to know many marbles she has altogether.

2. Draw a picture, and write an equation to show and solve the problem.

3. Using equal groups, show the equation $5 \times 4 = 20$.

4. Show the multiplication equation $1 \times 4 = 4$ as repeated addition.

5. Write the addition equation $2 + 2 + 2 = 6$ as multiplication.

6. Show the multiplication equation $4 \times 2 = 8$ as repeated addition.

7. Write the addition equation $3 + 3 + 3 + 3 + 3 = 15$ as multiplication.

Use the following information to answer the next question.

Phillip sold 3 glasses of lemonade for 2 dollars each. He wanted to know how much money he collected in total.

8. Draw a picture, and write an equation to show and solve the problem.

Use the following information to answer the next question.

Roger has 3 bottles of soda. Each bottle will fill 4 glasses. Roger wants to know how many glasses he can fill with soda altogether.

9. Draw a picture, and write an equation to show and solve the problem.

Use the following information to answer the next question.

Polly has 4 boxes of pencils and wants to know how many pencils she has. When she looks in the boxes, she discovers that the boxes are empty!

10. Draw a picture, and write an equation that shows and solves the problem.

Lesson 2   DIVISION

Multiplication and division are related like addition and subtraction. Division is the opposite of multiplication. In multiplication, you find the total number of objects in a certain number of equal groups. In division, you group a number of items to find how many groups can be made. In other words, you group a number into equal parts. The **quotient** is the answer to a division problem. Objects can be divided into groups in two different ways. The two ways are equal sharing and equal grouping.

Equal sharing is when you have a given number of items and you separate them into a given number of groups. Each group ends up with an equal number of items.

The picture shows 10 triangles being divided into 2 groups.

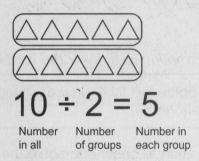

$$10 \div 2 = 5$$

Number in all   Number of groups   Number in each group

The answer to the problem tells how many triangles are in each group. The answer (quotient) is 5. If there are 10 triangles, 2 equal groups of 5 can be made.

Equal grouping is when a given number of items is repeatedly taken away from a given quantity. The number of times the items are taken away is the answer or quotient.

There are 10 triangles in this picture as well, but the triangles are being taken away 2 at a time until there are no more in the group. The question is about how many groups of triangles can be made. If you have 10 triangles, you can make 5 equal groups with 2 triangles in each group.

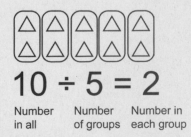

$$10 \div 5 = 2$$

Number in all   Number of groups   Number in each group

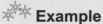 **Example**

Sherry has 10 apples. She wants to share them with 5 of her friends. How many apples can she give each friend? Show this problem using equal sharing.

Solution

To solve this problem using equal sharing, remember that you have a given number of items to separate into a given number of groups. Each group will end up with an equal number of items.

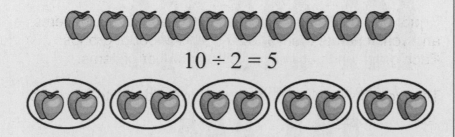

$$10 \div 2 = 5$$

Sherry gives each of her friends 1 apple. She is left with 5 apples, so she can give her friends another apple. Sherry can give each friend 2 apples.

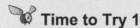 **Time to Try 1**

A group of 12 campers goes hiking in the woods. The hiking leader wants to make equal groups of 4 to go on the paths. He wonders how many campers he should put in each group. Using equal sharing, show how the hiking leader can solve the problem.

NOTES

✳ Example

Mrs. Jones has many students in her choir. She wants to group 15 of the girls into groups of 3. How many equal groups can she make? Show the problem using equal groupings.

Solution

Mrs. Jones starts making groups of 3 by separating 3 students at a time. She can make 5 groups of 3 students.

1 group   1 group   1 group

1 group   1 group

🐝 Time to Try 2

Chad picks 12 flowers. He bundles the flowers into groups of 6. How many friends can Chad give bundles to?

Use equal grouping to show how Chad can find out how many friends he can give the flowers to.

Division problems can be shown as division equations as well as by pictures. It is often easier to write an equation than draw a group of pictures. However, you can always draw a picture to help you describe a division equation or problem. To draw a picture for a division equation, you can draw equal groups or show equal sharing.

✻ Example

Write an equation to show the following problem, and then solve it. You can draw a picture to help you solve the problem.

Kirsten's mom orders pizza for Kirsten's birthday party. She orders one large pizza. It has 10 pieces. There are 5 girls altogether at the party. How many pieces of pizza does each girl get?

Solution

You need to know how many pieces of pizza there are in total (10). The next thing you need to know to write your division equation is how many girls are sharing the pizza (5). To find the answer or quotient for the equation $10 \div 5 = \square$, draw a picture of five girls. Now, begin dividing the pizza by giving each girl a piece of pizza one at a time. Keep doing that until all of the pizza has been given out. Check to see if each girl has an equal number of pieces. If she has, you have correctly completed the problem.

The division equation that shows and solves the problem is $10 \div 5 = 2$.

Each girl gets two pieces of pizza.

NOTES

 Time to Try 3

Jermaine has 20 pieces of chocolate. He is eating lunch with 3 friends. He wants to be sure that all of them get an equal amount of chocolate, including himself. He wonders how many pieces of chocolate each boy should get.

Write an equation to show and solve Jermaine's problem. You can draw a picture to help you solve the problem.

REPEATED SUBTRACTION

Division can also be shown as repeated subtraction. Repeated subtraction means that you subtract the same number from the total number until you have nothing left.

For example, the division equation $12 \div 4 = 3$ is the same as subtracting 4 again and again until you get to zero.

Start with the total.
$12 - 4 = 8, 8 - 4 = 4, 4 - 4 = 0$

It takes 3 groups of subtraction to get to 0, so the answer is 3.
$12 \div 4 = 3$

Example

How can the equation $8 \div 2 = 4$ be shown as repeated subtraction?

Solution

The equation $8 \div 2 = 4$ is the same as subtracting 2 from 8 a total of 4 times.
$8 - 2 = 6, 6 - 2 = 4, 4 - 2 = 2, 2 - 2 = 0$

It takes 4 groups of subtraction to get 0, so the answer is 4.

 Time to Try 4

Show the division equation $20 \div 4 = 5$ as repeated subtraction.

You can also show how division is related to subtraction by writing division expressions or equations from repeated subtraction equations.

 Example

Write the repeated subtraction equations as a division equation.
$12 - 3 = 9, 9 - 3 = 6, 6 - 3 = 3, 3 - 3 = 0$

Solution

Start with the first number. That number will be your dividend (12), the first number in the equation. It will be the number that you are taking away from. Next, look at the number being subtracted. That number is the divisor (3). The number of times you subtract the divisor from the dividend is the answer (or quotient).

The division equation is $12 \div 3 = 4$.

 Time to Try 5

Here is a series of repeated subtraction equations.
$15 - 5 = 10, 10 - 5 = 5, 5 - 5 = 0$

Write the repeated subtraction equations as a division equation.

DIVIDING BY ZERO

Like in multiplication, when you divide a number by zero, the answer will always be zero. This is shown by the division equation $3 \div 0 = 0$. The equation means you have a total of 3 items but no groups, so there is nothing in each group. You can not divide zero by a number either because you cannot make a number of groups from nothing.

PRACTICE EXERCISES

1. Using equal sharing, draw a picture to show the division equation $12 \div 4 = 3$.

Use the following information to answer the next question.

Madina wants to share 20 cupcakes with her 5 friends. She wants to know how many cupcakes she can give each friend.

2. Using equal sharing, show and solve Madina's problem.

Use the following information to answer the next question.

Savin has a bag of 25 oranges. He wants to divide them into groups of 5.
He wonders how many groups he can make.

3. Using equal groupings, show how many groups Savin can make with the oranges.

Use the following information to answer the next question.

Joni has 12 cookies. She wants to divide them equally between herself and 2 friends.
She wonders how many cookies each of them will get.

4. Draw a picture, and write a division equation to show and solve Joni's problem.

Use the following information to answer the next question.

Portia and her 2 brothers sold lemonade from a stand. They made 9 dollars in total. Portia wants to know how much money each of them will get if they split the money equally.

5. Draw a picture, and write a division equation to show and solve the problem.

6. Show the equation $6 \div 3 = 2$ as repeated subtraction.

7. Show the division equation $16 \div 4 = 4$ as repeated subtraction.

Use the following information to answer the next question.

$$9 - 3 = 6, 6 - 3 = 3, 3 - 3 = 0$$

8. Write the repeated subtraction sentences as a division expression.

Use the following information to answer the next question.

This group of number sentences shows repeated subtraction.
$$15 - 3 = 12, 12 - 3 = 9, 9 - 3 = 6, 6 - 3 = 3, 3 - 3 = 0$$

9. Write the repeated subtraction as a division equation.

Lesson 3 ARRAYS

An array is a group of items arranged in rows and columns. Arrays are used to show equal groupings. Arrays can also be used to show multiplication. For example, the array below shows there are 4 rows of balls with 5 balls in each row. The same array also shows there are 5 columns of balls with 4 balls in each column.

To write a multiplication equation for the array, count the rows and the number in each row. The total is the answer.
$4 \times 5 = 20$, $5 \times 4 = 20$

✳ Example

Write a multiplication equation for this array of cars.

Solution
There are 4 rows of cars. Each row has 4 cars.
The multiplication equation is $4 \times 4 = 16$.

There are 16 cars in all.

Time to Try 1

Here is an array of pizza slices.

Write a multiplication equation that describes the array.

CREATING ARRAYS

You can create arrays to show multiplication equations. Each array must show a grid of rows and columns. The rows represent one of the factors and the columns represent the other factor. The total number of items in the rows and columns is the product.

It does not matter in which order you multiply the two numbers. The answer will be the same.

Example

Create an array that shows the multiplication equation 3×2.

Solution

To create an array, order the grid to show objects in rows and columns. In the multiplication equation $3 \times 2 = \square$, there are 3 rows with 2 in each row. The array would look like this.

This array represents the equation $3 \times 2 = 6$.

NOTES

 Time to Try 2

Create an array that shows the multiplication equation 3×4.

MULTIPLICATION AND DIVISION ARE RELATED

Arrays can also be used to show how multiplication and division are related. When looking at an array, you can see that the number of rows and columns show equal groups of a certain amount.

For example, the array above shows there are 2 rows of circles with 3 circles in each row. You could also write it as 3 columns of circles with 2 circles in each column. Both ways show 6 circles. The multiplication equations you could write from this array are $2 \times 3 = 6$ and $3 \times 2 = 6$.

Looking at the same array, you could also write division equations. When using an array to show division, start with all of the objects as the dividend. The number of objects in each row would be the divisor. The number of rows would be the quotient (answer).

To write the division equation for this array, start with the number of circles altogether (6). The number of rows is 2, and the number in each row is 3. The division equation would be $6 \div 2 = 3$.

You could also write a division equation with the number of circles in each row as the divisor (3) and the number of rows as the quotient (2). The division equation would be $6 \div 3 = 2$. Both division equations are related.

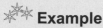 **Example**

Write the multiplication and division equations for this array of stars.

Solution

To write the multiplication equations for the array, count the rows of stars (3). Next, count the number of stars in each row (4). The total number of stars is the product. Remember that the order of the factors does not matter. The answer is the same.

$4 \times 3 = 12$

$3 \times 4 = 12$

To write the division equations for the array, start with the total number of stars (12). Next, use either the number of rows or the number of stars in each row as your divisor. The number you do not choose is the quotient.

$12 \div 3 = 4$

$12 \div 4 = 3$

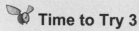 **Time to Try 3**

Here is an array of soccer balls.

Write the multiplication and division equations that represent the array.

PRACTICE EXERCISES

Write the multiplication equation that represents each of the following arrays.

1.

2.

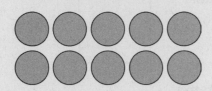

3.

4. Create an array that shows the multiplication equation 5×5.

5. Create an array that shows the multiplication equation $3 \times 2 = 6$.

Use the following array of shamrocks to answer the next question.

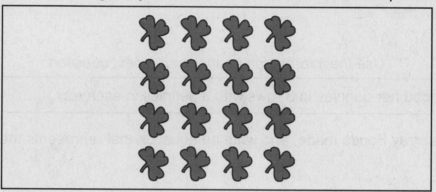

6. Write multiplication and division equations for the array.

Use the following array of stop signs to answer the next question.

7. Write multiplication and division equations for the array.

Use the following array of ducks to answer the next question.

8. Use the array of ducks to write multiplication and division equations.

Use the information to answer the next question.

Fonda arranged her pennies in 3 rows with 3 pennies in each row.

9. Draw the array Fonda made, and write an equation that represents the array.

Use the following information to answer the next question.

Ben has 5 disks. He places them in 5 equal groups.

10. Use an array to find out how many disks Ben places in each group.

REVIEW SUMMARY

- Multiplication is used to find the total number of items made up of equal-sized groups. It is also used to find the total number of items in a given number of groups.
- Multiplication can be described as repeated addition.
- When any number is multiplied by zero, the answer is always zero.
- Division is the opposite of multiplication. In division, a number of items is grouped to find out how many groups can be made. Objects are divided into groups in two ways.
  - Equal sharing is when a given number of items is separated into a given number of groups so that each group has the same number of items.
  - Equal grouping is when a given number of items is repeatedly taken away from a given quantity. The number of equal groups taken away is the answer.
- Division can be described as repeated subtraction.
- When a number is divided by zero, the answer is always zero.
- Arrays are items or objects that are arranged in rows and columns. Arrays are used to show equal groupings.
- Arrays can also be used to show how multiplication and division are related.

PRACTICE TEST

1. Using equal groups, show the multiplication equation $2 \times 5 = 10$.

2. Show the multiplication equation $4 \times 3 = 12$ as repeated addition.

3. Write the repeated addition equation $1 + 1 + 1 + 1 = 4$ as multiplication.

Use the following information to answer the next question.

Jenna has 3 groups of 2 apples. She wonders how many apples she has altogether.

4. Draw a picture, and write an equation to show and solve Jenna's problem.

Use the following information to answer the next question.

Rijiv collects toy cars. He separates them into 4 groups with 4 cars in each group. He wants to know how many cars he has altogether.

5. Draw a picture, and write an equation to show how many toy cars Rijiv has.

Use the following information to answer the next question.

Harris sells 8 candy bars for 2 dollars each. He wants to know much money he should collect.

6. Draw a picture, and write an equation to show how much Harris should collect.

Use the following information to answer the next question.

Lulu has 5 cookies. She wants to share them with 5 of her friends. She needs to know how many cookies she can give each friend.

7. Use equal grouping to show how many cookies Lulu can give each friend.

Use the following information to answer the next question.

Chen has 9 tomato plants. He puts them in trays. Each tray holds 3 plants.

8. Use equal groupings to show how many trays of tomato plants Chen will use.

Use the following information to answer the next question.

Daniel has 5 microscopes to distribute to his classmates. There are 20 students in his class. Daniel needs to know how many students have to share each microscope.

9. Draw a picture, and write an equation to show and solve Daniel's problem.

10. Show the equation $16 \div 4 = 4$ as repeated subtraction.

Use the following information to answer the next question.

Here is a series of subtraction equations.
    $25 - 5 = 20, 20 - 5 = 15, 15 - 5 = 10, 10 - 5 = 5, 5 - 5 = 0$

11. Write the repeated subtraction equations as a division equation.

Use the following information to answer the next question.

Tom and 3 of his friends have 16 eggs to decorate for Easter. Each person is going to decorate the same number of eggs.

12. Draw a picture, and write an equation to show how many eggs each person will decorate.

Use the following information to answer the next question.

Mr. Rabbit has 12 carrots. He wishes to share the carrots with 3 of his rabbit friends. This means 4 rabbits will be sharing the carrots.

13. Draw a picture, and write an equation to show how many carrots each rabbit will get.

14. Create an array to show the equation $5 \times 2 = 10$, then write the related division equations.

Use the following array of baseballs to answer the next question.

15. Write a multiplication equation that represents the array.

237

16. Create an array to show the multiplication equation $1 \times 5 = 5$, and write the related division equations for the array.

Use the following array of cars to answer the next question.

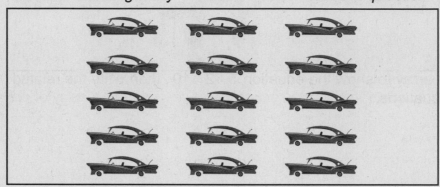

17. Write the multiplication and division equations for the array of cars.

Use the following array of presents to answer the next question.

18. Write multiplication and division equations to represent the array of presents.

Use the following array of curling rocks to answer the next question.

19. Use the array to find out how many curling rocks there are altogether.

Use the following array of batteries to answer the next question.

20. Use the array of batteries to write multiplication and division equations.

SOLVING EQUATIONS

When you are finished this unit, you will be able to…
• understand what an equation is
• understand that a symbol represents the unknown number in an equation
• explain what a symbol in an equation represents
• write an equation for a problem using a symbol to represent the unknown
• use the strategies of counting up or counting down to solve equations
• use base ten blocks to solve equations
• use the inverse operations of addition and subtraction to solve equations

Lesson	Page	Completed on
1. Understanding Equations and Symbols	242	
2. Solving Equations that Contain an Unknown	249	
Review Summary	255	
Practice Test	256	
Answers and Solutions	at the back of the book	

PREREQUISITE SKILLS AND KNOWLEDGE

Prior to starting this unit, you should be able to…
• determine quantities that are equal and not equal
• see that the sides of an equation are equal or not equal

Lesson 1 UNDERSTANDING EQUATIONS AND SYMBOLS

An **equation** is a number sentence. It uses an equal sign (=) to show that the amount on one side has the same value as the amount on the other side. The values on both sides are equal. For example, look at this equation.

$3 + 5 = 8$

$8 = 8$

When both sides of the equal sign (=) are the same, you know the equation is correct.

An equation is always written horizontally. If the numbers are written vertically, it is not considered to be an equation.

Equation	Not an Equation
$2 \times 8 = 16$	8 $\times 2$ 16

SYMBOLS IN EQUATIONS

Symbols can be signs, letters, pictures, or shapes that stand for something else. Symbols are often used in equations. The symbol in an equation represents a number that is not shown. This mystery number is called an unknown.

For example, the symbol ▲ is used in the equation 2 + 3 = ▲. The symbol ▲ stands for the unknown number.

SYMBOLS REPRESENT UNKNOWNS

In a math problem, there is always an unknown.
The unknown is what you are trying to find out when you solve the problem.   The value of the unknown is the solution to the problem. A symbol stands for the unknown in an equation.

The symbol that represents the unknown can be located anywhere in the equation. It might stand for the sum in an addition problem. It might be the number you are adding to another number. It might be the number you are subtracting from a number. When you see a symbol in an equation, you must find the number that the symbol stands for.

In 2 + 3 = ▲, the symbol ▲ represents the sum of 2 plus 3.

In 1 + ● = 6, the symbol ● represents the number that must be added to 1 to get a sum of 6.

In ☐ – 4 = 7, the symbol ☐ represents the number that 4 is subtracted from to get 7.

EXPLAINING WHAT A SYMBOL REPRESENTS

Before you can solve an equation, you need to understand what the symbol represents.

✸✸ Example

Explain what the symbol ▲ represents in the equation 9 – 2 = ▲.

Solution

The symbol ▲ represents the unknown number in the equation.

It represents the answer when 2 is subtracted from 9.

🦋 Time to Try 1

Explain what the ■ represents in the equation ■ + 4 = 10.

SAME UNKNOWN, DIFFERENT SYMBOLS

You can use different symbols to represent the same unknown in an equation. For example, in 5 + ● = 9, the symbol ● represents the number that must be added to 5 to get the sum of 9.

The same equation can be written as 5 + m = 9. The symbol m represents the number that must be added to 5 to get the sum of 9.

It does not matter what symbol is used. The unknown is still the same. Both ● and m represent the same unknown in the equation.

NOTES

 Example

Rewrite the equation 14 + ▲ = 19 two times using a different symbol to represent the same unknown.

Solution

Choose two different shapes, signs, or letters to represent the unknown. The unknown is the number that must be added to 14 to get the sum of 19.

Here are two ways you can represent the same unknown.
14 + ● = 19
14 + *A* = 19

 Time to Try 2

Rewrite the equation *F* – 8 = 14 two times using a different symbol each time to represent the same unknown.

EXPRESSING PICTURE PROBLEMS AS EQUATIONS

Sometimes, pictures are used to show a problem. Look at the picture problem carefully to determine what the unknown is. Then, write an equation to express the picture problem.

Follow these steps to help you write the equation.
• Use numbers to represent the items shown in the picture.
• Use a symbol to represent the unknown.
• Pay close attention to whether the items are being added or subtracted. Sometimes the plus or minus signs are shown. Sometimes you need to determine the operation by examining the pictures.

Example

Write an equation to express this picture problem.

To write the equation, follow these steps.
• Identify the items in the problem.
• Identify the unknown.
• Identify the operation needed.
• Write the equation that expresses the picture problem.

Solution
  • The items shown in the picture problem are apples.
  • The unknown is the total number of apples.
  • Choose a symbol to represent the unknown.
  • The + sign is a clue to add.
  • An equation that expresses the picture problem is $7 + 9 = \blacktriangle$.

Time to Try 3

This picture shows some balloons floating away from a larger bunch of balloons.

Choose a symbol to represent the unknown, and write an equation to express the picture problem.

NOTES

EXPRESSING WORD PROBLEMS AS EQUATIONS

Sometimes, a problem is written in words. The words tell you what you have to find. They also tell you what operation to use.

To write an equation for a word problem, read the problem carefully. Then, follow these steps.
- Identify what the unknown represents.
- Choose a symbol to represent the unknown.
- Determine the operation needed (+ or −) to express the equation.

Example

Carla had 24 candies. She shared some with her sister. When Carla counted her candies, she had 14 left.

Identify the unknown.
Identify the operation needed.
Write an equation to express the problem using the letter ▲ to represent the unknown.

Solution

The unknown (▲) is how many candies Carla gave to her sister.

The word *left* is a clue to subtract.

An equation that expresses the problem is 24 − ▲ = 14.

Time to Try 4

Phil has 13 toy cars. His brother Joey has 11 cars. How many cars do the boys have altogether?

Write an equation to express the problem using the letter *N* to represent the unknown.

PRACTICE EXERCISES

1. Explain what the symbol ☐ in the equation 8 + ☐ = 11 stands for.

2. Explain what the symbol ▲ in the equation 7 − ▲ = 5 represents.

3. The equation ☐ + 12 = 24 has an unknown. Rewrite the equation twice using a different symbol each time to represent the same unknown.

4. Use two different symbols to represent the unknown in the equation 10 − 8 = ●.

The apples in the picture express a problem

5. Choose a symbol to represent the unknown, and write an equation to express the problem.

The juice boxes shown express a problem.

6. Choose a symbol to represent the unknown, and write an equation to represent the problem shown in the picture.

Use the following information to answer the next question.

Caleb picked some carrots from the garden. He gave 15 carrots to his neighbour and had 12 carrots left. How many carrots did Caleb pick?

7. Let a square ☐ represent the unknown, and write an equation to express the problem.

Use the following information to answer the next question.

Dayton had 8 old pencil crayons left from last year. His grandmother gave him a package of 12 new pencil crayons when school began. How many pencil crayons does Dayton have now?

8. Let a square ☐ stand for the unknown, and write an equation to represent the problem.

Lesson 2   SOLVING EQUATIONS THAT CONTAIN AN UNKNOWN

You have been expressing picture problems and word problems as equations with an unknown. The unknown value in each equation is represented by a symbol. The operation to use is shown in the picture or described with words. Your job has been to write the equation. Now, you are going to solve equations that have one unknown.

There are several strategies you can use to solve such equations. A strategy is a plan that helps you determine the solution.

Here are five strategies that can help you find the unknown in equations.
- Guess and check
- Counting up
- Counting down
- Using base ten materials
- Using inverse operations

GUESS AND CHECK

To use guess and check, first make the most reasonable guess that you can. Then, check to see if you are correct. If you are not correct, make another guess.

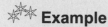 **Example**

Use the strategy of guess and check to solve the equation $14 + \bullet = 22$.

> *Solution*
>
> Since you know that $14 + 10 = 24$, a reasonable guess would be a number less than 10.
>
> Make a guess of 7.
> Check your answer. Replace the symbol $\bullet$ with 7.
> $14 + 7 = 21$
>
> You can see that the guess is one less than the answer of 22. So, add 1 more to your next guess.
>
> Make a guess of 8.
> Check your answer. Replace the symbol $\bullet$ with 8.
> $14 + 8 = 22$
>
> You know that the solution to the equation is 8.

NOTES

COUNTING UP

To count up, start with the lesser number and count up to the greater number. The number of counts is the unknown number in the equation. Counting up is a good strategy to use when the two numbers are close to each other.

 Example

Use the strategy of counting up to solve the equation $16 + \square = 21$. Explain your work.

Solution
Count up from 16 to 21.
17, 18, 19, 20, 21

There are 5 counts from 16 to 21, so the unknown number is 5.
$$16 + 5 = 21$$
$$21 = 21$$

The solution is $16 + 5 = 21$.

 Time to Try 1

Use the strategy of counting up to solve the equation $27 + \square = 31$. Explain your work.

COUNTING DOWN

To count down, start with the greater number and count down to the lesser number. The number of counts is the unknown number in the equation. Counting down is a good strategy to use when the two numbers are close to each other.

 Example

Use the strategy of counting down to solve the equation $36 - 29 = \square$.

Solution
Count down from 36 to 29.
35, 34, 33, 32, 31, 30, 29

There are 7 counts from 36 to 29, so the unknown number is 7.

$36 - 29 = 7$

$7 = 7$

 Time to Try 2

Use the strategy of counting down to solve the equation $17 - \square = 13$. Explain your work.

USING BASE TEN BLOCKS

To use base ten blocks, represent each number in the equation with ten rods and units. Then, add or subtract the units first. Next, add or subtract the ten rods.

 Example

Use base ten blocks to solve the equation $21 + \square = 27$.

Solution

Step 1

The equation $21 + \square = 27$ can be modelled with base ten blocks.

Two ten rods and 1 unit represent the number 21.
Two ten rods and 7 units represent the number 27.

Step 2

One way to solve this problem is to add base ten blocks to the number on the left side (21) until you make the number on the right side (27). Then, count the number of blocks you added. You added 6 units, so 6 is the unknown number.

$21 + 6 = 27$

NOTES

 Time to Try 3

Use base ten blocks to solve the equation 45 − 13 = ●.

USING INVERSE OPERATIONS

Inverse operations are opposite operations. Addition and subtraction are inverse operations. For example, if you know that 2 + 4 = 6, then you know that 6 − 4 = 2.

- You can use addition to solve subtraction problems.
- You can use subtraction to solve addition problems.

 Example

Use the inverse operation, subtraction, to solve the equation $15 + N = 25$. Show your work.

> *Solution*
> If you know that 15 + N = 25, then you know that
> 25 − 15 = N.
> $$15 + N = 25$$
> $$N = 25 - 15$$
> $$N = 10$$
> $$15 + 10 = 25$$
> $$25 = 25$$

 Time to Try 4

Use the inverse operation, addition, to solve the equation ▲ − 19 = 6. Show your work.

PRACTICE EXERCISES

1. Use the strategy of counting up to solve the equation $22 + \triangle = 27$. Show your work.

2. Use the strategy of counting up to solve the equation $78 + \square = 82$. Show your work.

3. Use the strategy of counting down to solve the equation $50 - \square = 47$. Show your work.

4. Use the strategy of counting down to solve the equation $18 - x = 14$. Show your work.

5. Use base ten blocks to solve the equation $52 + 35 = \bullet$. Draw base ten blocks to show your work.

6. Use base ten blocks to find the solution to the equation $33 - 12 = \bullet$. Draw base ten blocks to show your work.

7. Use the inverse operation, subtraction, to solve the equation $N + 12 = 36$.

8. Use the inverse operation, addition, to solve the equation $K - 15 = 42$.

REVIEW SUMMARY

- An equation is a number sentence that uses an equal sign (=) to show that both sides of the equation have the same value.
- A symbol can be used to represent an unknown number in an equation.
- A symbol can be a letter, a sign, or a shape.
- The same unknown in an equation can be represented by different symbols.
- Written problems and picture problems can be represented as equations with an unknown.
- A strategy is a plan that you can use to help you solve a problem.
- Solve equations using a strategy that works best for you.
- These strategies can be used to solve equations.
  - Guess and check
  - Counting up
  - Counting down
  - Base ten materials
  - The inverse operations of addition and subtraction

PRACTICE TEST

1. In the equation $12 + \square = 33$, explain what the symbol $\square$ represents. Do not solve for $\square$.

Use the following information to answer the next question.

2. Choose a symbol to stand for the unknown, and write an equation to represent the problem.

Use the following information to answer the next question.

Shaylah had 5 pink erasers. Her mom gave her a package of 6 white erasers. How many erasers does Shaylah have now?

3. Use a square ($\square$) to represent the unknown, and write an equation that expresses the given problem.

4. Use the strategy of counting down to solve the equation $33 - x = 28$. Show your work.

5. Use the inverse operation of subtraction to solve the equation $\square + 15 = 45$. Explain your work.

6. Rewrite the equation $47 - r = 19$ two times using a different symbol each time to represent the unknown.

7. Use base ten blocks to solve the equation $45 - 22 = \blacktriangle$.

8. Use the counting-up strategy to solve the equation $89 + \blacktriangle = 93$. Show your work.

9. Explain what the symbol $\blacktriangle$ in the equation $93 - \blacktriangle = 15$ represents.

10. Use the inverse operation, addition, to solve the equation $\triangle - 28 = 56$. Show your work.

Use the following information to answer the next question.

Hudson had a group of hockey cards. After he gave 22 cards to his cousin Cameron, he had 29 cards left. How many cards did Hudson have to begin with?

---

11. Using a square ($\square$) to represent the unknown, write an equation that expresses the given problem.

12. Use the strategy that works best for you to solve the equation $N + 48 = 88$. Explain your strategy.

PATTERNS

When you are finished this unit, you will be able to...
• describe, extend, and create increasing and decreasing patterns
• explain the rule for a given pattern
• describe and create patterns using a pattern rule

Lesson	Page	Completed on
1. Introduction to Patterns	260	
2. Patterns Using Pattern Rules	266	
Review Summary	276	
Practice Test	277	
Answers and Solutions	at the back of the book	

PREREQUISITE SKILLS AND KNOWLEDGE

Prior to starting this unit, you should be able to...
• describe, extend, and create a repeating pattern using numbers and objects
• define odd and even numbers

Lesson 1 *INTRODUCTION TO PATTERNS*

Patterns are formed when numbers, shapes, colours, or actions are repeated. Patterns can be seen everywhere you look. They are found in necklaces, music, sports, numbers, objects, and on paper or clothing. Here is an example of a repeating pattern showing two big triangles followed by two smaller triangles.

INCREASING PATTERNS

An increasing pattern has numbers that increase in value with each term of the pattern. It is sometimes called a growing pattern.

For example, the pattern 3, 6, 9, 12, 15 is an increasing or growing pattern. Each number is formed by adding 3 to the number before it.

DECREASING PATTERNS

A decreasing pattern has numbers that decrease in value with each term of the pattern. It is sometimes called a shrinking pattern.

For example, the pattern 20, 16, 12, 8, 4 is a decreasing or shrinking pattern. Each number is formed by taking away 4 from the number before it.

✸ Example

Is the pattern increasing or decreasing in the given number pattern?
333, 433, 533, 633, 733

Solution
The pattern is increasing.

The numbers in the pattern are increasing in value. The pattern starts at 333 and increases by 100 for each term.

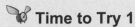 **Time to Try 1**

Is the pattern increasing or decreasing in the given number pattern?
320, 310, 300, 290, 280

Skip counting is a good way to make a number pattern.
You have already practiced skip counting by 5s, 10s, 25s, and 100s. When you skip count forward by a number, the number sequence increases by that number. When you skip count backward by a number, the number sequence decreases by that number.

Example

Compare the given skip counting patterns.
101, 201, 301, 401, 501
121, 131, 141, 151, 161

Solution

To compare the number patterns, look to see what number the pattern is increasing by. In the first pattern, each number is increasing by 100. In the second pattern, each number is increasing by 10.

Time to Try 2

Compare the given skip counting patterns.
354, 349, 344, 339, 334
475, 465, 455, 445, 435

PATTERNS USING CHARTS

Patterns can be found everywhere on a hundred chart.
Look for patterns in the rows, columns, and diagonals.

1	2	3	4	5	6	7	8	9	10
11	12	13	14	15	16	17	18	19	20
21	22	23	24	25	26	27	28	29	30
31	32	33	34	35	36	37	38	39	40
41	42	43	44	45	46	47	48	49	50
51	52	53	54	55	56	57	58	59	60
61	62	63	64	65	66	67	68	69	70
71	72	73	74	75	76	77	78	79	80
81	82	83	84	85	86	87	88	89	90
91	92	93	94	95	96	97	98	99	100

When you read down a column, each number ends with the same digit. For example, each number in the second column ends in a 2. Only the digits in the tens place change. There is another pattern going from the top left to the bottom right on the diagonal. Each number grows by eleven and forms the pattern 1, 12, 23, 34, 45, and so on. Try to find other patterns on the hundred chart.

 Example

When you look across the rows from left to right on the hundred chart, what pattern do you see?

Solution

The numbers increase in value. The pattern you see is that the numbers increase by 1 each term.

NOTES

Time to Try 3

Starting at the number 71, what pattern do you see for the circled numbers?

1	2	3	4	5	6	7	⑧	9	10
11	12	13	14	15	16	⑰	18	19	20
21	22	23	24	25	㉖	27	28	29	30
31	32	33	34	㉟	36	37	38	39	40
41	42	43	㊹	45	46	47	48	49	50
51	52	(53)	54	55	56	57	58	59	60
61	(62)	63	64	65	66	67	68	69	70
(71)	72	73	74	75	76	77	78	79	80

Patterns can also be made from sounds or actions. Music is made by repeating notes in different patterns. Dancing is done by repeating steps in different patterns.

Example

Hudson created the following pattern as he tapped his foot. The first time, he tapped his foot 1 time. The second time, he tapped his foot 2 times. The third time, he tapped his foot 3 times. How many times will he tap his foot the fourth time?

Solution

The pattern is growing by 1 each time. Since Hudson tapped his foot 3 times the third time, he will tap his foot 4 times the fourth time.

PRACTICE EXERCISES

Use the following information to answer the next question.

The numbers 12, 10, 8, 6, 4, 2 forms a pattern.

1. Is the given number pattern increasing or decreasing?

2. In the number pattern 5, 10, 15, 20, is the pattern increasing or decreasing?

Use the following information to answer the next question.

Two number patterns are shown here:
12, 17, 22, 27, 32, 37
50, 55, 60, 65, 70, 75

3. Compare the given skip counting patterns. What numbers are the two patterns increasing by?

Use the following information to answer the next question.

Two number patterns are shown here:
88, 78, 68, 58, 48
808, 708, 608, 508, 408

4. Compare the skip counting patterns shown. What numbers are the two skip counting patterns decreasing by?

Use the following information to answer the next question.

Ray made the following pattern with sticks. The first figure he made has 1 stick. The second figure he made has 2 sticks. The third figure he made has 3 sticks. The fourth figure he made has 4 sticks.

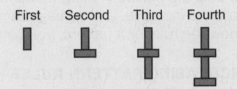

First   Second   Third   Fourth

5. How many sticks will Ray use to make the fifth figure?

Use the following information to answer the next question.

1	2	3	4	5	6	7	8	9	10
11	12	13	14	15	16	17	18	19	20
21	22	23	24	25	26	27	28	29	30
31	32	33	34	35	36	37	38	39	40
41	42	43	44	45	46	47	48	49	50
51	52	53	54	55	56	57	58	59	60
61	62	63	64	65	66	67	68	69	70
71	72	73	74	75	76	77	78	79	80
81	82	83	84	85	86	87	88	89	90
91	92	93	94	95	96	97	98	99	100

6. In the hundred chart shown, what pattern do you see going down the shaded column from 1 to 91?

Lesson 2   PATTERNS USING PATTERN RULES

All patterns follow a pattern rule. Finding the rules for different patterns can help you extend or continue a pattern. Look for the similarities, the differences, and the order the numbers or objects are placed in the pattern. Some patterns repeat, some patterns increase, and some patterns decrease. Once you know the rule for a pattern, you can extend it.

INCREASING PATTERN RULES

Look at the following increasing pattern.
6, 11, 16, 21, 26, 31, 36…

You can see that the numbers are increasing. Each time, the number increases by 5. If the numbers increase by 5 each time, the next three numbers will be 41, 46, 51. The pattern rule is that you add 5 to the number to get the next number in the sequence.

✻ Example

Find the pattern rule, and fill in the blanks to complete this number pattern.
1, 3, 5, 7, ___, ___, ___

Solution

To complete the pattern, look for the difference between the numbers. To find the difference, subtract the lesser number from the greater number. The difference between the first two numbers is 2 because 3 − 1 = 2.

Check the difference between the next two numbers to see if the difference is also 2.
5 − 3 = 2

If the difference between each pair of numbers is 2, you have found the pattern rule.

$$\overset{(+2)}{1,} \ \overset{(+2)}{3,} \ \overset{(+2)}{5,} \ \overset{(+2)}{7,} \ \overset{(+2)}{9,} \ \overset{(+2)}{11,} \ 13$$

Since each number goes up by 2, the rule is to add 2 each time to get the next term.

You can also count up from one number to the next. The number of counts it takes to get to the next number is the number that the pattern is increasing by. Starting at 1, count up to 3 (1, 2, 3). It takes 2 counts to get from 1 to 3.

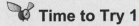 **Time to Try 1**

Find the pattern rule, and fill in the blanks to complete this number pattern.
21, 31, 41, ___, ___, ___

DECREASING PATTERN RULES

Look at the following decreasing number pattern.
26, 24, 22, 20, 18, 16…

The first thing to notice about the numbers is that they are decreasing in value. The numbers decrease by 2 each time. If the numbers become less by 2 each time, the next three numbers will be 14, 12, 10. Since you subtract 2 from one number to get the next number in the sequence, the pattern rule is to subtract 2.

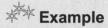 **Example**

Find the pattern rule, and continue the pattern for the next three numbers.
84, 79, 74, ___, ___, ___

Solution

To find the pattern rule, look for the difference between the numbers. To find the difference, subtract the lesser number from the greater number. The difference between the first two numbers is 5 because $84 - 79 = 5$. Check the difference between the next two numbers to see if the difference is also 5.
$79 - 74 = 5$

Since the difference between each pair of numbers is 5, you have found the pattern rule.

$$84, \overset{(-5)}{\ } 79, \overset{(-5)}{\ } 74, \overset{(-5)}{\ } 69, \overset{(-5)}{\ } 64, \overset{(-5)}{\ } 59$$

The pattern rule is to subtract 5 from each term to get the next term.

You can also count down from one term to the next term. The number of counts it takes to get to the next term is the number that the pattern is decreasing by. Starting at 84, count down to 79.

84, 83, 82, 81, 80, 79

NOTES

It takes 5 counts to get from 84 to 79.

The pattern rule is to subtract 5. The next three numbers are 69, 64, 59.

$74 - 5 = 69$, $69 - 5 = 64$, $64 - 5 = 59$

 Time to Try 2

Find the pattern rule, and continue the pattern for three more terms.
143, 136, 129, ___, ___, ___

PATTERN RULES FOR SHAPES AND OBJECTS

Patterns can also be shown with pictures, designs, and shapes. You can continue any pattern once you determine the pattern rule.

 Example

How many stars are needed in fifth figure if the pattern continues?

1   2   3

Solution

To figure out the rule, look at the number of stars used for the first and second figures. There are 2 more stars in the second figure than the first. Move on to the third figure. There are 2 more stars in the third figure than the second. You have found the pattern rule. Since 2 stars are added to each new figure, the pattern rule is to add 2.

Use the pattern rule to predict the number stars in the fourth figure. Since each figure goes up by 2 stars, add 2 stars to the number of stars in figure 3 ($5 + 2 = 7$).

There will be 7 stars in figure 4.

Follow the same steps to find the number of stars needed in figure 5 ($7 + 2 = 9$). There will be 9 stars in figure 5 if the pattern continues.

Drawing pictures is a good strategy to use to figure out this pattern rule. Draw the stars in figures 4 and 5.

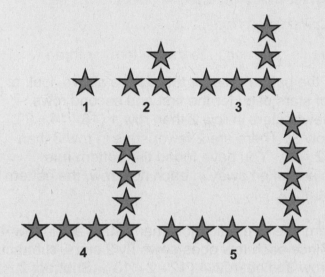

Time to Try 3

The balls used in these designs form a pattern.

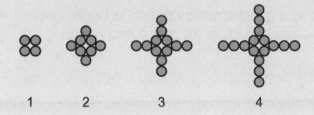

If the pattern continues, how many balls are needed in figure 5?

NOTES

✳ Example

Determine the pattern rule to find how many stars there will be in rows 4 and 5 of the given pattern.

Row 1 ☆☆☆☆☆☆☆☆☆☆☆☆☆☆☆☆

Row 2 ☆☆☆☆☆☆☆☆☆☆☆☆☆☆

Row 3 ☆☆☆☆☆☆☆☆☆☆☆☆

Solution

To figure out the pattern rule for the picture above, look at the number of stars used for the first and second rows. There are 2 fewer stars in row 2 than row 1 ($16 - 14 = 2$). Move on to row 3. There are 2 fewer stars in row 3 than row 2 ($14 - 12 = 2$). You have found the pattern rule. Since 2 stars are taken away in each new row, the pattern rule is to subtract 2.

Use the pattern rule to predict how many stars are in row 4 and row 5. Since each row goes down by 2 stars, subtract 2 stars from row 3 to get row 4 ($12 - 2 = 10$). Subtract 2 stars from row 4 to get row 5 ($10 - 2 = 8$).

There will be 10 stars in row 4 and 8 stars in row 5.

Drawing a picture is a good strategy to use to figure out this pattern rule. Draw the stars for row 4 and row 5.

Row 4 ☆☆☆☆☆☆☆☆☆☆

Row 5 ☆☆☆☆☆☆☆☆

🐝 Time to Try 4

Determine the pattern rule, and find how many hearts are needed in shapes 4 and 5 of the pattern.

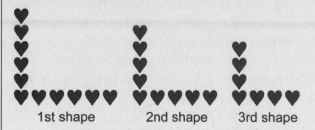

1st shape   2nd shape   3rd shape

You can describe the starting point of a given pattern as part of the pattern rule to extend it. Look at the number pattern 42, 44, 46, 48. This is a growing pattern. Each term increases by 2. This number pattern starts at 42.

The pattern rule is to start at 42 and add 2 each time.

✳ Example

Describe the starting point and the pattern rule for the set of numbers 37, 40, 43, 46, 49.

Solution

To describe the pattern rule, determine how the pattern is changing. The numbers are becoming greater, so the pattern is increasing or growing. To find out by how much, count up 3 counts (37, 38, 39, 40), or subtract 40 – 37 = 3. The pattern rule is to start at 37 and add 3 to each term.

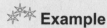 Time to Try 5

Describe the starting point and pattern rule for the decreasing pattern 94, 90, 86, 82, 78.

Sometimes you need to find a number that is missing in a number pattern. You can find the missing number by using the pattern rule.

✳ Example

What number is missing from the given number pattern?
265, 275, 285, _____, 305, 315

Solution

To find the pattern rule, look for the difference between the numbers. Starting with the first number in the pattern, find the difference between it and the second number.
The difference is 10. The digit in the tens place value position is going up by one, so the pattern is growing by 10 each term. The pattern rule is to add 10.

To find the missing number, add 10 to the number before the blank (285 + 10 = 295). The missing number is 295. You can check your answer by adding 10 to 295. If you get 305, which is the next number in the pattern, 295 is the missing number.

NOTES

 Time to Try 6

Here is a number pattern with a number missing.
620, 615, 610, _____, 600, 595

What number is missing from the given number pattern?

CREATING PATTERNS USING PATTERN RULES

A pattern rule is a plan that tells you how to make a pattern. It tells you what number to start the pattern with, what operation to use, and the number to use with the operation to get the next term. Sometimes, it tells you how many terms should be in the number sequence.

To create a pattern, you need to start with a pattern rule and then follow it.

 Example

Make a decreasing pattern that has five terms and follows this pattern rule: Start with 54 and subtract 3 each time.

Solution
Start at 54. Subtract 3 from 54 (54 – 3 = 51). The second number in the pattern is 51. Subtract 3 from 51 (51 – 3 = 48). The third number in the pattern is 48. Subtract 3 from 48 (48 – 3 = 45). The fourth number in the pattern is 45. Subtract 3 from 45. (45 – 3 = 42). The fifth number in the pattern is 42.

The pattern is 54, 51, 48, 45, 42.

 Time to Try 7

Make an increasing pattern that has five terms and uses the pattern rule to start at 35 and add 9 to each term.

PRACTICE EXERCISES

Use the following information to answer the next question.

Here is a pattern of numbers with three terms missing.
14, 21, 28, ___, ___, ___

1. Describe the pattern rule, and continue the pattern to fill in the three missing terms.

Use the following information to answer the next question.

The numbers 558, 568, 578, 588, 598, 608 form an increasing pattern.

2. Describe the starting point and the pattern rule for the increasing pattern.

Use the following information to answer the next question.

842, 742, 642, 542, 442

3. Describe the starting point and pattern rule for the decreasing pattern.

Use the following information to answer the next question.

Jason makes a pattern of shapes by stacking boxes.

1   2   3   4

4. If the pattern continues, how many boxes will Jason need for the fifth figure?

Use the following information to answer the next question.

Here is a number pattern with one term missing.
50, 150, 250, ___, 450

5. What number is missing from the given number pattern?

6. Start at 10 and add 1, then 2, then 3, and so on to make a pattern that has five terms.

7. Start at 639, and subtract 9 for six terms.

Use the following information to answer the next question.

Jill makes a cross pattern using squares.

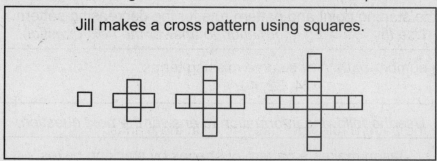

8. Determine the pattern rule, and find how many boxes are needed for the fifth figure.

274

Use the following information to answer the next question.

A growing number pattern.

 ② ⑦ ⑫ ⑰ ◯

9. Describe the pattern rule, and find the missing number.

10. Make an increasing pattern with four terms using this pattern rule: start at 23, and add 6 to each term.

11. Create a number pattern using this pattern rule: start at 250, and subtract 20 for five terms.

Use the following information to answer the next question.

The following number pattern has some missing terms.
24, 32, 40, ___, ___, ___

12. Determine the pattern rule, and use it to fill in the blanks.

13. What number is missing from the number pattern 340, 325, 310, 295, ___, 265?

REVIEW SUMMARY

- Patterns are formed when numbers, shapes, colours, or actions are repeated. Patterns can grow, shrink, or repeat.
- An increasing or growing pattern has numbers that increase in value with each term.
- A decreasing or shrinking pattern has numbers that decrease in value with each term.
- Patterns can be found on a hundred chart in the rows, columns, and diagonals.
- Patterns follow a pattern rule.
  - Pattern rules help you extend or continue a pattern.
  - Pattern rules can also be used for shapes and objects.
  - Pattern rules help you find a missing number in a sequence of numbers.
- To find the pattern rules for different patterns, look for similarities, differences, and the order in which the numbers or objects are placed.
- A pattern rule tells you what number to start the pattern with, what operation to use, and the number to use with the operation to get the next term.

PRACTICE TEST

Use the following information to answer the next question.

The numbers 622, 624, 626, 628, 630 form a number pattern.

1. Is the given number pattern increasing or decreasing?

Use the following information to answer the next question.

The numbers 191, 181, 171, 161, 151 form a number pattern.

2. Is the pattern increasing or decreasing in the given number pattern?

3. Compare the given skip counting patterns.
   220, 230, 240, 250, 260
   260, 250, 240, 230, 220

4. Compare the given skip counting patterns.
   66, 61, 56, 51, 46
   205, 200, 195, 190, 185

Use the following information to answer the next question.

1	2	3	4	5	6	7	8	9	10
11	12	13	14	15	16	17	18	19	20
21	22	23	24	25	26	27	28	29	30
31	32	33	34	35	36	37	38	39	40
41	42	43	44	45	46	47	48	49	50
51	52	53	54	55	56	57	58	59	60
61	62	63	64	65	66	67	68	69	70
71	72	73	74	75	76	77	78	79	80
81	82	83	84	85	86	87	88	89	90
91	92	93	94	95	96	97	98	99	100

5. Starting at the number 95, what pattern do you see for the shaded numbers on the given hundred chart?

Use the following information to answer the next question.

Lila made a tower using a snowball pattern. In step 1 of the pattern, Lila used 1 snowball. In step 2, Lila used 3 snowballs. In step 3, Lila used 5 snowballs. In step 4, Lila used 7 snowballs.

Step 1   Step 2   Step 3   Step 4

6. How many snowballs will Lila use in step 5 of the pattern?

Use the following information to answer the next question.

Here is a number pattern with some of the numbers missing.
92, 94, 96, 98, ___, ___, ___

7. Find the pattern rule, and fill in the blanks to complete the given number pattern.

Use the following information to answer the next question.

The number pattern 11, 21, 31, ___, ___, ___ has some missing numbers.

8. Find the pattern rule, and fill in the blanks to complete the number pattern.

9. Find the pattern rule, and continue the following pattern for three more numbers.
234, 229, 224, ___, ___, ___

10. State the pattern rule for the following numbers, and complete the pattern by filling in the blanks.
57, 82, 107, ___, ___, ___

Use the following information to answer the next question.

The blocks in these three figures form a pattern.

11. If the pattern continues, how many blocks will be needed in figure 4?

Use the following diagram to answer the next question.

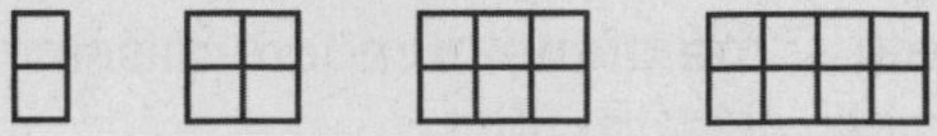

12. Determine the pattern rule to find how many blocks will be needed in figure 5 and figure 6 of the pattern.

Use the following information to answer the next question.

64, 67, 70, 73, 76

13. Describe the starting point and the pattern rule for the given set of numbers.

Use the following information to answer the next question.

124, 120, 116, 112, 108

14. Describe the pattern rule and include the starting point for the given decreasing pattern.

Use the following information to answer the next question.

This number pattern has a missing term.
325, 300, 275, _____, 225, 200

15. What number is missing from the given number pattern?

Use the following information to answer the next question.

The pattern rule is to start with 72 and subtract 3 from each term to get the next term.

16. Using the pattern rule, make a decreasing pattern that has four terms.

Use the following information to answer the next question.

The pattern rule is to start at 26 and add 7 to each term to get the next term.

17. Using the pattern rule, make an increasing pattern that has five terms.

Use the following information to answer the next question.

1	2	3	4	5	6	7	8	9	10
11	12	13	14	15	16	17	18	19	20
21	22	23	24	25	26	27	28	29	30
31	32	33	34	35	36	37	38	39	40
41	42	43	44	45	46	47	48	49	50
51	52	53	54	55	56	57	58	59	60
61	62	63	64	65	66	67	68	69	70
71	72	73	74	75	76	77	78	79	80
81	82	83	84	85	86	87	88	89	90
91	92	93	94	95	96	97	98	99	100

18. From the hundred chart shown, what pattern do you see for the shaded numbers beginning at number 41?

Use the following information to answer the next question.

1	2	3	4	5	6	7	8	9	10
11	12	13	14	15	16	17	18	19	20
21	22	23	24	25	26	27	28	29	30
31	32	33	34	35	36	37	38	39	40
41	42	43	44	45	46	47	48	49	50
51	52	53	54	55	56	57	58	59	60
61	62	63	64	65	66	67	68	69	70
71	72	73	74	75	76	77	78	79	80
81	82	83	84	85	86	87	88	89	90
91	92	93	94	95	96	97	98	99	100

19. On the given hundred chart, what is the pattern rule for the shaded numbers going diagonally from 10 to 91?

TIME

When you are finished this unit, you will be able to...
• relate passage of time by events
• relate events by how long it takes to complete them
• determine the amount of seconds in a minute, minutes in an hour, hours in a day, days in a week, and weeks in a year
• create a calendar to record days of the week, dates, and personal events.

Lesson	Page	Completed on
1. Time Measurement	284	
2. Units of Time	292	
Review Summary	300	
Practice Test	301	
Answers and Solutions	at the back of the book	

PREREQUISITE SKILLS AND KNOWLEDGE

Prior to starting this unit, you should be able to...
• tell the months of the year in order
• tell the number and name of the days in a week
• read a date on a calendar

Lesson 1 *TIME MEASUREMENT*

NOTES

Time is used to measure how long an event is or to find the amount of space between past, present, or future events. Seconds, minutes, hours, days, weeks, months, and years can all be used to measure time. All of the units used to measure time are related to one another. One minute is made up of 60 seconds, and one hour has 60 minutes. There are 24 hours in one day, 7 days in a week, and about 4 weeks (sometimes with an extra 1 to 3 days) in a month. There are 12 months in one year. There are 365 days in every year except for a leap year, which has 366 days. A leap year happens every four years.

60 seconds = 1 minute	
60 minutes = 1 hour	
24 hours = 1 day	
7 days = 1 week	
4 weeks = 1 month	

Each of these units of time can be used to measure how much time has passed; however, some units of time are more appropriate to measure certain events. The units of time measurement written in order from the shortest amount of time to the longest are seconds, minutes, hours, days, weeks, months, years.

12 months = 1 year
52 weeks = 1 year
365 days = 1 year
366 days = 1 leap year

 Example

What measure of time would you use to measure how long it would take to blink?

Solution

To decide whether you would use seconds, minutes, hours, days, weeks, months, or years to measure the time it would take to blink, determine if blinking is a short or long event. Blinking occurs very quickly so most likely it would be measured using seconds.

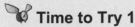

 Time to Try 1

What measure of time would you use to measure how long it would take to clean your room?

 Time to Try 2

What measure of time would you use to measure the length of your favourite movie?

Some activities take longer than others. Can you think of something that takes a second to do? Seconds are a very short period of time. Think of things that happen immediately such as the time it takes to clap or cough.

Minutes are a little longer. If you were thinking of things you could do in a minute, you might think of brushing your teeth or walking in from the car to your house. You could watch a show or go to soccer practice in an hour. A week is the length of spring break.

Example

Would you be able to walk to school in a second?

Solution

No, depending on where you lived, it would more likely take several minutes to walk to school.

 Time to Try 3

Would you be able to wash your car in an hour?

PASSAGE OF TIME

Passage of time is the amount of time between when something begins and when it ends. For example, piano lessons begin at 2:00 and end at 2:30. The passage of time between 2:00 and 2:30 is $\frac{1}{2}$ hour or 30 minutes. When using a clock to measure the passage of time, you would use words like seconds, minutes, and hours.

60 seconds = 1 minute
60 minutes = 1 hour
45 minutes = $\frac{3}{4}$ hour
30 minutes = $\frac{1}{2}$ hour
15 minutes = $\frac{1}{4}$ hour
24 hours = 1 day

Counting to the nearest half hour or hour makes it easier to calculate the passage of time.

 Example

John left the house at 8:30 and arrived at school at 9:10. How long did it take John to get to school?

Solution

From 8:30 to 9:00 (nearest hour) it is 30 minutes. From 9:00 to 9:10, it is 10 minutes. Add 30 and 10 together.

It took John 40 minutes to get to school.

 Time to Try 4

Jill went out with her mom on Saturday. They left the house at 10:15 A.M. and arrived home at 6:45 P.M. How long was Jill gone for?

The **days** of the week are listed in order in the table below. The days of the week always follow the same order. Tuesday is always the day after Monday, and Friday is always the day before Saturday. Sunday is the first day of the week and Saturday is the last day of the week.

Sunday	Monday	Tuesday	Wednesday	Thursday	Friday	Saturday

You can measure the passage of time using days and weeks as well.

Example

Seth took a book out of the library on Monday morning and returned it on Thursday after school. How many days did Seth have the book?

Solution

You would count Monday, Tuesday, Wednesday, and Thursday—Seth had the book for four days. You must count Thursday because Seth returned the book at the end of the day.

Seth had the book for 4 days.

Time to Try 5

Sally went to basketball camp on Friday morning and returned on Thursday night. How many days was she gone for?

The **months** of the year follow a specific order as well. The order of months never changes. The day after December 31 is January 1, which is the first day of a new year. There are 12 months in one year and 365 days in one year.

Months	Days
January	31
February	28
March	31
April	30
May	31
June	30
July	31
August	31
September	30
October	31
November	30
December	31

Every fourth year is a **leap year**. In a leap year, there are 366 days. The extra day is placed in February (Feb 29).

You can also measure the passage of time using months or years.

 Example

Frank plays soccer in the summer but not in the winter. If Frank's last soccer game is at the end of September and he starts playing again in May, how long is Frank's break between soccer seasons?

Solution

Count the months between September and May but do not count them in your counting.

October, November, December, January, February, March, April.

Frank's break between soccer seasons lasted 7 months.

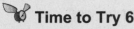 **Time to Try 6**

Mimi went on a world cruise. She left on March 22 and returned on August 8. How many days was Mimi gone?

Minutes, hours, and days are standard units for measuring time, but you can measure how time passes using non-standard measurements. You could measure time by how long a TV show lasts—some shows are 30 minutes, others are 1 hour. You could measure shorter periods of time by how long a commercial break lasts—2 to 3 minutes.

PRACTICE EXERCISES

1. What measure of time would you use to measure how long your Math class is?

2. What measure of time would you use to measure the how long a professional hockey game lasts?

3. Your lacrosse team plays in a tournament with 15 other teams. What unit of measurement would be used to measure the length of time the tournament takes?

4. Could you play a game of monopoly in seconds?

5. Iman started his homework at 7:15 P.M. and finished at 7:50 P.M. How long did Iman spend doing his homework?

6. Nathan went to a Boy Scout camp on the morning of Saturday, July 17, and returned on the evening of Sunday, July 25. How many nights was Nathan gone?

7. Jesse attends hip hop dance classes from November 1 to March 31. How many months does Jesse attend dance classes?

8. Massimo was born on January 8, 1997. How old is he on January 8, 2010?

9. Match the events with the approximate time each should likely take.

____	Ice Hockey Season	1. 1 second
____	Watch a movie	2. 1 minute
____	Snap your fingers	3. 2 weeks
____	Tie your shoes	4. 2 hours
____	Go on a holiday	5. 5 months

10. Whalen begins reading his book at 11:45 A.M. and reads until 1:30 P.M. For how many minutes did Whalen read his book?

Lesson 2   UNITS OF TIME

The following time relationships can help you solve problems involving time.

60 seconds = 1 minute
60 minutes = 1 hour
24 hours = 1 day
7 days = 1 week
4 weeks = 1 month
12 months = 1 year
52 weeks = 1 year
365 days = 1 year

❋ Example

John ran across the field in 180 seconds. How many minutes did it take John to run across the field?

Solution

There are 60 seconds in 1 minute. Subtract 60 seconds from the total number of seconds and count how many times you subtract to reach zero. This will find out how many minutes are in 180 seconds.

$$180 - 60 = 120$$
$$120 - 60 = 60$$
$$60 - 60 = 0$$

John ran across the field in 3 minutes.

Time to Try 1

Kyle walked his dog around the block. It took him 540 seconds. How many minutes did it take Kyle to walk his dog around the block?

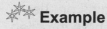 **Example**

Mark started his homework at 4:00 P.M. and stopped at 7:00 P.M. For many minutes did Mark study?

Solution

First, count how many hours Mark worked on his homework.
4:00 P.M. – 5:00 P.M. = 1 hour
5:00 P.M. – 6:00 P.M. = 2 hours
6:00 P.M. – 7:00 P.M. = 3 hours

There are 3 hours from 4:00 P.M. to 7:00 P.M.

Next, find how many minutes are in 3 hours. Add 60 minutes 3 times.
60 + 60 + 60 = 180.

Mark did homework for 180 minutes.

 Time to Try 2

Ariel went to a concert. She left at 1:00 P.M. and returned home at 5:00 P.M. How many minutes was she gone.

Calendars help organize all of the things that need to be done in a month. A calendar page displays the months of the year as well as the days of the week.

JUNE

MON	TUES	WED	THU	FRI	SAT	SUN
May 30	31	June 1	2	3	4	5
6	7	8	9	10	11	12
13	14	15	16	17	18	19
20	21	22	23	24	25	26
27	28	29	30	July 1	2	3

NOTES

There are 12 months in one year. Each year begins on the first day of January. The following shows the months in order:

Months	Days
January	31
February	28
March	31
April	30
May	31
June	30
July	31
August	31
September	30
October	31
November	30
December	31

The months repeat in the same order every year. The first letter in each month must be capitalized any time a month is written.

Each month has a certain amount of days. If you can't remember how many days are in a month, you can use a calendar. Calendars follow the same order every year.

Time to Try 3

Juanita is filling in a quick reminder of months and holidays or celebrations in her notebook. She has missed writing a few of the months.

Complete the months of the year for Juanita.

Month	Holiday/Celebration
January	New Year's Day
	Valentine's Day
	St. Patrick's Day
April	Easter
May	Mother's Day
	Father's Day
	Canada Day
	Civic Holiday
September	Back to School
	Thanksgiving/Halloween
November	Remembrance Day
	Christmas

There are seven days in a week. Each week begins on Sunday. The order of the days is as follows:

Sunday	Monday	Tuesday	Wednesday	Thursday	Friday	Saturday

Just like the months of the year, the days of the week repeat their order. The first letter in the name of the day needs to be capitalized any time it is written.

NOTES

You can create a calendar to help you organize your monthly activities and special events.

When creating a calendar, label the month at the top, then fill in the days of the week starting with Sunday on the left. The days should be in order: Sunday, Monday, Tuesday, Wednesday, Thursday, Friday, and Saturday.

Next, you number the days of the month. June has 30 days, and the first day of the month in the year 2010 is a Tuesday. Begin numbering the calendar on the first Tuesday in the first row and number all the days to 30.

JUNE

SUN	MON	TUES	WED	THU	FRI	SAT
		1	2	3	4	5
6	7	8	9	10	11	12
13	14	15	16	17	18	19
20	21	22	23	24	25	26
27	28	29	30			

 Time to Try 4

Choose a month and create a calendar for dates and special events.

PRACTICE EXERCISES

1. How many minutes are equal to 480 seconds?

2. How many weeks are equal to 4 years?

3. How many hours are there in 3 days?

4. How many seconds are there in 4 minutes?

5. Match the times on the left with time on the right equal to it,

   ___ 3 days   1. 180 seconds
   ___ 6 weeks   2. 120 minutes
   ___ 3 minutes   3. 42 days
   ___ 600 seconds   4. 72 hours
   ___ 2 hours   5. 10 minutes

6. Marley watches cartoons from 9:00 A.M. to 10:15 A.M. on Saturday mornings. For how many minutes does Marley watch cartoons?

7. Paul ran 3 laps of the track in 8 minutes. How many seconds did it take him?

8. Millie likes to play games on the computer. She plays from 2:15 P.M. to 3:45 P.M. How many minutes does Millie spend playing computer games?

9. Alton begins an exercise program on January 17 and completes it on March 2. How many days did Alton's exercise program last?

Use the following information to answer the next question.

The first day of December 2010 is a Wednesday. Pam's birthday is December 12, and Floyd's is December 21.

10. Create a calendar for December 2010, and mark the birthdays and Christmas on the calendar.

December 2010

SUN	MON	TUES	WED	THU	FRI	SAT

Use the following information to answer the next question.

The first day of the April 2112 will be Sunday. Good Friday will be April 13, and Easter will be April 15. Greg has a birthday on April 3, and Ted has a birthday on April 25.

11. Create a calendar for April 2112, and mark these dates on the calendar.

April 2112

SUN	MON	TUES	WED	THU	FRI	SAT

Use the following information to answer the next question.

February 2116 will be a leap year. The first day of the month will be a Monday. Valentine's Day will be February 14, and Family Day will be February 22. Meike has a birthday on February 7, and Rick has a birthday on Feb 12.

12. Create a calendar for February 2116, and mark these dates on the calendar.

February 2116

SUN	MON	TUES	WED	THU	FRI	SAT

REVIEW SUMMARY

- Time can be measured by seconds, minutes, days, weeks, months, and years. It can also be measured by TV shows, commercials, or counting.
- 24 hours = 1 day, 60 minutes = 1 hour, and 60 seconds = 1 minute
- The passage of time is the amount of time between the beginning and end of an event. Some events are quick and take only a few seconds, such as the time it takes to blink or snap your fingers. Other events can last for hours or longer, such as playing a game of soccer.
- Each week begins on Sunday. The order of the days is as follows: Sunday, Monday, Tuesday, Wednesday, Thursday, Friday, Saturday. The days of the week repeat their order.
- Listed in order, the months are January, February, March, April, May, June, July, August, September, October, November, December. The months repeat in the same order each year.
- Calendars can be used to organize a month or year. You can use a calendar to find out how many days are in a month.
- Leap years occur every 4 years. In a leap year, there are 29 days in February.

PRACTICE TEST

1. What measurement of time would be used to measure the time it takes to pour a glass of milk?

2. What measurement of time would you use to measure how long the football season lasts?

3. Would you be able to run a marathon in minutes?

4. Max believes he can eat six hot dogs in 1 minute. Is this a reasonable measurement of time?

5. Sheila begins writing her book report at 4:30 P.M. She finishes at 5:15 P.M. How many minutes did it take Sheila to write her book report?

6. Laurel attends a computer camp during the summer. She left for camp Tuesday morning and returned Monday night. How many days was Laurel at the camp?

7. Dean goes snowmobiling with his father. They start at 10:00 A.M. and finish at 3:00 P.M. How many hours did they spend snowmobiling?

8. Jongho is updating his stamp collection. He begins at 9:35 A.M. and finishes at 10:10 A.M. How many minutes did Jongho spend updating his stamp collection?

9. Whitney spends Saturday morning helping her mother bake cookies. They begin at 9:15 A.M. and finish at 11:45 A.M. How long did they spend baking cookies?

10. Ross plays soccer from May 1 until August 31. For how many months does he play soccer?

11. Chloe brushed her teeth for 120 seconds. For how many minutes did she brush her teeth?

12. Kunwar plays with his blocks for 2 hours and 35 minutes. How many minutes does he play with his blocks?

13. Basil likes to watch television. He started watching at 1:15 and finished at 3:10. How many minutes did Basil watch television?

14. Akhil runs a candy store. He opens at 8:30 A.M. and closes at 9:00 P.M. How many hours is the candy store open?

15. Gillian attends a summer camp. She leaves Wednesday morning and returns Monday evening. How many days is Gillian at camp?

16. Jack leaves to visit his grandmother on the evening of July 25 and returns home on the morning of August 8. How many days was Jack away?

17. Archie goes shopping for his mother. He leaves at 10:30 A.M. and returns at 1:05 P.M. How many minutes was Archie gone?

Use the following information to answer the next question.

The first day of March 2112 is a Thursday. St. Patrick's Day will be March 17. Doctor Seuss's birthday will be March 2. The International Day of the Woman will be March 8, and the first day of Spring will be March 21.

18. Create a calendar for the month of March 2112, and mark these dates on the calendar.

March 2112

SUN	MON	TUES	WED	THU	FRI	SAT

Use the following information to answer the next question.

The first day of September 2114 will be a Monday. September 6 will be Read a Book Day, September 9 will be Teddy Bear Day, September 13 will be National Peanut Day, and September 22 will be Elephant Appreciation Day.

19. Create a calendar for the month of September 2114, and mark these days on the calendar.

September 2114

SUN	MON	TUES	WED	THU	FRI	SAT

Use the following information to answer the next question.

The first day of December 2116 will be a Thursday. December 4 will be National Cookie Day, December 17 will be National Maple Syrup Day, December 25 will be Christmas Day, and December 26 will be Boxing Day.

20. Create a calendar for December 2116, and mark these days on your calendar.

December 2116

SUN	MON	TUES	WED	THU	FRI	SAT

LENGTH AND PERIMETER

When you are finished this unit, you will be able to...
• provide referents for estimating length in centimetres and metres
• estimate length using referents
• explain how centimetres (cm) and metres (m) are related
• measure and record the length, height, and perimeter of an object
• draw a line of a given length using a ruler
• sketch a line segment
• make different shapes when given a specific perimeter

PREREQUISITE SKILLS AND KNOWLEDGE

Prior to starting this unit, you should be able to...
• estimate, measure, and record the length using non-standard units
• use a ruler to measure length

Lesson 1   *ESTIMATING LENGTH*

Centimetres and metres are units used to measure length, height, width, and perimeter.

- Length is how long something is.
- Height is the distance from the top to the bottom of something.
- Width is the distance from one side to the other side of something.
- Perimeter is the distance around the outside of something.

REFERENTS

The width of your fingernail is approximately one centimetre. One centimetre would also be the width of a large paper clip. Can you think of other items that would be one centimetre?

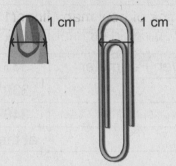

1 cm   1 cm

Stand with your arms stretched out to your sides. The distance from the tip of your middle finger on your left hand to the tip of your middle finger on your right hand is approximately one metre. One metre is also the size of a giant footstep or the height of a door from the doorknob to the floor.

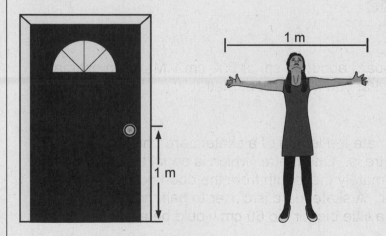

1 m

1 m

ESTIMATING LENGTH

Sometimes an exact measurement is not needed. Perhaps you are trying to decide which piece of licorice is the longest or whose chair is the tallest. In each of these situations, it is okay to make an approximate measurement. If you are measuring the width, length, or height of furniture to see if it fits in a room, you may want to be a little bit more precise.

You can estimate the length of an object using what you know about the length of other objects.

 Example

Estimate the length of a crayon using what you know about the width of your finger.

Solution

To estimate how long a crayon is, think of how many finger widths would fit along the crayon. You could estimate the length of a crayon to be about 8 finger widths, which would be about 8 cm.

 Time to Try 1

Estimate the length of a glue stick.

Example

Is a skateboard about 60 cm or 600 cm? Make an estimate based on what you know about metres.

Solution

To estimate the length of a skateboard, think of how long one metre is. One metre (which is equal to 100 cm) is approximately the length from the doorknob on a door to the floor. A skateboard is closer to half that length or maybe a little bigger, so 60 cm would be a good estimate.

NOTES

Time to Try 2

Is a car about 1 m or about 3.5 m long? Make an estimate based on what you know about metres.

RELATIONSHIP BETWEEN CENTIMETRES AND METRES

Usually, the shorter the object or distance, the smaller the unit used. The longer the object or distance, the larger the unit used. For example, the length of a pencil is best measured in centimetres. The height of a classroom is best measured in metres.

1 m = 100 cm
100 cm = 1 m

You can show 100 centimetres is equivalent to 1 metre by comparing rulers to metre sticks. You could also use centimetre cubes and build them up against a metre stick.

PRACTICE EXERCISES

Use the following information to answer the next question.

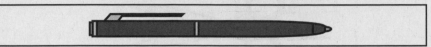

1. Estimate the length of a pen using what you know about the width of your finger.

Use the following information to answer the next question.

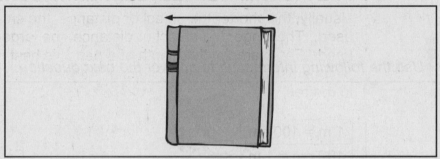

2. Estimate the width of your math book in centimetres.

Use the following information to answer the next question.

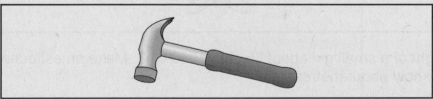

3. Would a hammer be about 25 cm or 250 cm long? Make an estimate.

Use the following information to answer the next question.

4. Is a pair scissors about 20 cm or 200 cm? Make an estimate based on what you know about the length of your finger.

Use the following information to answer the next question.

5. Is the height of a small girl about 95 cm or 950 cm? Make an estimate based on what you know about metres.

Use the following information to answer the next question.

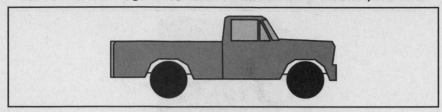

6. Is a pick-up truck about 1 m or about 6.5 m? Make an estimate based on what you know about metres.

Use the following information to answer the next question.

7. Estimate the length of a bus based on what you know about metres.

Use the following information to answer the next question.

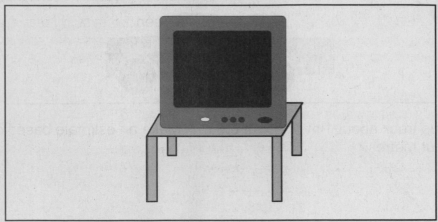

8. Estimate the length of a TV table based on what you know about **metres**.

9. Can the length of a marker be estimated in metres? Explain.

Use the following information to answer the next question.

10. Can the length of a computer mouse from where the wire connects to the tip of the other end be estimated in centimetres? If yes, estimate the length.

Lesson 2   Measuring Length

Rulers, measuring tapes, and metre sticks are some of the measuring tools that can be used to find out the exact length, height, width, perimeter, or distance of something. To get an accurate measurement when you use one of these measuring tools, be sure to line up the edge of the object with the line on the measuring tool that shows zero.

Most Grade 3 students have a ruler that is 30 cm. The first part of the ruler looks like this one. Each number on the ruler is one centimetre.

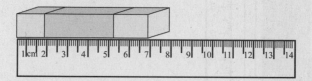

How long is the eraser according to this ruler? Look at the numbers along the ruler. The eraser's edge is at the 7. The eraser is 7 cm long.

☀ **Example**

Use a ruler to measure. The length of the line shown is ___ cm.

Solution

Line up your ruler with the first part of the line. Follow the line down the ruler until it stops. Look at what number it has stopped at (6). Write the number with units on the line.

<u>6 cm</u>

🦋 **Time to Try 1**

The length of the line shown is ___ cm.

NOTES

You can also use a metre stick to measure.

 Example

Sue and Barb measured the height of their fence with a metre stick. How high is the fence?

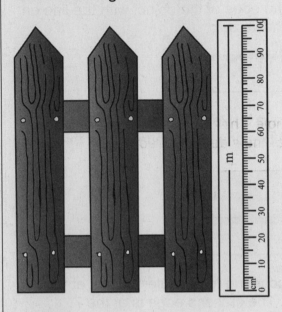

Solution

The metre stick starts at 0, so the bottom of the fence should be lined up with the 0. Then, look at the number that lines up with the top of the fence. The fence is 1 m (or 100 cm) high.

You can also measure shapes. When you measure a shape, remember to line up your ruler with the end of the side of the shape you are measuring.

To measure the bottom of a triangle, use your ruler.

The bottom of the triangle is 3 cm

Example

Use a ruler to measure the height of the rectangle shown. Remember—height is the distance from the top to the bottom of something. The height of the rectangle is ____ cm.

Solution

To measure the rectangle's height, use your ruler. Line up the zero with the end of the side of the rectangle.

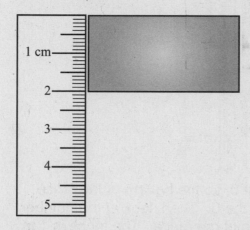

The height of the rectangle is 2 cm.

 Time to Try 2

Use a ruler to measure the length of each side of the given shape.

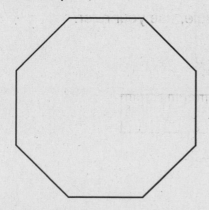

NOTES

Three-dimensional (3-D) objects can also be measured with a ruler. Three dimensional objects have three possible measurements: length, width, and height. (Height is how high an object is, width is how wide it is, and length is how long it is.)

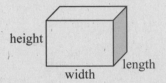

You can find the measurement of each side by measuring with your ruler.

 Example

Find the width of the given shape.

Solution

To find the width of the shape, line your ruler up with the edge of the shape, and measure the width of the shape. The width of the shape is 5 cm.

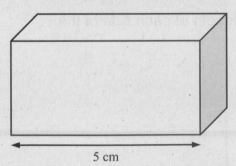

5 cm

Time to Try 3

Find the length of the given shape using your ruler.

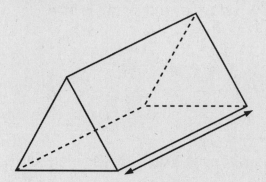

PRACTICE EXERCISES

Measure the length of each of the following objects in centimetres using your ruler.

1.

2.

3.

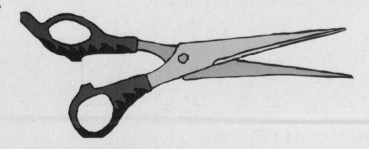

Use the following information to answer the next question.

A bookshelf is as shown. Ben measures the height of the bookshelf with a metre stick.

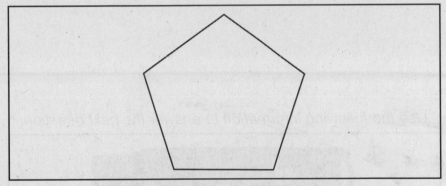

4. If the arrow beside the bookshelf is 30 cm and the height of the bookshelf is 3 arrow lengths, how tall is the bookshelf in total?

Use the following information to answer the next question.

5. Use a ruler to measure the bottom of the given shape.

Use the following information to answer the next question.

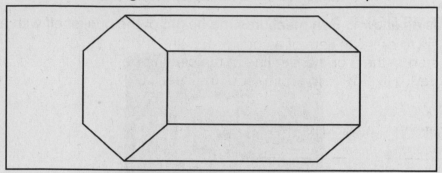

6. Find the length of the bottom of the given prism using your ruler.

Use the following information to answer the next question.

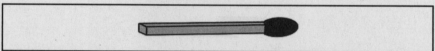

7. Use a ruler to measure the length of the matchstick in centimetres.

Use the following information to answer the next question.

8. Cindy measures the length of her USB drive as 2 cm, and her sister Jane measures it as 7 cm. Who is correct?

Lesson 3   DRAWING LINES

DRAWING ITEMS USING A RULER

When you begin to draw an item of a specific length, remember to start at the 0 or the first line of the centimetre ruler. Then, draw a line up to the number of the specific length.

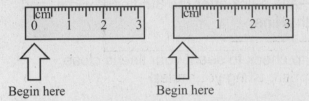

Begin here   Begin here

Remember not to start at the edge of the ruler unless the ruler has a 0 or a line at the very edge of it.

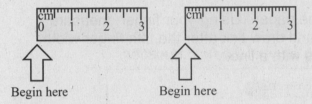

Begin here   Begin here

Mrs. Wilson asks Pam to draw a pencil that is 11 cm long. Pam's ruler starts with a 0 after a small space, so she puts her pencil at the 0 and draws a small line. She then draws another small line at number 11. She then turns the space between the two small lines into a drawing of a pencil.

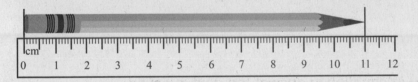

✸ Example

Draw a line that is 14 cm long.

Solution

Begin by placing your ruler on the paper and marking where the zero is. Draw your line along the ruler's edge until you reach the number 14. Stop at the tick for the number 14.

🐝 Time to Try 1

Draw a line that is 18 cm long.

NOTES

NOTES

DRAWING A LINE WITHOUT A RULER

You can draw a line without a ruler by estimating the length from what you already know about centimetres. A centimetre is about the width of your finger. To estimate a line approximately 8 centimetres long, mark where your line will begin, and use your finger width to measure out 8 cm. You can do this by placing 8 fingertips, finger over finger, one after another. Place a tick after the 8th finger width, and connect the ticks with a line.

You can use a ruler to check to see if your line is close.

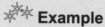 **Example**

Sketch a line that is 5 cm long without using a ruler.

Solution

Draw a tick on the paper. Using your finger, measure 5 finger widths, and draw tick after the fifth finger width. Connect the ticks with a line.

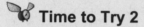 **Time to Try 2**

Sketch a line that is 11 cm long without using a ruler.

PRACTICE EXERCISES

1. Draw a line that is 10 cm long.

2. Draw a line that is 12 cm long.

3. Draw a vertical line that is 7 cm long. Remember vertical means up and down.

4. Sketch a line that is 8 cm long without using a ruler.

5.   How would you draw a line that is 15 cm long without using a ruler?

6.   Explain how to draw a line that is 13 cm long without using a ruler.

Lesson 4   PERIMETER

PERIMETER

Perimeter is the distance around the outside of a shape.
To find the perimeter of a shape, add the lengths of all the
sides of the shape together. When you write the perimeter,
be sure to write the unit used when measuring the lengths of
the side. For example, you could write perimeter as 12 cm
or 30 m.

USING CENTIMETRE GRID PAPER

You can use grid or graph paper to help you find the perimeter
by counting the number of units.

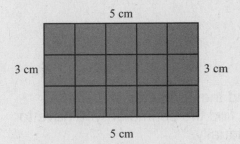

To find the perimeter of the given shape, add the lengths of all
four sides:
5 + 3 + 5 + 3 = 16 cm

✳ Example

What is the perimeter of the given square if each side is
4 cm long?

Solution

To find the perimeter, measure the length of each of the
four sides. Each side is 4 cm long. Add the four lengths
together.
4 cm + 4 cm + 4 cm + 4 cm = 16 cm

Because the shape is a square and all four sides are the
same length, you can also multiply to find the perimeter.
$4 \times 4 = 16$

NOTES

NOTES

🦋 Time to Try 1

Find the perimeter of the given square.

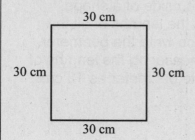

Sometimes, you will need to find the perimeter of a shape whose sides are not equal. To find the perimeter, you have to add all the sides together individually.

USING GEOBOARDS

The following diagram is an example of a geoboard.

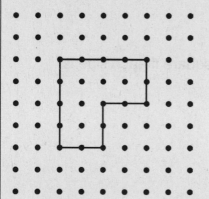

When finding the perimeter of a figure on a geoboard, one unit is the length between two pegs that are side by side.

To find the perimeter, add the number of units that make up the lengths of all six sides.

$4 + 4 + 2 + 2 + 2 + 2 = 16$ units

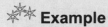 **Example**

Find the perimeter of the given shape.

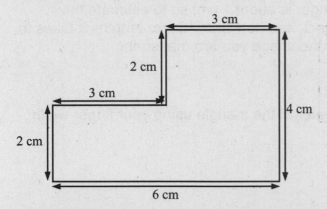

Solution

The perimeter of the figure = the sum of all the sides
$$= (2+3+2+3+4+6)\,\text{cm}$$
$$= 20\ \text{cm}$$

 Time to Try 2

Each block on the grid represents 1 metre. Find the perimeter of the given shape.

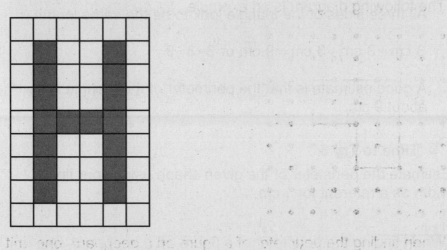

NOTES

You do not always need an exact answer when you are measuring perimeter. Sometimes you can estimate or make a guess based on what you know about length. You know that the width of your finger is about 1 cm, so to estimate the perimeter of an object, see how many finger lengths it takes to make the length of the shape you are measuring.

 Example

Estimate the perimeter of the triangle using your finger width as a referent.

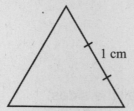

Solution

One side of the triangle is broken into three parts. Each part looks to be about the same size and width as your finger. Since you know that one finger width is 1 cm, the whole side would be about 3 cm long (1 + 1 + 1 = 3).

All three sides of the triangle look to be the same length.

3 cm + 3 cm + 3 cm = 9 cm or 3×3=9

A good estimate is that the perimeter of the triangle is about 9 cm.

 Time to Try 3

Estimate the perimeter of the given shape using your finger width as a referent for 1 cm.

PRACTICE EXERCISES

Find the perimeter of the following shapes.

1. Trapezoid

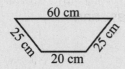

60 cm
25 cm 25 cm
20 cm

2. Hexagon

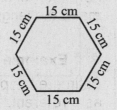

15 cm
15 cm 15 cm
15 cm 15 cm
15 cm

3. Triangle

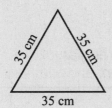

35 cm 35 cm
35 cm

Use the following diagram to answer the next question.

The given figure represents the size and shape of Maria's garden.

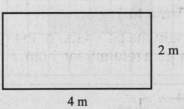

2 m

4 m

4. What is the perimeter?

Use the following diagram to answer the next question.

The given figure represents the size and shape of a room.

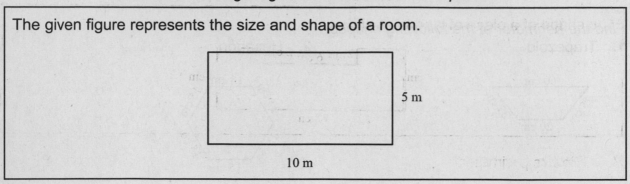

5 m

10 m

5. What is the perimeter?

Use the following diagram to answer the next question.

Each block on the grid represents 1 metre.

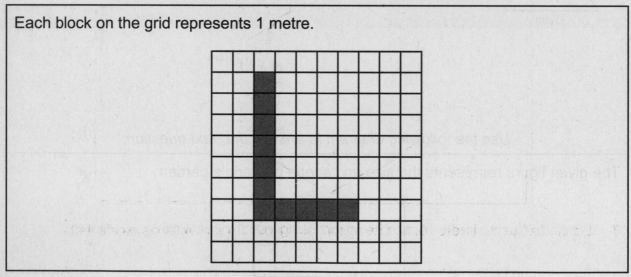

6. Find the perimeter of the given shape.

Use the following diagram to answer the next question.

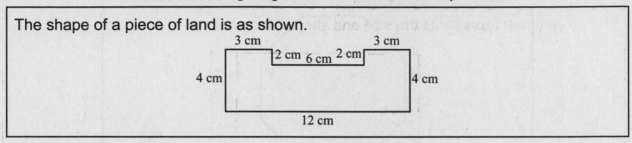

The shape of a piece of land is as shown.

3 cm 2 cm 6 cm 2 cm 3 cm

4 cm   4 cm

12 cm

7. Find its perimeter.

Use the following information to answer the next question.

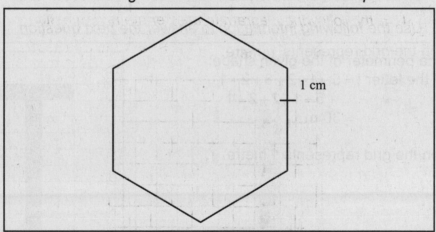

1 cm

8. Estimate the perimeter of the hexagon using your finger width as a referent.

Use the following information to answer the next question.

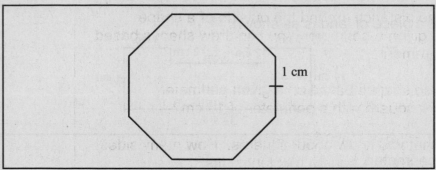

1 cm

9. Estimate the perimeter of the octagon using your finger width as a referent.

Use the following information to answer the next question.

Jack found the perimeter of the given shape:
Perimeter of the letter $I = 5 + 1 + 2 + 8 + 2 + 1$
$$+ 5 + 1 + 2 + 2 + 1$$
$$= 30 \text{ m}$$

Each block on the grid represents 1 metre.

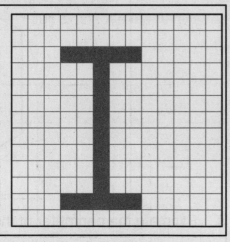

10. Is Jack correct?

Lesson 5 CONSTRUCTING SHAPES FOR A GIVEN PERIMETER

Perimeter is the distance around the outside of a shape. When you are given a perimeter, you can draw shapes based on that measurement.

Let's draw some shapes based on a given perimeter. Can you draw a square with a perimeter of 16 cm?

Think about what you know about squares. How many sides does a square have? A square has four sides.

What do you know about each of those sides? All sides of a square are the same length.

If the perimeter of the square is 16 cm and there are four sides of equal length, you can divide 16 by 4 to determine the length of each side.
16÷4=4

Use centimetre grid paper to draw your square.
On centimetre grid paper, each square is one centimetre wide and one centimetre tall. You may find it helpful to colour your square to make it stand out.

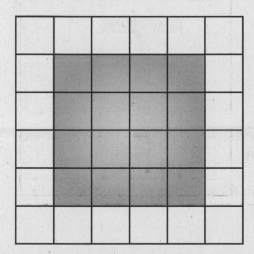

Once you have drawn your square, check your work by adding the lengths of the four sides together.
4+4+4+4=16

How would you solve a similar problem given the perimeter of a rectangle?

Think about what you know about a rectangle. A rectangle has four sides with two pairs of equal sides.

NOTES

Draw a rectangle with a perimeter of 16 cm.

One way to begin is by finding four numbers that add together to make 16. Remember that a rectangle has two pairs of equal sides, so you must find two sets of numbers that add together to make 16.

For example,
$7+7+1+1=16$

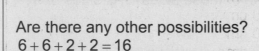

Are there any other possibilities?
$6+6+2+2=16$

$5+5+3+3=16$

In this case, there are three possible rectangles that you could draw with a perimeter of 16 cm.

Another strategy you can try in these types of questions is to divide the total perimeter by 2.
$16 \div 2 = 8$

Then, find all the combinations that total 8.
$7+1=8$
$6+2=8$
$5+3=8$

You do not need to list the opposite combinations
(e.g., $1+7$, $2+6$, or $3+5$).

Let's practice the second strategy.

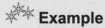 Example

Draw all the possible combinations for a rectangle (including a square) with a perimeter of 20 cm.

Solution

Divide the perimeter by 2: $20 \div 2 = 10$. Find all the combinations of numbers that total 10.

9 + 1:   9 + 9 + 1 + 1 = 20 cm
8 + 2:   8 + 8 + 2 + 2 = 20 cm
7 + 3:   7 + 7 + 3 + 3 = 20 cm
6 + 4:   6 + 6 + 4 + 4 = 20 cm
5 + 5:   5 + 5 + 5 + 5 = 20 cm

Draw the rectangles using centimetre grid paper. Be sure to label each side.

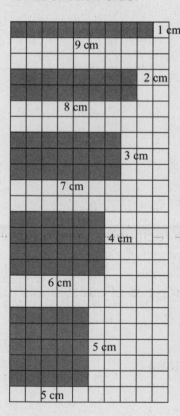

NOTES

 Time to Try 1

Draw 2 shapes with a perimeter of 12 cm.

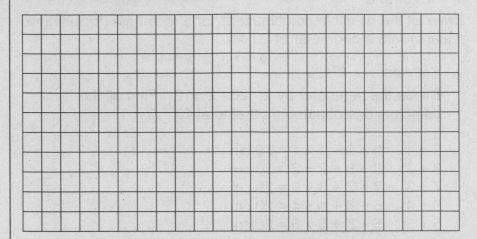

PRACTICE EXERCISES

1. Using centimetre grid paper, draw a square with a perimeter of 20 cm and one rectangle with a perimeter of 36 cm. Be sure to label the sides of your drawings.

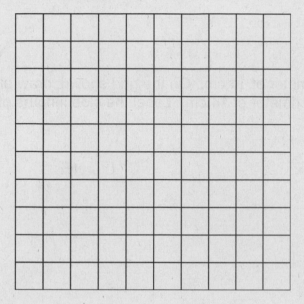

2. Draw a square with a perimeter of 16 cm. Be sure to label the sides of your drawings.

3. Draw all of the rectangles with a perimeter of 18 cm.

4. The length and width of a rectangle is 3 cm by 5 cm. What is the perimeter of the rectangle?

5. Daniel has a painting board with a perimeter of 14 cm. On the grid shown, draw all possible rectangles that each have a perimeter of 14 cm. Label the side lengths of each rectangle.

Use the following information to answer the next question.

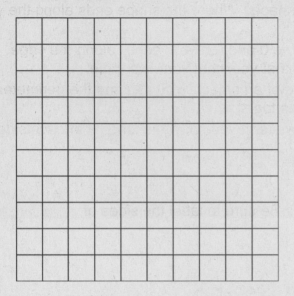

6. The possible combinations of perimeters for rectangles are shown. Find the perimeter of the rectangles.

REVIEW SUMMARY

- Length is how long something is. Height is the distance from the top to the bottom of something. Width is the distance from one side to the other side.
- Length, height, width, perimeter, and distance can be measured using different units of measurement such as centimetres (cm) and metres (m).
- Standard units of measurement are related to one another.
  100 cm = 1 m
- You can estimate how long an object is using referents or things that are about the measure of a centimetre or metre.
- You can measure an object or shape with a ruler, measuring tape, or metre stick. Place the ruler at the edge of the object or shape. Where the shape ends along the ruler is the length.
- You can draw a line using a ruler. Start at the 0 and run your pencil along the edge until you come to the number for the length that you want your line to be.
- Perimeter is the distance around the outside of an object. You can find the perimeter of a shape by adding the lengths of the sides together.
- You can also draw a shape for a given perimeter if you know the lengths of each side and how many sides it has.

PRACTICE TEST

Use the following diagram to answer the next question.

1. Estimate the length of the pair of sunglasses in the box using what you know about the length of your finger.

Use the following diagram to answer the next question.

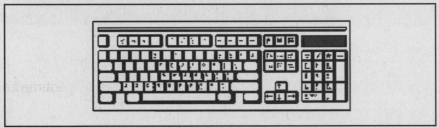

2. Is a real computer keyboard about 40 cm or 400 cm long? Make an estimation based on what you know about the length of your finger.

Use the following diagram to answer the next question.

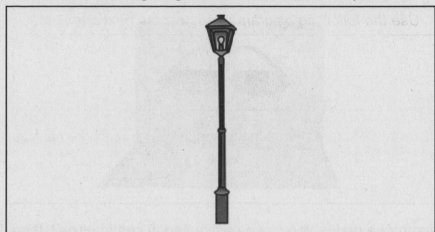

3. Estimate the length of a real lamppost based on what you know about metres.

4. In real life, which of the following objects is **best** estimated in centimetres?

A.

B.

C.

D.

Use the following diagram to answer the next question.

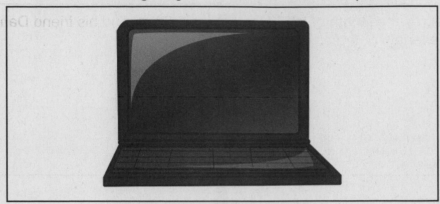

5. Can the length of a real laptop can be estimated in centimetres? If so, find its estimated length.

Use the following diagram to answer the next question.

6. Use a ruler to measure the height of the given object in centimetres.

Use the following information to answer the next question.

Robert measures the length of the given box as 1.2 cm, and his friend Daniel measures the length of the box as 5 cm.

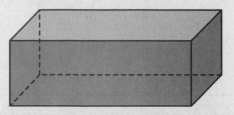

7. Who is correct?

8. Draw a line that is 9 cm long.

9. How would you draw a line that is 16 cm long without using a ruler?

Use the following information to answer the next question.

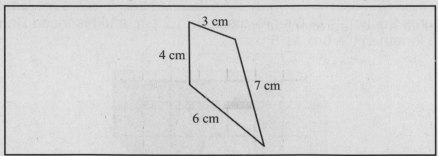

10. Find the perimeter of the given shape.

Use the following information to answer the next question.

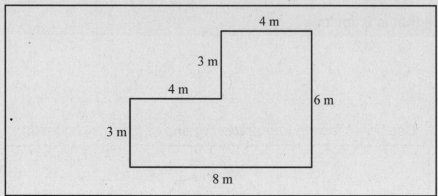

11. Find the perimeter of the given shape.

Use the following information to answer the next question.

Each block on the grid represents 1 metre.

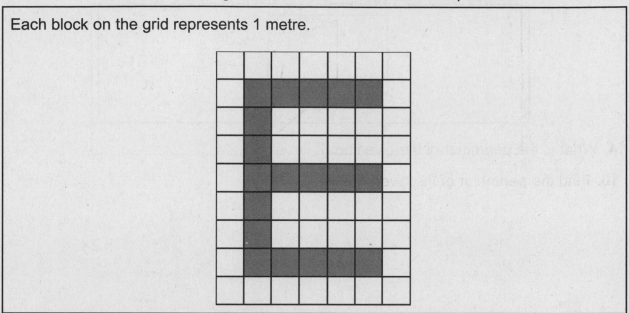

12. Find the perimeter of the given shape.

Use the following information to answer the next question.

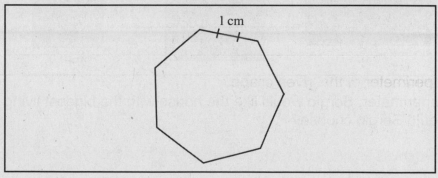

13. Estimate the perimeter of the heptagon using your finger width for a referent.

Use the following information to answer the next question.

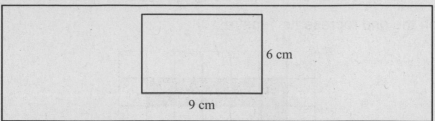

14. What is the perimeter of the given box?

Use the following information to answer the next question.

Sergio is looking for a new house. The living rooms of the three houses he is considering are shown.

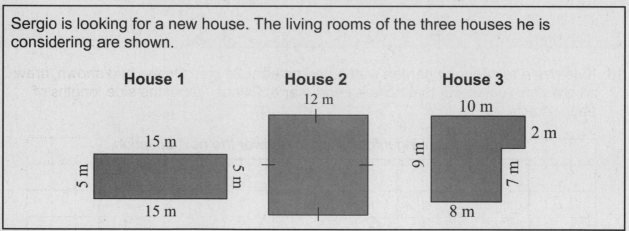

15. Based on perimeter, Sergio would like the house with the biggest living room. Which house should Sergio choose?

16. Draw all the possible shapes of the rectangles with a perimeter of 22 cm.

17. The perimeter of a rectangle is 32 cm. List the possible lengths and widths of the rectangle.

18. Kyle has a rectangular garden with a perimeter of 24 cm. On the grid shown, draw all possible rectangles that have a perimeter of 24 cm. Label the side lengths of each rectangle.

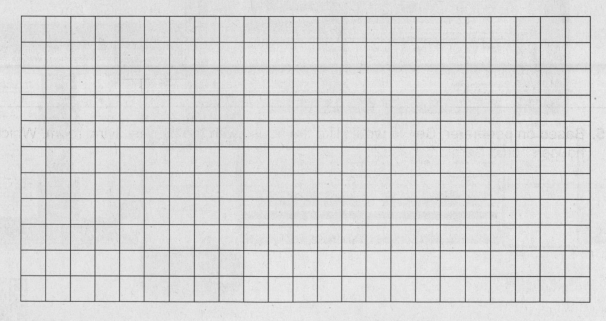

MASS

When you are finished this unit, you will be able to...
- provide a referent for grams and kilograms
- estimate weight using a referent for grams and kilograms
- measure and record the weight of objects in grams (g) and kilograms (kg) using a balance and weight scale
- explain the relationship between grams and kilograms

PREREQUISITE SKILLS AND KNOWLEDGE

Prior to starting this unit, you should be able to...
- estimate, measure, and record the weight of objects
- read a scale

Lesson 1   ESTIMATING WEIGHT

Mass refers to how heavy an object is. In Canada, we measure mass in grams and kilograms. A gram is about as heavy as a jellybean, and a kilogram is about as heavy as a textbook.

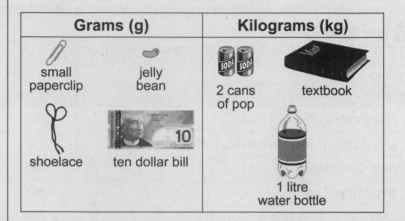

Grams (g)		Kilograms (kg)	
small paperclip	jelly bean	2 cans of pop	textbook
shoelace	ten dollar bill		1 litre water bottle

Can you think of any other items that weigh 1 gram or 1 kilogram?

When you use an object that has the same weight as a gram or kilogram, you are using a referent. It can help you determine the weight of other items.

Sometimes, you will have a question about the weight of an object, but an exact measurement will not be necessary. In some cases, an estimate will do. To make an estimate about how heavy something is, look at how big the object is and what it is made of. A peacock feather is quite large, but it is very light. A magnet, on the other hand, is small, but it is solid and surprisingly heavy.

To help you make an estimate, you can use what you know about grams and kilograms. Remember, one gram is about the weight of a jellybean. A kilogram is about the weight of a textbook.

✳✳ Example

Estimate how much the watermelon weighs: about 4 g or about 4 kg?

Solution

Pretend you have four jellybeans in your hand. Do you think a watermelon would weigh the same? Probably not. Four jellybeans are not as heavy as a watermelon. The best estimate is the other choice, which is 4 kg. A 4 kg watermelon weighs about as much as 4 textbooks.

 Time to Try 1

Estimate how much the soccer ball weighs: about 50 g or about 500 g?

To make objects that equal a certain mass, use a balance scale or a referent such as a jellybean to estimate. One jellybean equals approximately 1 gram. One way to create a figure out of clay that equals 5 g is to place 5 jellybeans on one side of a balance scale and then build a figure that would balance the scale. If the scale balances, both sides weigh approximately 5 g.

 Example

Approximately how much do the two computer disks weigh?

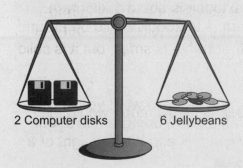

2 Computer disks   6 Jellybeans

Solution

Since the scale is balanced, the weight of the jellybeans is the same as the weight of the two computer disks. To find out approximately how much the two computer disks weigh, count the number of jellybeans on one side of the scale. Remember that one jellybean weighs approximately 1 g. There are 6 jellybeans, so they weigh about 6 g. This means that the two computer disks also weigh about 6 g.

Time to Try 2

How many jellybeans would it take to balance a scale with only one computer disk?

RELATIONSHIP BETWEEN GRAMS AND KILOGRAMS

Grams and kilograms are related to each other. There are 1 000 grams in 1 kilogram.

1 000 grams = 1 kilogram

You can think of it as 1 kilogram is equal to a textbook, so 1 textbook = 1 000 grams.

 Example

How much would the book weigh in grams?

Solution

The weight of an average textbook is about 1 kilogram. Since 1 textbook = 1 kilogram, 1 textbook would be around 1 000 grams.

 Time to Try 3

Each group has about 25 jellybeans. How much would they weigh in total?

PRACTICE EXERCISES

Use the following diagram to answer the next question.

1. What is the weight of a DVD: about 2 g or about 200 g?

Use the following diagram to answer the next question.

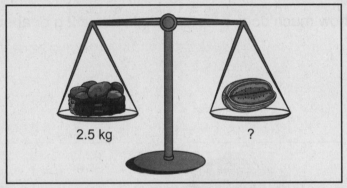

2. Approximately how much does the watermelon weigh?

Use the following diagram to answer the next question.

Paper clip

3. If a small paper-clip weighs 1 gram, how many paper-clips are in 1 kilogram?

Estimate how much the given object weighs.

Use the following information to answer the next question.

4. Approximately how much does a laptop weigh: about 2 g or about 2 kg?

Use the following information to answer the next question.

5. Does a cabbage have a weight of about 3 g or about 300 g?

Use the following information to answer the next question.

6. Does a mango weigh about 2 g or about 200 g?

Use the following information to answer the next question.

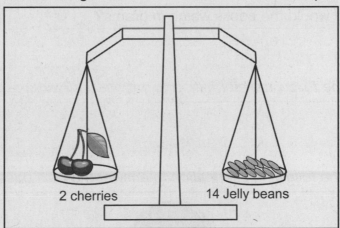

2 cherries   14 Jelly beans

7. Approximately how much do the two cherries weigh?

Use the following information to answer the next question.

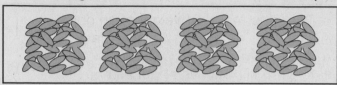

8. Each group has about 30 jellybeans. How much would they weigh in total?

Use the following information to answer the next question.

9. About how much would the books weigh in grams?

Use the following information to answer the next question.

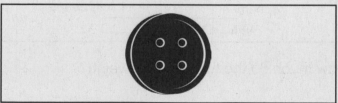

10. If a small button weighs 1 gram, how many buttons are in 1 kilogram?

Lesson 2   MEASURING AND RECORDING WEIGHT

A **scale** is used to measure the mass or weight of an object. A scale tells you how heavy the object is. Weight (mass) is measured in grams (g) or kilograms (kg). One gram is about as heavy as a jellybean. One kilogram is about as heavy as a textbook.

The weight or mass of an object can be found by using a weigh scale or a balance scale. To measure the weight or mass of an object using a weigh scale, place the object on the scale and read the weight.

 Example

What is the weight of the oranges?

Solution

Read the scale. The weight that the scale shows is the weight of the objects on the scale.
1 kilogram (1 kg)

 Time to Try 1

What is the weight of the following object?

A **balance scale** is a set of two scales used to weigh objects. This scale is often used when the weight or mass of objects are being compared. The object on the side of the scale that is lower weighs more, while the object on the higher side of the scale weighs less.

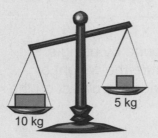

Both objects weigh the same when a scale is balanced.

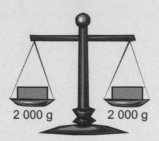

☀ Example

How much does the cat weigh?

Solution

The kitten has a mass of 2 kg. When the two sides of a balance scale are even with each other (balanced), the two sides have equal masses. That means that the 1 kg mass plus the mass of the kitten are equal to 3 kg.

Time to Try 2

How much does the chair weigh?

Does an object have the same mass if you change its shape? Let's check and see.

✳ Example

Is the mass of an apple the same when the shape of the apple is changed?

Solution

The mass of an apple can be measured with a balance. A balance compares the mass of two objects. Place the apple on one side of the balance. Add weights to the other side of the balance until the two sides balance. Since you know the mass of the weights, you can add up the weights, and the sum will be the mass of the apple.

If you cut the apple up into smaller pieces and weigh it again, it will weigh the same. Cutting up the apple does not change its mass. All the pieces of the apple are still there. Cutting the apple has only made the apple a different shape.

 Time to Try 3

Record the mass of the blocks on the scale. Each block weighs one gram.

The connecting blocks weigh 9 grams. Now, change the shape of the blocks, and re-weigh it to see if the mass is the same.

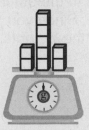

Will the blocks weigh the same?

PRACTICE EXERCISES

Write the weight of the objects shown below.

Use the following information to answer the next question.

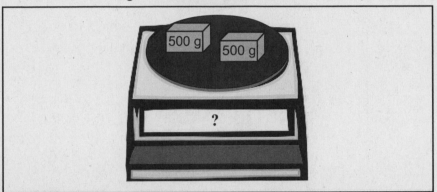

1. The boxes weigh _____.

Use the following information to answer the next question.

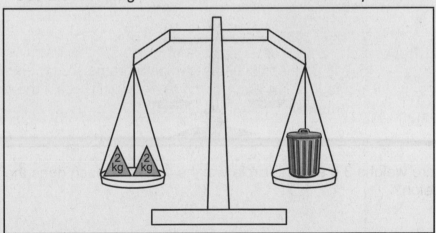

2. The garbage can weighs _____.

Use the following information to answer the next question.

3. The books weigh _____.

Use the following information to answer the next question.

4. If the square weighs 3 g and the circle weighs 4 g, how much does the triangle weigh?

Use the following information to answer the next question.

5. What is the weight of the tomatoes in grams?

Use the following information to answer the next question.

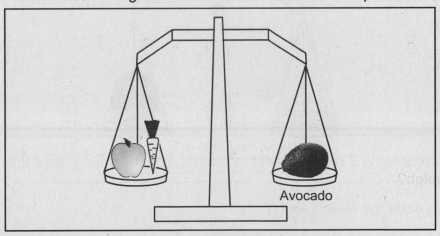

Avocado

6. If the carrot weighs 75 g and the apple weighs 150 g, how much does the avocado weigh?

Use the following information to answer the next question.

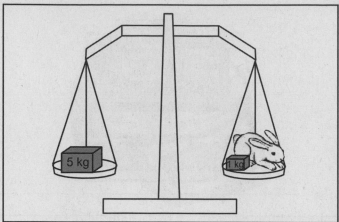

7. How much does the rabbit weigh?

Use the following information to answer the next question.

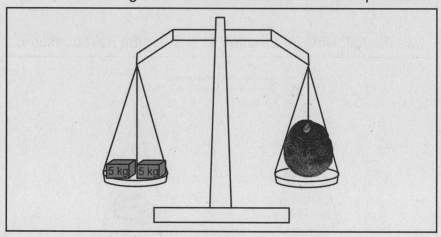

8. How much does the melon weigh?

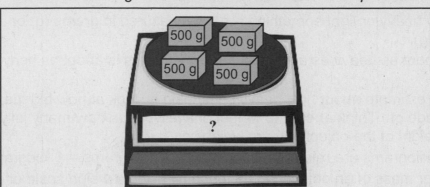

9. Write the total weight of the objects on the scale in kilograms.

REVIEW SUMMARY

- Mass is how heavy or light something is. It is measured in grams (g) or kilograms (kg).
- A gram is about as heavy as a jellybean and a kilogram is about as heavy as a textbook.
- To make an estimate about how heavy something is, look at how big the object is and what it is made of. Think about the weight of a jellybean: how many jellybeans would equal the weight of the object you are weighing.
- Grams and kilograms are related to each other: 1 000 grams = 1 kilogram.
- The weight or mass of an object can be found by using a weigh scale or a balance scale. Place the object on a scale and read the weight.
- When a balance scale is balanced, the objects on each side of it weigh the same.

PRACTICE TEST

Estimate how much the given object weighs.

Use the following information to answer the next question.

1.   Approximately how much does a pumpkin weigh: 6 g or 6 kg?

Use the following information to answer the next question.

2.   Approximately how much does a cake weigh: 60 g or 600 g?

Use the following information to answer the next question.

3.   Approximately how much does a pineapple weigh: 1 gram or 1 kg?

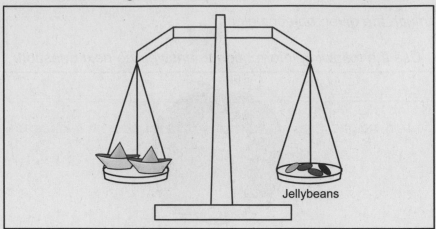

4. Approximately how much do the two paper boats weigh?

Use the following information to answer the next question.

5. About how much do the books weigh in grams?

Use the following information to answer the next question.

Each group has about 50 jellybeans.

6. How much would they weigh in total?

Use the following information to answer the next question.

7. If a small vitamin weighs 1 gram, how many vitamins are in 1 kilogram?

Use the following information to answer the next question.

3 kg

8. What is the weight of the apples in grams?

Use the following information to answer the next question.

9. How much does the puppy weigh?

Use the following information to answer the next question.

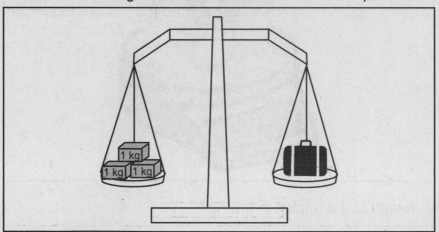

10. How much does the suitcase weigh?

Use the following information to answer the next question.

11. What is the total weight of the eggs in grams?

Use the following information to answer the next question.

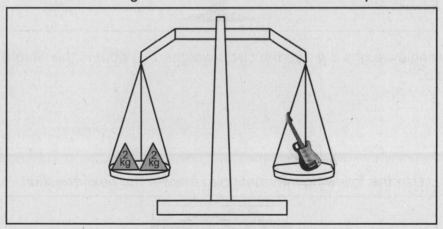

12. What is the weight of the guitar in kilograms?

Use the following information to answer the next question.

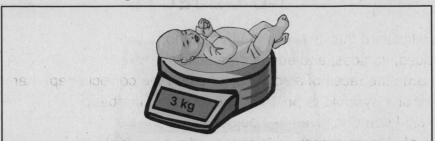

13. What is the weight of the baby in grams?

Use the following information to answer the next question.

14. If the rectangle weighs 8 g and the circle weighs 7 g, what is the weight of the triangle?

Use the following information to answer the next question.

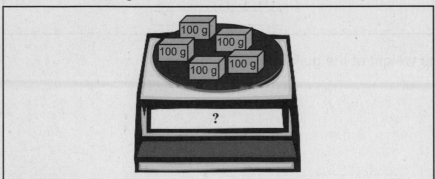

15. What is the weight of the boxes?

3-D OBJECTS

When you are finished this unit, you will be able to…
• count the faces, vertices, and edges on a solid
• show and name the faces of a solid object using the correct shape names
• tell the name of a pyramid or prism by the shape of the base
• construct a skeleton of a given 3-D object
• sort a group of objects according to faces, edges, or vertices

PREREQUISITE SKILLS AND KNOWLEDGE

Prior to starting this unit, you should be able to…
• define shapes
• differentiate between faces, vertices, and edges
• explain what a 3-D object is
• identify and name 3-D objects, such as a cube, sphere, cone, cylinder, prism, and pyramid

Lesson 1   3-D OBJECTS

A solid is a three-dimensional (3-D) object. The types of 3-D solids that we will study in this lesson are 3-D solids that are made up of faces, vertices, and edges.

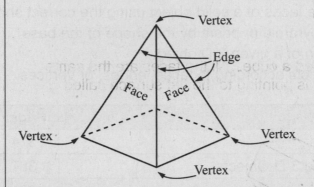

A **face** is a flat surface on a 3-D object. It is described by using the names of two-dimensional shapes like squares, rectangles, and pentagons. The faces of the given shape are triangle-shaped.

An **edge** is where two surfaces join together. Two of the triangle-shaped faces on the square-based pyramid meet to create an edge.

A **vertex** is where three or more edges meet to form a corner. The top of the square-based pyramid is where four of the edges meet to form a point. This is a vertex. Each corner at the base of a pyramid is also a vertex.

✸ Example

Identify the following parts of a 3-D solid as a face, vertex, or edge.

a)

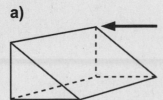

Solution

Look at the first object. It is a triangular prism. The arrow is pointing to where the edges meet to form a corner called a vertex.

374

b)

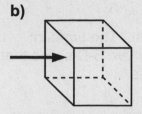

Solution

This object is called a cube. All the faces are the same sizes. The arrow is pointing to the flat surface called a face.

c)

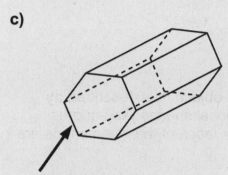

Solution

This object is called a hexagonal prism. The prism is named by its base, which is the shape of a hexagon. The arrow is pointing to where the two faces meet, which is called an edge.

🦋 Time to Try 1

Identify the following parts of a 3-D solid as a face, vertex, or edge.

a)

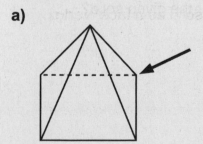

b)

c)

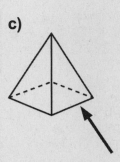

The faces of a 3-D object, are the sides and the bases.
You can describe the shapes of the faces using 2-D names.

✳ Example

What are the shapes of the faces for the given solid?

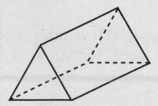

Solution

There are five faces on a triangular prism. Two of the
faces are triangles at each end of the prism. The other
three faces are rectangles on the sides.

Time to Try 2

What is the shape of the faces for the given solid?

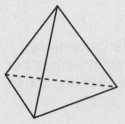

PRISMS

All **prisms** have rectangular faces. As well, all prisms will have two faces at opposite ends that are the same shape and size. These faces are not always rectangular. The shape of these faces gives the prism its name.

The following diagrams show a triangular prism and two rectangular prisms (remember that a square is a type of rectangle). The faces at the opposite ends are shaded to help you see how these faces name the prisms.

Triangular prism   Cube (square prism)   Rectangular prism

All **triangular prisms** have 5 faces, 9 edges, and 6 vertices.
All **cubes** and **rectangular prisms** have 6 faces, 12 edges, and 8 vertices.

PYRAMIDS

All **pyramids** have a base that gives the pyramid its name. All of the sides of all pyramids meet at one point called a vertex.

The following diagrams show two kinds of rectangular-based pyramids and one kind of triangular-based pyramid (remember that a square is a type of rectangle). The bases are shaded to help you see how the shapes of the bases name the pyramids.

Square-based
pyramid

Rectangular-based
pyramid

Triangular-based
pyramid

All **square-based pyramids** and **rectangular-based pyramids** have 5 faces, 8 edges, and 5 vertices.
All **triangular-based pyramids** have 4 faces, 6 edges, and 4 vertices.

The following chart shows the number of faces, edges, and vertices of some common pyramids and prisms.

	Faces	Edges	Vertices
Square-based pyramid	5	8	5
Rectangular-based pyramid	5	8	5
Triangular-based pyramid	4	6	4
Square prism (cube)	6	12	8
Rectangular prism	6	12	8
Triangular prism	5	9	6

Example

How many faces, edges, and vertices does the given
solid have?

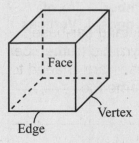

Solution

Count the faces (the flat sides of the object). There are 6.
Count the edges (where the faces meet). There are 12.
Count the vertices (where the edges meet at a corner).
There are 8.

 Time to Try 3

How many faces, edges, and vertices does the given
solid have?

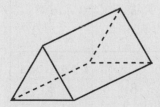

To sort a group of 3-D objects based on their faces, edges, or
vertices, you can first compare them by making a chart.

The number of vertices and edges and the number and
shapes of faces are different depending on the object.

NOTES

Example

a) Fill in the chart below.

Name of 3-D Object	Number of Faces	Shape of Face(s) (2-D)	Number of Edges	Number of Vertices
Cube				
Rectangular-based prism				
Square-based pyramid				
Rectangular-based pyramid				

Solution

Name of 3-D Object	Number of Faces	Shape of Face(s) (2-D)	Number of Edges	Number of Vertices
Cube	6	Square	12	8
Rectangular-based prism	6	Rectangle	12	8
Square-based pyramid	5	Square base and triangle sides	8	5
Rectangular-based pyramid	5	Rectangle base and triangle sides	8	5

b) Look at the chart above. How do the solids differ? How would you sort these objects according to number of vertices?

Solution

The pyramids and prisms/cube can be sorted into the number of vertices each object has. The cube and the rectangular prism have the same number of vertices (8). The pyramids (square and rectangular) have the same number of vertices (5).

5 Vertices	8 Vertices
Rectangular-based pyramid	Cube
Square-based pyramid	Rectangular-based prism

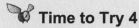 **Time to Try 4**

a) Fill out the chart below to help you sort the 3-D objects by vertices, edges, and faces.

Name of 3-D Object	Number of Faces	Shape of Face(s) (2-D)	Number of Edges	Number of Vertices
Cone				
Cylinder				
Cube				
Rectangular prism				

b) How would you sort the shapes according to the number of edges?

PRACTICE EXERCISES

Use the following diagram to answer the next question.

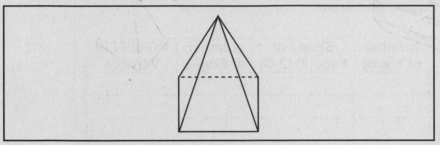

1. What are the shapes of the faces on the solid shown?

Use the 3-D figures below to answer the next questions.

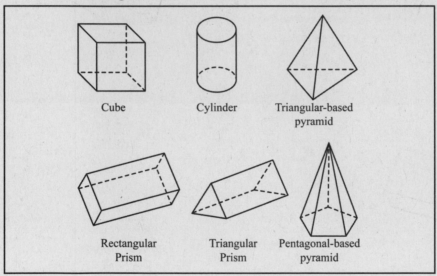

Cube   Cylinder   Triangular-based pyramid

Rectangular Prism   Triangular Prism   Pentagonal-based pyramid

Write the name of the 3-D figure above that has the following characteristics.

2. 2 circular faces

3. 9 edges

4. 12 edges

5. 4 vertices

6. 5 triangle-shaped faces, 1 pentagon-shaped face

Write the name of each of the following figures.

7.

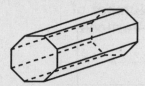

8.

9.

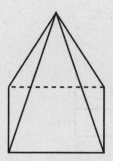

10.

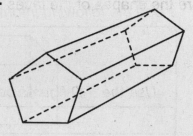

11.

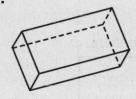

12. Sort the figures listed in questions **7** to **11** according to whether they are prisms or pyramids by writing their name in the appropriate side of the given table.

Prism	Pyramid

13. Fill in the number of faces, vertices, and edges of the 3-D objects in the table.

Name of 3-D Object	Number of Faces	Number of Edges	Number of Vertices
Triangular prism			
Cube			
Rectangle prism			
Triangular-based pyramid			

Use the following information to answer the next question.

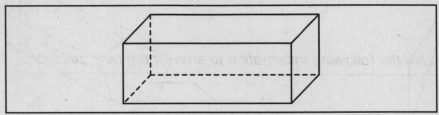

14. What is the shape of the faces for the solid?

Use the following information to answer the next question.

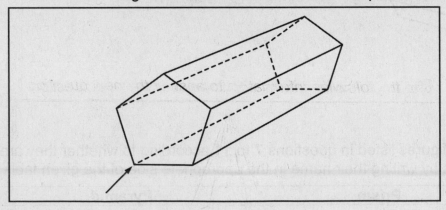

15. Identify the part of the given 3-D solid as a face, vertex, or edge.

Use the following information to answer the next question.

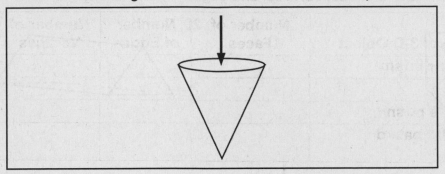

16. Identify the part of the given 3-D solid as a face, vertex, or edge.

Use the following information to answer the next question.

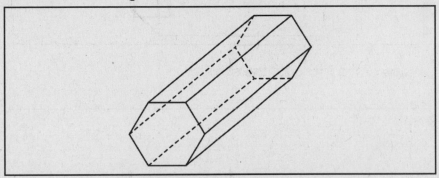

17. How many faces, edges, and vertices does the given solid have?

Use the following information to answer the next question.

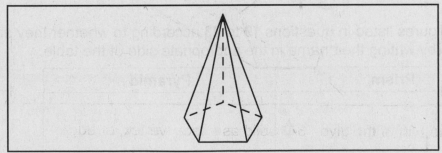

18. How many faces, edges, and vertices does the given solid have?

Write the name of each of the following figures.

19.

20.

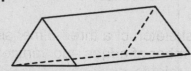

21.

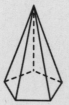

22.

23.

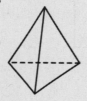

24. Sort the figures listed in questions **19** to **23** according to whether they are prisms or pyramids by writing their name in the appropriate side of the table.

Prism	Pyramid

Lesson 2   *CONSTRUCTING 3-D OBJECTS*

CONSTRUCTING SKELETONS OF THREE-DIMENSIONAL FIGURES

To make a skeleton of a three-dimensional figure, you need to know the number of edges and vertices of the figure. You can use straight objects, such as straws or toothpicks, to represent the edges of the shape. You can then use soft objects, such as marshmallows or modelling clay, to represent the vertices.

✳ **Example**

How would you make a skeleton of this cube using straws and marshmallows?

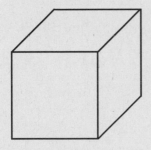

Solution

First, count the edges and vertices on the cube.

A cube has 12 edges. Since all the side lengths of a cube are the same length, you will need 12 straws that are all the same length.
A cube has 8 vertices, so you will need eight marshmallows.

Next, make a square-shaped base by connecting four straws and four marshmallows. Connect one straw to stand vertically from each marshmallow. These will form the side edges of the cube. Place a marshmallow on top of each vertical straw. Then, make the square-shaped top by connecting four straws to the marshmallows, as shown in the diagram.

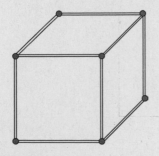

NOTES

 Time to Try 1

How would you make a skeleton of this triangular prism using straws and marshmallows?

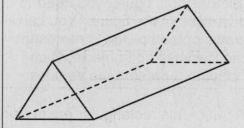

PRACTICE EXERCISES

Use the following diagram to answer the next question.

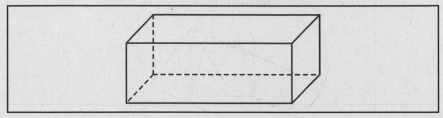

1. How would you make a skeleton of this rectangular prism using straws and marshmallows?

Use the following diagram to answer the next question.

Sam constructed a 3-D object with straws and marshmallows.

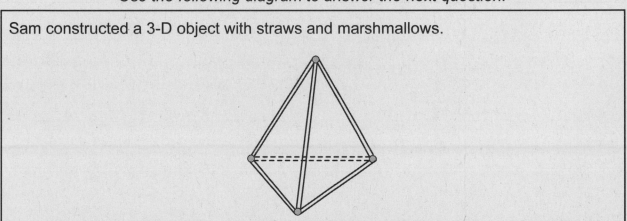

2. What object did he make?

Use the following diagram to answer the next question.

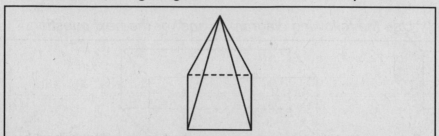

3. How would you make a skeleton of this square-based pyramid using straws and marshmallows?

REVIEW SUMMARY

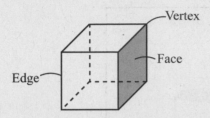

- A face is any flat surface on a prism or pyramid. A face is described by using the name of its two-dimensional shape, such as a triangle, square, or rectangle.
- An edge is where any two faces meet.
- A vertex is where at least three edges meet together. The edges form a corner or point at the vertex.

Name of 3-D Object	Number of Faces	Shape of Face(s) (2-D)	Number of Edges	Number of Vertices
Triangular prism	5	2 triangles 2 rectangles	9	6
Square-based pyramid	5	1 square 4 triangles	8	5
Cube	6	6 squares	12	8
Pentagonal-based pyramid	6	1 pentagon 5 triangles	10	6
Triangular-based pyramid	4	3 triangles	6	4

- You can sort 3-D objects according to how many vertices, edges, or faces they have.
- You can construct a skeleton of a 3-D object to help understand how many faces, edges, and vertices they have, as well as the shape of the faces.

PRACTICE TEST

Identify the parts of the given 3-D solids as a face, vertex, or edge.

1.

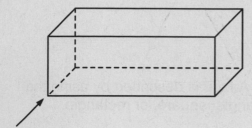

2.

3.

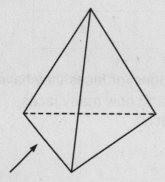

What is the shape of the faces for the following solids?

4.

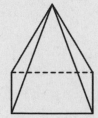

5.

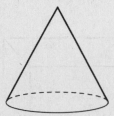

6.

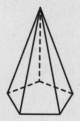

Look at the following solids. How many faces, edges, and vertices does each have?

7.

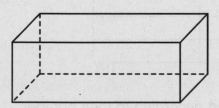

8.

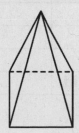

9.

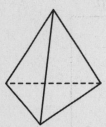

10.

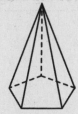

11.

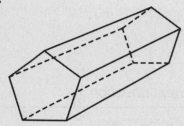

12. Fill out the following chart.

Name of 3-D Object	Number of Faces	Number of Edges	Number of Vertices
Triangular prism			
Pentagonal pyramid			
Cube			
Square-based pyramid			

13. How would you sort the shapes from the preceding chart according to their number of faces?

Use the following diagram to answer the next question.

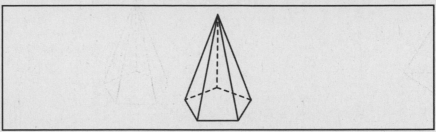

14. How would you make a skeleton of the pentagonal-based pyramid using straws and marshmallows?

Use the following information to answer the next question.

Mark's teacher asked him to construct a 3-D shape with 18 straws and 12 marshmallows. He made the following shape.

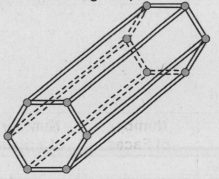

15. What shape did Mark make?

NOTES

STATISTICS AND PROBABILITY

When you are finished this unit, you will be able to…
• collect and organize information
• show information in lists, tally charts, and bar graphs
• answer questions from collected data
• create a bar graph
• draw conclusions from the data presented

PREREQUISITE SKILLS AND KNOWLEDGE

Prior to starting this unit, you should be able to…
• create and collect information about yourself
• choose a good way to collect and record information
• understand data presented in a pictograph

Lesson 1 *COLLECTING AND ORGANIZING INFORMATION*

NOTES

Information that is collected by asking questions, observing, or taking measurements is called data.

COLLECTING DATA

When you are collecting the data, there are two questions you need to ask:
• What is the best method to get the answers?
• What is the best method to record the answers?

You need to match the number of people answering your question to how you get the answers. For example, if you ask your class if they like chocolate or white cake best, you might want to ask everyone who likes chocolate cake to raise their hands. You would then do the same thing for white cake. If you were only asking five people, you could ask them one at a time.

It is important to collect data from the right people. For example, to find out how many Grade 3 students in Lander Elementary School are interested in going rock climbing, the Grade 3 students at that school must be surveyed. Data gathered from five students at Lander Elementary School or from the Grade 3 students at Hillside Elementary School would not be useful to discover how many Grade 3 students at Lander Elementary School are interested in rock climbing.

Example

Marc wants to collect data about what colour eyes each of his 27 classmates has. Marc's teacher gives him ten minutes to survey the students. What is the **best** method for Marc to collect the data?

Solution

The best way for Marc to collect his information is to have each student raise their hand or stand when he calls each eye colour. He could also have every student write down their eye colour on a piece of paper, but it would probably take longer than the ten minutes to record the total data.

It is important to keep track of the collected data. Tally charts, checklists, and line plots are three common ways to record data.

TALLY CHARTS

A tally chart is a popular way to record data. On a tally chart, a tally, or mark, is used to record the frequency of something.

Feelings of Students in a Grade 3 Class on a Particular Day	
Feeling	**Tally of Students**
Happy	‖‖‖‖
Sad	‖‖
Angry	‖
Confused	‖‖
Excited	‖‖‖
Tired	‖‖‖‖

Tally charts are good for organizing data gathered from questionnaires or surveys. A tally records answers easily in groups of five (‖‖). Every five tallies are bundled together. This makes it easy to find the total number of tallies. Count the bundled tallies by skip counting by fives.

NOTES

 Example

There are red, blue, and green marbles in a bag. Joey dumped the marbles out of the bag to see how many of each colour there were. The image below shows what he saw.

Fill in the tally chart to see how many of each marble Joey had.

R = red marbles
G = green marbles
B = blue marbles

Joey's Marbles

Colour	Tally
Red	
Blue	
Green	

Solution

Joey's Marbles

Colour	Tally
Red	卌 卌I
Blue	卌I
Green	卌 卌 卌

Make a tally mark in the box by the colour for each marble Joey counts. There are 11 red marbles, so you should have 11 ticks. Remember every group of 5 tallies has a line through it to bundle it. The tallies for the red marbles should look like 卌 卌I.

There are 6 blue marbles, so you should have 6 ticks (卌I).

There are 15 green marbles, so you should have 15 ticks (卌 卌 卌).

400

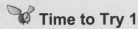 **Time to Try 1**

Arden asked her class what kind of pet they had at home. She found out that 5 people had dogs, 7 people had cats, 4 people had fish, 3 people had rabbits, 2 people had hamsters, 1 person had a snake, and 4 people had no pets. Fill in the tally chart below to show to show her results.

Pets of the Students in Grade 3B Class	
Pet	**Tally of Students**
Dog	
Cat	
Fish	
Rabbit	
Hamster	
Snake	
No Pet	

Each tally mark is equal to one pet.

NOTES

CHECKLISTS

You can use a checklist to organize the data you collect. To record information on a checklist, use a check mark in the column of the choice that is picked by the person you are questioning.

 Example

Gregory is interested in finding which one of three games is the most popular among his classmates. He decided to ask each of his classmates which game they like best: Doctor Dodge Ball, Capture the Flag, or Obstacle Baseball. Gregory has made a checklist to record the data he collects.

Name of Student	Doctor Dodge Ball	Capture the Flag	Obstacle Baseball
Trent		√	
Sherri			√
Abigail			√
Lane	√		
Dana			√
Michael		√	
Josh	√		
Julia	√		
Trevor	√		
Alysha		√	
Helen			√
Alden		√	
Carlos			
Teresa			
Sutton			
Hayden			
Luke			
Geneiva			
Tessa			
Jen			
Randy			

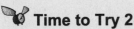 Time to Try 2

Complete the checklist on the previous page by filling in the rest of Gregory's data.

Carlos	Capture the Flag
Teresa	Obstacle Baseball
Sutton	Capture the Flag
Hayden	Doctor Dodge Ball
Luke	Doctor Dodge Ball
Geneiva	Obstacle Baseball
Tessa	Capture the Flag
Jen	Doctor Dodge Ball
Randy	Capture the Flag

LINE PLOT

A line plot is a number line where each number in a set of data is plotted by making a mark above that number. Usually, an X is used.

To make a number line plot, draw a line, and write the numbers you are using to show your information. Label them below the line. For example, your data can be from 1–10 or 0–100. Make sure your line is broken into equal lengths. Next, plot your data by placing an X over the correct number. If the number is repeated, place another X above the number.

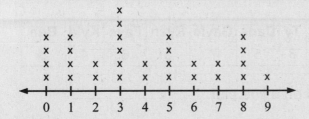

NOTES

 Example

Belinda collected the following data.
3, 2, 4, 3, 5, 3, 2, 3, 1, 3, 5

Plot the data collected on a line plot.

Solution

Begin by drawing a horizontal line. Place the numbers that fall within the range of the data (0–5) on the line. Make sure the ticks (numbers) are spread out evenly on the line.

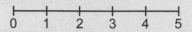

Next, plot the numbers on the line. The first number is a 3, so draw an X over the 3. The next number is a 2, so draw an X over the 2. Do this for all of the numbers, and remember that if one number is repeated you have to place the second X above the first X.

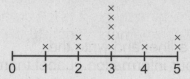

 Time to Try 3

Sandy asked her classmates how many hours a week spent reading. This is the data she collected.

Allie	Victor	Eli	Peter	Ty	Dana	Gayle	Ryan	Faye	Kyle	Ben
4	1	4	3	6	5	7	3	6	4	8

Plot the data collected on a line plot.

PRACTICE EXERCISES

Match the following questions with the group of people you would most likely survey to collect data.

1. What type of dog is the smartest?

2. What is your favourite subject in school?

3. What band instrument is the most fun to play?

4. What is the best movie playing this week?

A. Anyone who goes to school

B. People who own or have owned dogs

C. People who have seen a movie lately

D. Students who play an instrument

Use the following information to answer the next question.

Three students are arguing over what they think the most popular food is among Grade 4 students. Freddy thinks pizza is the most popular food, Norman thinks burgers are the most popular, and Maria thinks it is ice cream. They decide to survey the whole grade to resolve their disagreement. There are 75 students in Grade 4 at their school.

5. How should they organize their data?

Use the following information to answer the next question.

Emma went to the library and counted the number of males and females present over 30 minutes. This table gives the data she recorded.

| Males | IIII |
| Females | III |

6. According to Emma's record, how many people were present in the library?

Use the following information to answer the next question.

Favourite Type of Sandwich	Number of Students
Ham and Cheese	16
Turkey	13
Tuna	7
Egg Salad	4
Roast Beef	10

7. Display the information in the given table in a tally chart.

Use the following information to answer the next question.

Ryan surveyed 100 children and asked "What is your favourite lunch food?" Then, he tallied the results in a table.

Lunch Food	Boys	Girls
Pizza	8	6
Burger	12	12
Sandwich	4	6
Hotdog	14	12
Salad	2	24
Total	40	60

8. Display the information in the given table in a tally chart.

Use the following information to answer the next question.

Jack was playing a game with his friends. On each turn, the players spun a spinner. They recorded how many times the spinner landed on each of the numbers.

Spinner Number	Frequency
2	5
9	8
4	5
8	6
1	5
6	7
3	8
7	6

9. Display the information in the given table in a line plot.

Use the following information to answer the next question.

Gillian wants to know which sport her friends like the best. She asked each of her friends which sport they like best: swimming, soccer, or tennis. Gillian recorded the data she collected in a table.

Lynsey	Swimming
Caitlin	Swimming
Courtney	Tennis
Natalie	Swimming
Edward	Soccer
Amy	Soccer
Racheal	Tennis
Brad	Swimming
Vanessa	Soccer

10. Display the information in the given table in a checklist.

Use the following information to answer the next question.

Chase collected the following data: 2, 4, 5, 3, 1, 4, 2, 6, 5, 4, 2, 6, 4, 5, 1

11. Plot the data collected on a line plot.

Use the following information to answer the next question.

Carolyn surveyed the students in her class to find out how many pets each of her classmates owns. She recorded her results in the chart below.

Number of Pets	Tally	Frequency
0									
1											
2								
3			
4				

12. Complete the chart by recording the frequency of the number of pets each student owns.

Use the following information to answer the next question.

The given table shows the number of raffle tickets sold over 40 days.

Day	Number of Tickets Sold
0–10	35
11–20	25
21–30	36
31–40	23

13. Display the information from the given table in a tally chart.

Lesson 2 UNDERSTANDING DATA PRESENTED

After you have collected and recorded your data, you can use the information to answer questions. This information can be organized in many ways.

✱✱ Example

Mrs. Johnson works in the cafeteria. She is worried about the students' food choices. She has decided to observe the students, so she can determine if they are making good choices about what they eat. Mrs. Johnson decides to record the number of students who buy fruit and veggies or milk from the cafeteria at lunchtime. She also records the number of students who buy chocolate bars and chips or soft drinks. Their results are shown below.

Cafeteria Foods		
Food Item	Tally of Students	Frequency
Fruit/Veggies	卌 卌 卌 卌	
Milk	卌 卌 卌 卌 卌 ‖	
Chocolate Bars/Chips	卌 卌 卌 卌 卌 卌 卌 ‖‖	
Soft Drinks	卌 卌 卌 卌 卌 卌 卌 卌	

Total the tally marks for each food item, and enter the number next to the food item.

Solution

Each tally mark (|) represents one food item. Each group (卌) represents five items. Look at the marks across from the word Milk. Count them.

25 + 2 = 27

Fruit/Veggies	20
Milk	27
Chocolate Bars/Chips	38
Soft Drinks	41

According to Mrs. Johnson's data, 47 students bought fruit and veggies or milk (20 + 27), and 79 students bought chocolate bars and chips or pop (38 + 41). Mrs. Johnson had a reason to worry about the choices the students were making.

Time to Try 1

Answer the questions below using the tally chart.

Ways To Get to School	
Transportation	**Tally**
Bus	IIII
Parents drive	III
Walk	IIIIIIII
Skateboard	IIII
Ride bike	IIII
Rollerblade	I

a)   How many students walk to school?

b)   Is skateboarding more popular than bike riding?

c)   Which two ways of getting to school are used by the same number of students?

Checklists help organize data by recording information. Place a check mark in the column of the choice picked by the person you are questioning.

✳ Example

Mr. Frank wanted to order pizza for the students in the math club. He asked each student what type of pizza they wanted.

Name of Student	Cheese	Pepperoni	Ham and Pineapple
Todd	√		
Shelley		√	
Andrea			√
Lonnie		√	
Dina	√		
Mike			√
Joe		√	
Julie	√		
Trent		√	
Porter		√	
Hannah	√		
Hunter		√	

a) Which type of pizza is **most popular**?

Solution

To find out which pizza choice is most popular, count all of the students who chose cheese (4), pepperoni (6), and ham and pineapple (2). The most popular pizza was pepperoni.

b) Which type of pizza is **least popular**?

Solution

To find out which pizza choice is least popular, count all of the students who chose cheese (4), pepperoni (6), and ham and pineapple (2). The least popular pizza was ham and pineapple.

c) How many students are in the math club?

Solution

To find out how many students are in the math club, count all of the students who chose cheese (4), pepperoni (6), and ham and pineapple (2). Add these numbers together. There are 12 students in the math club.

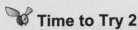 **Time to Try 2**

Mr. Frank also decided he was going to buy ice cream for the math club students. His results are recorded in the checklist below.

Name of Student	Chocolate	Vanilla	Strawberry
Todd		√	
Shelley		√	
Andrea			√
Lonnie	√		
Dina			√
Mike	√		
Joe		√	
Julie	√		
Trent		√	
Porter	√		
Hannah	√		
Hunter			√

a) Which type of ice cream is **most popular**?

b) Which students chose strawberry?

c) How many more students chose vanilla than chose strawberry?

BAR GRAPHS

Bar graphs organize data in bars along the *x*- and *y*-axes. You can use the data in a bar graph to answer questions and solve problems.

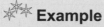 **Example**

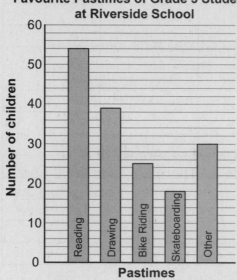

Favourite Pastimes of Grade 3 Students at Riverside School

a) Since the data was collected for the given graph, 8 new students have moved to Riverside School. Of these new students, 3 said that reading was their favourite pastime, 2 said drawing, 1 said bike riding, and 2 said gymnastics. How does this change the data represented in the graph?

Solution

Reading
Add the 3 new students to the 54 students shown on the graph to find the number of students who chose reading as their favourite pastime.
3 + 54 = 57

In all, 57 students chose reading.

Drawing
Add the 2 new students to the 39 students shown on the graph to find the number of students who chose drawing as their favourite pastime.
$2 + 39 = 41$

In all, 41 students chose drawing.

Bike Riding
Add the 1 new student to the 25 students shown on the graph to find the number of students who chose skateboarding as their favourite pastime.
$1 + 25 = 26$

In all, 26 students chose drawing.

Skateboarding
The number of students who chose skateboarding as their favourite pastime does not change because none of the new students chose it as their favourite pastime. There are still 18 students who chose skateboarding.

Other
Because gymnastics is not listed separately, it is considered an "other" pastime. Therefore, add the 2 new students to the 30 students shown on the graph to find the number of students who chose pastimes other than those listed in the graph.
$2 + 30 = 32$

In all, 32 students chose pastimes other than those listed in the graph.

b) Including the 8 new students, how many students were asked about their favourite pastime?

Solution

To find the total number of students who took part in this survey, use the information from part **a**. The 8 students are included in the new totals. Add the number of students who chose each pastime.
$57 + 41 + 26 + 18 + 32 = 174$

A total of 174 students were asked about their favourite pastime.

PRACTICE EXERCISES

Use the following information to answer the next question.

The children registered at the *Adventures R Us* summer camp voted for their favourite flavour of ice cream. The camp counsellor entered the data on a bar graph.

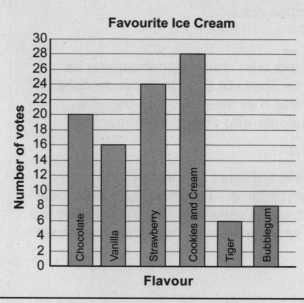

1. How many children took part in this survey?

2. What is the **most popular** flavour?

3. What is the **least popular** flavour?

4. How many children did **not** choose cookies and cream as their favourite flavour?

5. How many more votes did strawberry get than bubblegum?

Use the following information to answer the next question.

Cara asked some of the students in her class what their favourite school subject was. Her results are given in the checklist below.

Name of Student	Math	Language Arts	Science
Jask	√		
Susan		√	
Abby			√
Ava		√	
Lori	√		
Nathan	√		
Jacob		√	
Tash	√		
Billy			√
Parker	√		
Sam		√	
Lee			√

6. Which school subject is the **most popular**?

7. How many more students chose math than chose science as their favourite subject?

8. How many students did **not** choose language arts as their favourite subject?

Use the following information to answer the next question.

Justin recorded the number of vehicles that went by his house in one afternoon.

Vehicles	Tally Marks
Car	卌‖
Bus	卌
Bicycle	卌 卌‖‖

9. How many bicycles went by Justin's house?

10. How many more cars than buses went by Justin's house?

11. How many vehicles went by Justin's house in total?

Use the following information to answer the next two questions.

Pamela surveyed the students in her class because she wanted to find out how many pets each student owns. She recorded her results in the chart below.

Number of Pets	Tally
0	卌‖
1	卌‖‖‖
2	卌‖
3	‖
4	‖

12. How many students have exactly 2 pets?

13. How many students have 2 or more pets?

Lesson 3 **CREATING BAR GRAPHS**

A *bar graph* displays data using vertical or horizontal bars. These bars show quantity and the connection between two or more things and make it easy to compare data.

When creating a bar graph, be sure the numbers along the side go up in equal intervals. The numbers in the graph below go up by intervals of two.

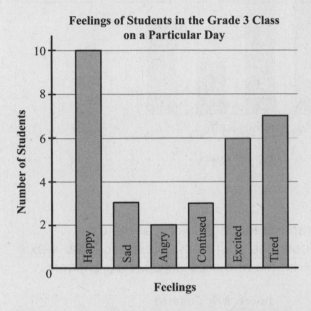

The parts of the bar graph are given below.

Title The title appears at the top of the graph and explains what the graph is about. The title of this graph is "Feelings of Students in the Grade 3 Class on a Particular Day."

x-axis The x-axis is the horizontal line at the bottom of the graph. The label along the x-axis is "Feelings." It shows students' different feelings.

y-axis The y-axis is the vertical line on the left side of the graph. The label on the y-axis is "Number of Students." It tells you how many students were questioned.

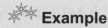 **Example**

Label the graph below.

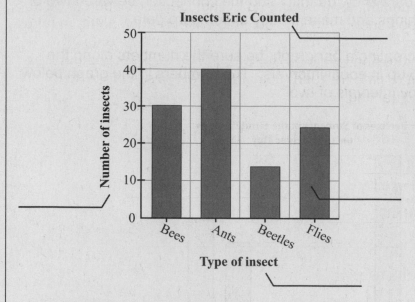

Solution

To create a bar graph, begin by looking at the data. Write a title that describes your data. Next, label the *x*-axis and *y*-axis with the labels and scales you have chosen.

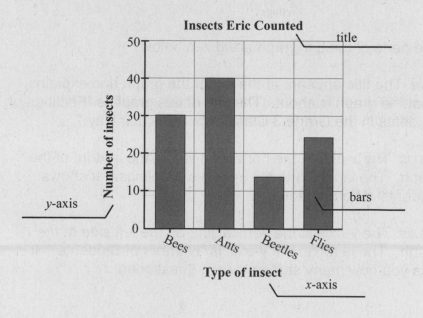

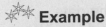 **Example**

Jerome is training for a triathlon. There are three parts to the race: running, swimming, and biking. Jerome needs to be in very good shape. He has decided to keep track of the number of hours he spends running, working out with weights, swimming, and biking each week. The table below shows the amount of time he spent doing these exercises in his first week of training.

Exercise	Time Spent in Hours
Running	9
Working with weights	10
Swimming	8
Biking	8

Graph the information in the table.

Solution

First, write a title for your graph. A good title would be something like "Jerome's Training Time."

Next, decide what information goes on each axis. Sports will go on the *x*-axis, and the number of hours spent training will go on the *y*-axis. For the *y*-axis, decide on a scale. A good scale for this question is 0–10.

Write Jerome's four sports along the *x*-axis: running, weights, swimming, and biking.

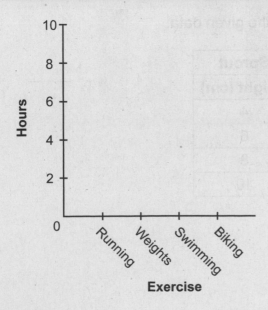

NOTES

Finally, draw in your bars so that they show the data. Jerome spends 9 hours running. The bar should be above the label running on the *x*-axis and should go up to the 9 on the *y*-axis. Since you are going up by 2s on the *y*-axis, you have to go halfway between the 8 and the 10. Jerome spends 10 hours on weights, so your bar should be above the label weights on the *x*-axis and should go up to the 10 on the *y*-axis. Jerome spends 8 hours swimming. The bar should be above the label swimming on the *x*-axis and go up to the 8 on the *y*-axis. Finally, Jerome also spends 8 hours biking. Draw your bar above the biking label on the *x*-axis and go up to 8 on the *y*-axis.

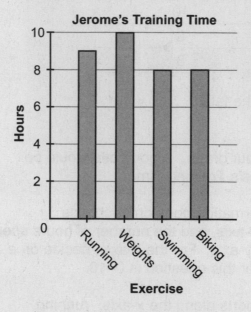

Time to Try 1

Create a bar graph for the given data.

Growth of a Bean Sprout	
Number of Days	**Height (cm)**
1	4
3	6
5	8
7	10

Bar graphs can be compared to determine what characteristics they share. Properly presented data is easy to read and understand.

✳ Example

Compare the following bar graphs and determine how they are the same.

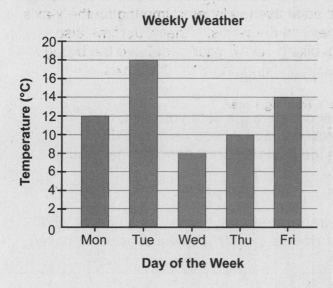

Weekly Weather

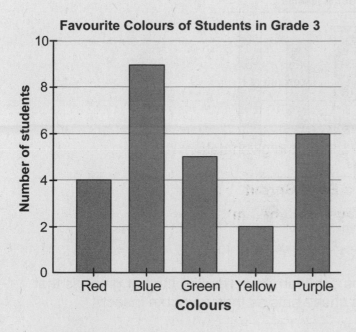

Favourite Colours of Students in Grade 3

Solution

Look at the bar graphs. Both have a title at the top to identify what the data in the graph is describing. Also, both have labels on the *x*- and *y*-axes, and the scale on the *y*- axis goes up in intervals of two.

DRAWING CONCLUSIONS

You can draw conclusions from the data presented in a bar graph. Drawing conclusions means to look at what information is given in the graph and make a prediction or an assumption.

When you read graphs, pay close attention to all the data shown. When you read graphs, you need to pay attention to all the data shown, such as the following information:
• Labels on the axes
• Information in the title
• The scales, or intervals, used

You can interpret or compare the data you read, and mathematical operations can be done using the data. You can look at all the data and draw conclusions about it.

 Example

The following bar graph shows the number of students who chose one of four favourite insects. Draw a conclusion based on the data shown.

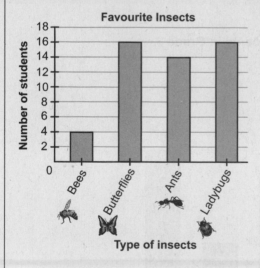

Solution

One fact you can learn from reading the bar graph is that 14 students chose ants as their favourite insect.

When you interpret the data in this graph, one fact you can learn is that 12 more students like ladybugs than bees.
$16 - 4 = 12$

A conclusion you can draw from the data shown is that of the four given insects, bees are the least popular.

NOTES

 Time to Try 2

Ken asks some students at his school what their favourite activity is. He makes a bar graph to show the results. What conclusions can he draw about the least popular and most popular activity?

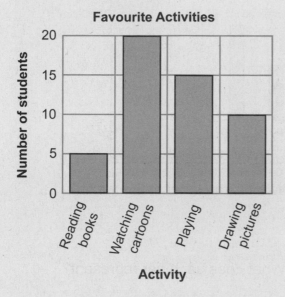

PRACTICE EXERCISES

Use the following information to answer the next four questions.

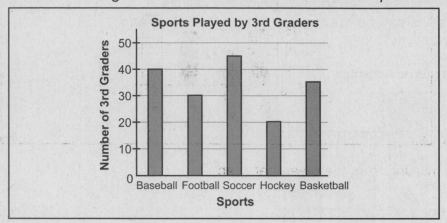

1. What is the title of this bar graph?

2. What is the label of the *x*-axis?

3. What is the label of the *y*-axis?

4. What does each bar represent?

Use the following information to answer the next four questions.

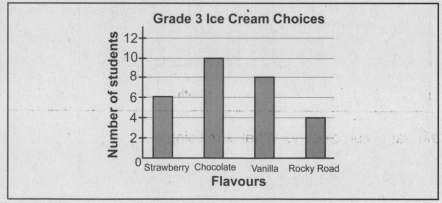

5. What is the title of this bar graph?

6. What is the label of the *x*-axis?

7. What is the label of the *y*-axis?

8. What does each bar represent?

Use the following information to answer the next question.

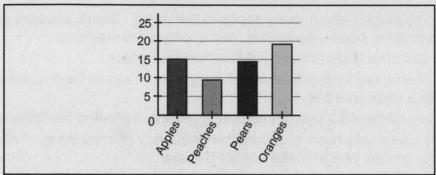

9. What is missing from the given bar graph?

Use the following information to answer the next question.

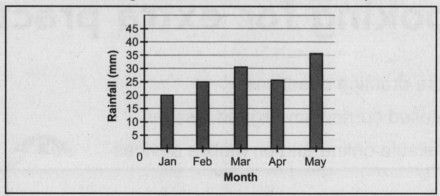

10. Look at the bar graph closely. What is missing?

REVIEW SUMMARY

- People have questions about many things in the world. Some answers can be found by asking questions, observing events, and taking measurements.
- Tally charts and checklists are two ways of recording data.
- Graphs are often used to organize and display data. Graphs help communicate information in a clear manner.
- There are many different types of charts and graphs, including the following types.
  - Tally charts use a tally mark to record the frequency of something. Tallies are bundled into groups of 5 to make counting easier.
  - A bar graph that uses bars to show quantity.
- Each type of chart or graph can be used to show the same information.
- To construct a bar graph, you need to include a title, labels for the *x*- and *y*-axes, a scale on the *y*-axis, and the two sets of data along the *x*- and *y*-axes.
- Graphs can help you solve problems and draw conclusions.

PRACTICE TEST

1. Dayton wants to see how much traffic goes by the school on Friday afternoons. One Friday, he records all the vehicles that drive past the school between 3:00 P.M. and 4:00 P.M. What would the **best** method be for Dayton to use to record his data?

2. Danielle wants to collect data about the most popular television show among the 29 students in her class. She makes a list of four television shows. Her teacher gives her ten minutes to survey her classmates. What is the **best** method for Danielle to use to collect her data?

Use the following information to answer the next question.

The following table shows the score that students earned on a quiz.

Score	Frequency
3	2
4	1
8	3
10	1
15	5
17	4
19	2

3. Create a line plot using the information in the given frequency chart.

Use the following bar graph to answer the next three questions.

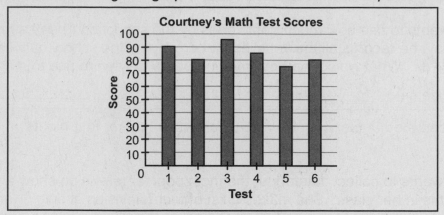

4. On which test did Courtney get her **highest** score?

5. On which tests did Courtney score 80?

6. What is Courtney's total score on all six tests?

Use the following information to answer the next two questions.

Students in Mr. Smith's class were asked to choose their favourite sport. Their responses were recorded in the given chart:

Sport	Tally of Students
Basketball	⦀⦀⦀⦀⦀
Hockey	⦀⦀⦀⦀ |||
Baseball	⦀⦀⦀ ||||
Tennis	⦀⦀ ||

7. How many students' responses were recorded in the chart?

8. How many more students chose hockey than chose tennis as their favourite sport?

Use the following information to answer the next two questions.

Sarah recorded the number of hours she slept each night for four nights.

Friday	卌			
Saturday	卌卌
Sunday	卌			
Monday	卌卌

9. How many hours did Sarah sleep on Friday night?

10. In total, how many hours did Sarah sleep on the four nights?

Use the following information to answer the next two questions.

Lisa recorded the height of five students in her class. She put the information in a chart.

Student	Height (in cm)
Julie	100
Chris	140
Ruby	130
John	100
Pam	100

11. Display the information from the chart in a bar graph.

12. How much taller than John is Chris?

Use the following information to answer the next question.

Mrs. Lefebvre asked the students in her Grade 3 class to vote for their favourite track 'n fun day activity. Each student chose one activity and wrote it on a slip of paper. Mrs. Lefebvre collected the slips of paper. The results are given.

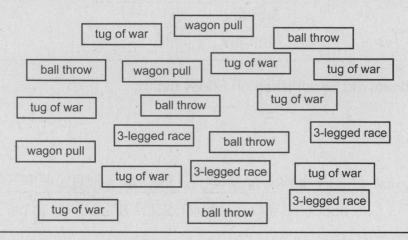

13. Create a tally chart to show the number of students who voted for each activity.

14. A local grocery store surveyed some of its customers to find out their favourite fruit. The results were recorded in the given frequency chart. Complete the chart by adding tally marks.

Fruit	Frequency	Tally
Apples	25	
Peaches	9	
Pears	14	
Oranges	22	

Use the following information to answer the next question.

The following data shows the height of each student in a Grade 3 class to the nearest centimetre.

134 140 129 141 135
130 134 134 135 140
141 131 132 135 131
130 140 137 131 138

15. Display the data on a line plot.

Use the following information to answer the next question.

Colleen collects data about the different hair colours of students in her school.
- Red hair: 23
- Light brown hair: 33
- Black hair: 25
- Dark brown hair: 28
- Blonde hair: 31

16. Display the information in a bar graph.

NOTES

Student Notes and Problems

ANSWERS AND SOLUTIONS

COUNTING

Lesson 1—Skip Counting up to 1 000

🦋 TIME TO TRY 🦋
ANSWERS AND SOLUTIONS

1. 244, 249, 254, 259, 264, 269
    The ones digits all end in a 4 or a 9.

2. 233, 243, 253, 263, 273, 283
    When you count by 10 in this number sequence, only the number in the tens place changes. It goes up by one. The digits in the hundreds and ones place remain the same.

3. 238, 338, 438, 538, 638, 738
    As you skip count forward by 100, you add 100 to the number before. The digits in the tens and ones places stay the same. The digit in the hundreds place goes up by one.

4. 425, 450, 475, 500, 525, 550
    Notice the pattern of the hundreds place number. As you skip count forward, the digits 25, 50, 75, and 00 repeat as the digit in the hundreds place increases.

5. 24, 27, 30, 33, 36, 39, 42
    Start counting at 24, and add 3 for each count. Each number is a multiple of 3, which means it is the product of a number that it multiplied by 3.

6. To find the number that the sequence is growing by, subtract the first number from the second number, then the next number from the number before it.
    $150 - 125 = 25$, $175 - 150 = 25$, $200 - 175 = 25$

    The sequence shows skip counting by 25s. You can also count up from the first number to the second.

PRACTICE EXERCISE
ANSWERS AND SOLUTIONS

1. 632, 637, 642, 647, 652, 657

3. 24, 28, 32, 36, 40, 44

5. 150, 175, 200, 225, 250, 275

7. 735, 745, 755, 765, 775, 785

9. 44, 144, 244, 344, 444, 544

11. 5

Lesson 2—Skip Counting Backward

🦋 TIME TO TRY 🦋
ANSWERS AND SOLUTIONS

1. 374, 369, 364, 359, 354, 349
    When you count backward by 5, the ones digit makes a pattern that ends in a 4 or a 9.

2. 478, 468, 458, 448, 438, 428
    When you subtract 10, the number in the tens place changes. The digits in the hundreds and ones places remain the same. The ones digits all end in 0. The tens digits go down by 1 each time.

3. 784, 684, 584, 484, 384, 284
When you skip count backward, the digit in the hundreds place gets smaller by 1 each time. The digits in the tens and ones places stay the same.

4. 9<u>75</u>, 9<u>50</u>, 9<u>25</u>, 9<u>00</u>, 8<u>75</u>, 8<u>50</u>
As you skip count backward, the digits 75, 50, 25 and 00 repeat. The digit in the hundreds place may also decrease as you count backward.

5. 42, 39, 36, 33, 30, 27
When you skip count backward, subtract 3 from the number you start with.
42 – 3 = 39, 39 – 3 = 36, 36 – 3 = 33, 33 – 3 = 30, 30 – 3 = 27

6. 48, 44, 40, 36, 32, 28
When you skip count backward, subtract 4 from the number you start with.
48, 44 (48 – 4 = 44), 40 (44 – 4 = 40), 36 (40 – 4 = 36), 32 (36 – 4 = 32), 28 (32 – 4 = 28)

7. The number 363 is incorrect.
To determine the mistake in the skip counting sequence, start with the first number. Then, subtract 10 from each number.
394 – 10 = 384, 384 – 10 = 374, 374 – 10 = 364, 364 – 10 = 354

The mistake is the number 363. The last number should be 354, not 363.

8. To find the missing number, continue the skip counting pattern. To find the pattern, count down from the first number (44) to the second number (40). You get 43, 42, 41, 40. That is four counts.

Now count down from the second number (40) to the next number (36). That is also 4 counts. The skip counting sequence is counting backward by 4s.

To fill in the blank, subtract 4 from the number before the blank. You get 32 – 4 = 28.

The number 28 is missing from the skip counting sequence.

PRACTICE EXERCISES
ANSWERS AND SOLUTIONS

1. 873, 868, 863, 858, 853, 848

3. 243, 233, 223, 213, 203, 193

5. 36, 32, 28, 24, 20, 16

7. 782, 682, 582, 482, 382, 282

9. To find the skip count backward pattern, subtract the third number from the second number. You get 42 – 39 = 3. Then subtract the fourth number from the third number to get 39 – 36 = 3.

This sequence shows skip counting backward by 3s. To find the missing first number, add 3 to the second number.
42 + 3 = 45

Lesson 3—Skip Counting with Money

TIME TO TRY
ANSWERS AND SOLUTIONS

1. 90¢
A dime is worth ten cents. To skip count forward by dimes, add 10 to each count.
10, 20, 30, 40, 50, 60, 70, 80, 90

2. To skip count forward by dimes, add 10 to each count.
10, 20 (10 + 10 = 20), 30 (20 + 10 = 30), 40 (30 + 10 = 40), 50 (40 + 10 = 50)

PRACTICE EXERCISES
ANSWERS AND SOLUTIONS

1. 10, 20, 30, 40
   There are 4 dimes. The total value of the dimes is 40 cents.

3. 5, 10, 15, 20, 25, 30, 35, 40
   There are 8 nickels, which have a total value of 40 cents.

5. 75¢, $1.00, $1.25, $1.50, $1.75, $2.00

7. 80¢, 70¢, 60¢, 50¢, 40¢, 30¢

9. $9.00, $8.00, $7.00, $6.00, 5.00, $4.00

Practice Test

ANSWERS AND SOLUTIONS

1. 527, 532, 537, 542, 547, 552

3. 822, 817, 812, 807, 802, 797

5. 32, 28, 24, 20, 16, 12

7. 625, 600, 575, 550, 525, 500

9. $2.75, $2.50, $2.25, $2.00, $1.75, $1.50

11. 504, 501, 498, 495, 492, 489

13. $2.75, $2.50, $2.25, $2.00, $1.75, $1.50

15. 225, 215, 205, 195, 185, 175

REPRESENTING NUMBERS

Lesson 1—Reading and Writing Numbers to 1 000

TIME TO TRY
ANSWERS AND SOLUTIONS

1. To write the number 800 in words, look at the digit in the hundreds place. It is an eight. Add the word *hundred* after.

   In words, the number 800 is written as eight hundred.

2. To write the number 243 in words, start from the left and move to the right. Write the name for the digit in the hundreds place, and add the word *hundred* after it, two hundred Next, write the tens and the ones places together. Do not forget to put in the hyphen, forty-three.

   The number 243 is written in words as two hundred forty-three.

PRACTICE EXERCISES
ANSWERS AND SOLUTIONS

1.

seven hundred eight — 99
ninety-nine — 780
twenty-eight — 992
nine hundred ninety-two — 28
seven hundred eighty — 708

3. The number of marbles written in words is six hundred thirty-two.

5. The number of pennies written in words is eight hundred six.

7. Rochelle owns forty-three dolls.

9. Dermot took two hundred fifty shots on goal.

11. Louise has 47 Barbie dolls.

Lesson 2—Representing Numbers in Other Ways

🐰 TIME TO TRY 🐰
ANSWERS AND SOLUTIONS

1. To build the number 437 using the fewest blocks, look at each place value position. Use the base ten blocks to show the value. Units are each worth one, so use them to show the number in the ones position. Ten rods each have a value of 10, so use them to build the number in the tens position. The number in the hundreds place value position can be built most easily with hundred flats that each have a value of 100.

There is a 7 in the ones position. Use 7 units to represent this value. The 3 in the tens place can be shown using 3 ten rods. The value of the number in the hundreds position is 400. Use 4 hundred flats to show this amount.

This picture shows the fewest base ten blocks used to build the number 437.

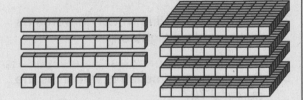

2. There are 6 flats (600), 3 rods (30), and 9 units (9) in the picture. The number shown by the base ten blocks is 639.

3. There are many ways to represent the number 626 with money. Remember that 1 loonie has a value of 100 cents, 1 dime has a value of 10 cents, and 1 penny has a value of 1 cent.

You can represent the number 626 with 6 loonies, 2 dimes, and 6 pennies.

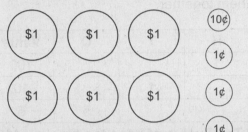

Another way to show the number 626 is with 1 five-dollar bill, 1 loonie, 1 quarter, and 1 penny.

PRACTICE EXERCISES
ANSWERS AND SOLUTIONS

1.

$$\begin{array}{ll} 6 \text{ flats} & = 600 \\ 3 \text{ rods} & = 30 \\ \underline{19 \text{ units}} & = \underline{19} \\ & 649 \end{array} \Rightarrow 600 + 30 + 19 = 649$$

Ten units could be traded for one rod, which would leave nine single units.

3. The picture shows the fewest base ten blocks that can be used to build the number 297.

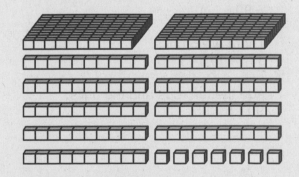

Check your answer.
200 + 90 + 7 = 297

5. The base ten blocks are incorrect.

To see if these base ten blocks equal 125, add up their values. Write the values in a place value chart, and add them together.

H	T	O	Value
1			100
	1		10
		5	5
Total value of base ten blocks: 115			

7. The addition sentence $150 - 25$ is correct. Line up the place value positions, and subtract.

$$
\begin{array}{r}
1\overset{4}{\cancel{5}}\overset{10}{\cancel{0}} \\
-\ 2\ 5 \\
\hline
1\ 2\ 5
\end{array}
$$

9. The written form of the number is correct. Start from left to right. Write the name for the digit in the hundreds place and add the word *hundred* after it. That gives you one hundred. Next, write the tens and ones places together, *twenty-five*. 125 is written *one hundred twenty-five*.

11. The base ten blocks are incorrect. Count the base ten blocks. There are 9 ten rods.
$10 + 10 + 10 + 10 + 10 + 10 + 10 + 10 + 10 = 90$

There are 5 units.
$1 + 1 + 1 + 1 + 1 = 5$

Add the ten rods and the units.
$90 + 5 = 95$

13. 453
There are 4 hundreds' flats, five tens' rods, and 3 ones' units. No regrouping is necessary.

15. 479
Regroup the tens to make one hundred flat out of 10 rods. This leaves 7 rods in the tens place. There are 4 hundred flats, 7 ten rods, and 9 one units.

17. ___ 8 loonies, 5 dimes, 1 nickel, 3 pennies

√ one 5 dollar bill, 3 loonies, 6 dimes, 8 pennies

√ one five dollar bill, 2 loonies, 4 quarters, 5 dimes, 3 nickels, 3 pennies

√ 8 loonies, 1 quarter, 4 dimes, 3 pennies

$800 + 50 + 5 + 3 = 858$
$500 + 100 + 60 + 8 = 868$
$500 + 200 + 100 + 50 + 15 + 3 = 868$
$800 + 25 + 40 + 3 = 868$

Practice Test

ANSWERS AND SOLUTIONS

1.

479 — four hundred forty-four
408 — four hundred seventy-nine
460 — four hundred eight
444 — four hundred sixty

3. The number 818 is written in words as eight hundred eighteen.

5. Seven hundred seven is written as the numeral 707.

7. The base ten blocks represent the number 364.

There are 3 flats (300), 6 rods (60) and 4 units (4). The number shown by the base ten blocks is $300 + 60 + 4 = 364$

9. The base ten blocks in the picture represents the number 127.

There is 1 flat (100), 2 rods (20), and 7 units (7). The number shown by the base ten blocks is $100 + 20 + 7 = 127$.

11.

seven hundred twenty-four   1 flat, 3 unit
five hundred nineteen   2 flats, 3 rods, 3 units
one hundred three   7 flats, 2 rods, 4 units
two hundred thirty-three   5 flats, 1 rod, 9 units

13. √ $301 - 214 = 87$
   √ $657 - 570 = 87$
   √ $928 - 841 = 87$
   ___ $114 - 17 = 97$

15. The subtraction sentence 864 – 397 represents the number 467.

17. The subtraction sentence 715 – 140 represents the number 575.

19. The total amount of money represents the number 735.
- 7 loonies equal 700 (100 + 100 + 100 + 100 + 100 + 100 + 100)
- 3 dimes equal 30 (10 + 10 + 10).
- 5 pennies equal 5 (1 + 1 + 1 + 1 + 1).

700 + 30 + 735

Place Value

Lesson 1—Value of a Digit

🦋 TIME TO TRY 🦋
ANSWERS AND SOLUTIONS

1. 42<u>8</u>
The value of the digit in the ones place is 8.

2. 5<u>5</u>4
The value of the digit in the tens column is 50.

3. <u>3</u>21
The value of the digit in the hundreds column is 300.

4. The value of the hundreds place is 100, in the tens place is 10, and in the ones place is 1.

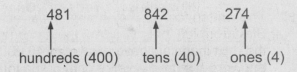

     481   842   274
     ↑   ↑   ↑

hundreds (400)   tens (40)   ones (4)

In the number 481, the digit 4 is in the hundreds place and has a value of 400.

In the number 842, the digit 4 is in the tens place and has a value of 40.

In the number 274, the digit 4 is in the ones place and has a value of 4.

5.

H	T	O
6	7	9

PRACTICE EXERCISES ANSWERS AND SOLUTIONS

1.

Hundreds	Tens	Ones
400	60	7

400 hundred flats equal 40 000, 60 ten rods have a value of 600, and 7 units equal 7. The total value shown in this table is (40 000 + 600 + 7) 40 607.

	Hundreds	Tens	Ones
√	4	6	7

4 hundred flats have a value of 400, 6 ten rods equal 60, and the value of 7 units is 7. The total value shown in this table is (400 + 60 + 7) 467.

	Hundreds	Tens	Ones
√			467

467 units have a value of 467.

Hundreds	Tens	Ones
400		67

400 hundred flats have a value of 40 000 and 67 units have a value of 67. The total shown in this table is (40 000 + 67) 40 067.

3. 2⑤1   50

The value of the 5 in the tens place position is worth 50.

5. The value of the digit 6 is 6 ones. The number is 54**6**.

7. The value of the number 100 is 1 hundred so the number is **1**23.

9. 31⑧   10

Lesson 2—Place Value with Base Ten Blocks

✿ TIME TO TRY ✿ ANSWERS AND SOLUTIONS

1. First, look at the digit in the ones place (4). Draw 4 units in the ones column of your place value chart.

Next, look at the digit in the tens place (4). Draw 4 rods in the tens column.

Finally, look at the digit in the hundreds place (4). Draw 4 flats in the hundreds column.

This is the place value chart that represents the number 444.

2. To show the number 452 using the fewest base ten blocks, determine the place value for each digit.

There is a 4 in the hundreds place. That means there are 4 hundreds or 4 flats (400) in the hundreds place value column.

There is a 5 in the tens place. That means there are 5 tens or 5 rods (50) in the tens place value column.

Finally, there is a 2 in the ones place. That means there are 2 ones or 2 units in the ones place value column.

This number can be shown by drawing 4 flats, 5 rods, and 2 units.

H	T	O

PRACTICE EXERCISES
ANSWERS AND SOLUTIONS

1. There is 1 flat in the hundreds place that represents 1 hundred.
   $1 \times 100 = 100$

   There are 4 ten rods in the tens place that represent 4 tens.
   $4 \times 10 = 40$

   There are 0 units in the ones place so there are 0 ones.
   $0 \times 1 = 0$

   The number represented by the base ten blocks is 140.

3. For the number 345, look at the ones place (5). Draw 5 units in the ones column of the place value chart.

   Next, look at the tens place (4). Draw 4 rods in the tens column.

   Finally, look at the hundreds place (3). Draw 3 flats in the hundreds column.

H	T	O

5. For the number 196, look at the ones place (6). Draw 6 units in the ones column of the place value chart.

   Next, look at the tens place (9). Draw 9 rods in the tens column.

   Finally, look at the hundreds place (1). Draw 1 flat in the hundreds column.

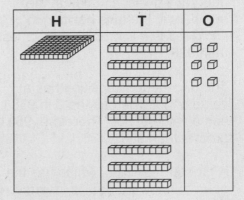

H	T	O

7. There are 4 flats in the hundreds place that represent 4 hundreds.
   $4 \times 100 = 400$

   There are 0 ten rods in the tens place that represent 0 tens.
   $0 \times 10 = 0$

   There are 5 units in the ones place that represent 5 ones.
   $5 \times 1 = 5$

   The number represented by the base ten blocks in the place value chart is 405. Remember to put the 0 in as a place holder for the tens place.

Lesson 3—Comparing and Ordering

✿ TIME TO TRY ✿
ANSWERS AND SOLUTIONS

1. **a)** Both numbers have a 9 in the hundreds position. Look at the numbers in the tens position to find out if 958 is greater than or less than 938.

    The 5 in the tens position has a value of 50, whereas the 3 in 938 has a value of 30. Therefore, 958 is greater than 938.

    A greater than sign, which has the open part toward 958, is inserted.

    958 > 938

    b) All of the digits in both numbers are the same. These two numbers have equal values.

    An equal sign is inserted.

    434 = 434

2. To find the missing numbers, look at the space and the numbers on either side of the space.

    Either count up by 1 from the number on the left, or count back by 1 from the number on the right.

    Begin by looking at the second row. The number before the space is 27. One more would be 28.

    Next, look at the seventh row. The number to the right of the space is 77. One less would be 76.

Finally, the last row has a space right after the number 91. So the next number would be 92.

The missing numbers on the hundred chart are 28, 76, and 92.

3. To place the numbers in order from greatest to least, look at and compare the digits in the greatest place value position.

    Step 1
    Start by making a table to order the numbers.

Th	H	T	O
1	0	0	0
	9	2	9
	8	3	9
	8	1	8
	9	5	5

    The greatest place value position is the thousands position. Only the number 1 000 has a number in this position, so this makes it the greatest number.

    Step 2
    Look at the digit in the hundreds position.

    The numbers with a 9 in the hundreds place value position are greater than those with an 8 in the hundreds position. The numbers 929 and 955 both have the same value in the hundreds position, so move to the place value position to the right, and compare those digits.

    The number 929 has a 2 in the tens position, and the number 955 has a 5 in the tens position. Since 5 is greater than 2, 955 comes next in line, followed by 929.

Step 3

Look at the last two numbers, 839 and 818. They both have the same value in the hundreds position, so move to the next place value position. The number 839 has a 3 in the tens position, and the number 818 has a 1. Since 3 is greater than 1, 839 is the next number, and 818 is the last number.

Step 4

Write the numbers in descending order: 1 000, 955, 929, 839, and 818.

4. **Step 1**

Start by creating different numbers. Use a chart to help. Make sure that only 1 digit is in each place value position. For example, if you write a 3 in the hundreds place, the 4 or 8 must go in the tens place or the ones place. Whichever digit you choose to write in the tens position, the other digit would go in the ones.

The following numbers can be made by using 3, 4 and 8.

348
384
438
483
834
843

Step 2

Order the numbers from least to greatest.

Compare the digits in the hundreds place.

The digit 3 is the least digit, so 348 and 384 would be first and second numbers. Looking at the tens place, the digit 4 is less than 8, so 348 would be first number, followed by 384.

Looking at the hundreds place again, the digit 4 is the next least digit, so 438 and 483 would be the next two numbers. Looking at the tens place, the digit 3 is less than 8, so 438 would be the third number, and 483 would be next.

Finally, the last two numbers are 834 and 843. Look at the digits in the tens place again. The digit 3 is less than 4, so 834 would be the next number, and the number 843 would be the greatest number.

Step 3

Write the sequence of numbers in order from least to greatest: 348, 384, 438, 483, 834, 843

PRACTICE EXERCISES
ANSWERS AND SOLUTIONS

1. To complete this comparison, you need to figure out if 555 is greater or less than 667. To do this, look at the first digit in the hundreds position. The 5 with a value of 500 is less than the 6 with a value of 600. The open end of the symbol should point toward 555, so the less than symbol is used to show that 555 is less than 667.

   555 < 667

3. All of the digits in these two numbers are identical. Therefore, use an equal symbol to show that the two numbers are equal.

   213 = 213

5. To list the number of marbles students' collections from least to greatest begin by looking at the digit in the hundreds position. The number whose digit has the least value is the first digit to be listed. The number 167 has a 1 in the hundreds position with a value of 100. All other numbers have a value of 200 or more in the hundreds position. This means that Jason's collection has the least number of marbles.

Look again at the hundreds position for the remaining numbers. The next least numbers of marbles are 276 and 286. Both numbers have a 2 in the hundreds place value position, so to compare them further, look at the digit in the tens position. The number with the lower digit is the next least number. The digit 7 (value of 70) is less than the digit 8 (value of 80). Rebecca's marble collection has the second least number of marbles, and Craig's collection has the third least.

You are now left with Taneisha and Gillian's collections. Both girls have more than 300 marbles. To finish this comparison, you need to look at the digit in the tens place of the numbers 328 and 319. 328 has a 2 in the tens place with a value of 20, and 319 has a 1 in the tens place with a value of 10. The 1 is less than 2, so Taneisha's collection is second greatest, and Gillian has the greatest marble collection.

	167	Jason
LEAST	276	Rebecca
↓	287	Craig
GREATEST	319	Taneisha
	328	Gillian

7. **Step 1**
To put the numbers in order from greatest to least, start by looking at the digits in the greatest place value position. Look at the digits in the hundreds place. There is an 8 in all of the numbers, so move to the tens place.

Step 2
There is a 7 in 871, a 6 in 867, and 8 in 887. The digit 8 is greatest, so 887 is the first number. The digit 7 is the next greatest, so 871 is the second number. The least number is 867.

Step 3
Placed in order from greatest to least, the numbers are 887, 871, and 867.

9. Look at the chart to see which rows have spaces. To determine which numbers are missing, look at the numbers on either side of the spaces.

The missing numbers in the chart are 14, 30, 44, 67, and 95.

Practice Test

ANSWERS AND SOLUTIONS

1.

H	T	O
9	5	1

3. The digit in the tens position is 4.
$4 \times 10 = 40$

The value of the 4 in the number 346 is 40.

5. To figure out the answers, think "What number multiplied by 100 equals 400?" It is 4 because $4 \times 100 = 400$.

The correct number is 421.

7. There are 7 flats in the hundreds place that represent 7 hundreds (700).

There are 5 ten rods in the tens place that represent 5 tens (50).

There is 1 unit in the ones place that represents 1 one.

The number is 751.

9. For the number 231, look at the ones place first. Draw 1 unit in the ones column of the place value chart.

Next, look at the tens place. Draw 3 rods in the tens column.

Finally, look at the hundreds place. Draw 2 flats in the hundreds column. This place value chart represents the number 231.

Th	H	T	O

11. The 2 (200) is worth less than the 3 (300). Therefore, 243 is less than 327. A less than sign with the closed end pointing toward 243 is inserted in the space.

243 $\leq$ 327

13. Step 1
To put the numbers in order from least to greatest, look at the digits in the hundreds place. There is a 5 in 582 and 536. There is a 4 in 425. Since 4 is less than 5, 425 is the first number.

Step 2
Since the other two numbers have the same digit (5), move to the tens place. There is an 8 in 582 and a 3 in 536. Since 3 is less than 8, the next number is 536. The greatest number is 582.

Step 3
Placed in order from least to greatest, the numbers are 425, 536, and 582.

15. Step 1
Start by creating 6 different numbers. Make sure that each digit is used once in the number. For example, if you write a 4 in the hundreds place, the 2 or 6 must go in the tens place or the ones place. Which ever digit you choose to write in the tens position, the other digit would go in the ones. The following numbers can be made by using 2, 4 and 6.

426
462
264
246
642
624

Step 2
Next, order the numbers from least to greatest.

Compare the digits in the hundreds place. Since 2 hundreds are smaller than 4 or 6, start with 264 and 246. Move to the right to compare the tens. 4 is less than 6 so 246 is the first number and 264 is the second number.

Since 4 hundreds is smaller than 6 hundreds, compare 426 and 462. Move to the right to compare the tens. 2 is less than 6 so the next two numbers would be 426 then 462.

Finally compare the numbers with 6 in the hundreds. Move to the right to compare the tens. 4 is less than 6 so the next two numbers are 624 and 642.

Step 3
Write the sequence of numbers in order from least to greatest: 246, 264, 426, 462, 624, 642

SORTING

Lesson 1—Sorting Numbers

🦋 TIME TO TRY 🦋
ANSWERS AND SOLUTIONS

1. These numbers are sorted by the number of digits they have. The numbers that have 1 digit are less than 10.
    The numbers that have 2 digits are 10 or greater.

    The 1-digit numbers are 1, 3, 7, 4.
    The 2-digit numbers are 19, 45, 63.

2. Remember that even numbers end in 0, 2, 4, 6, 8 and can be divided evenly into groups of 2. Odd numbers end in 1, 3, 5, 7, 9 and cannot be evenly divided into groups of 2.

    The even numbers are 20, 34, 58, 76.
    The odd numbers are 7, 15, 23, 39, 67.

3. The whole numbers are 26, 1, 12.

    The fractions are $\frac{2}{3}$, $\frac{1}{4}$, $\frac{1}{5}$.

    To sort numbers as fractions or whole numbers, remember that fractions are shown as one number over another number. The fractions $\frac{2}{3}$, $\frac{1}{4}$, and $\frac{1}{5}$ are numbers with a numerator (top number) and a denominator (bottom number). The numbers 26, 1, and 12 are whole numbers.

4. List the numbers less than 12.
    2, 5, 6, 9

    The even numbers less than 12 are 2, 6.

    The odd numbers less than 12 are 5, 9.

    List the numbers greater than 12.
    15, 16, 19, 20, 21 24, 25

    The even numbers greater than 12 are 16, 20, 24.

    The odd numbers greater than 12 are 1 5, 19, 21, 25.

    Make a table to show the numbers sorted correctly.

	Even	Odd
Less than 12	2, 6	5, 9
Greater than 12	16, 20, 24	15, 19, 21, 25

5. The numbers in the top boxes are odd numbers. The numbers in the bottom boxes are even numbers.

Odd	1, 3, 5, 7	11, 13, 15, 17
Even	2, 4, 6, 8	10, 12, 14, 16, 18

    The top left box and bottom left box numbers are less than 9.

    The top right box and bottom right box numbers are greater than 9.

    This table shows the sorting rules used.

	< 9	> 9
Odd	1, 3, 5, 7	11, 13, 15, 17
Even	2, 4, 6, 8	10, 12, 14, 16, 18

PRACTICE EXERCISES
ANSWERS AND SOLUTIONS

1. The whole numbers are 15, 4, 10.
The fractions are $\frac{1}{8}, \frac{2}{5}, \frac{4}{6}, \frac{1}{2}$.

3. The numbers that are less than 20 are 6, 15, 5, and 13.

The numbers that are greater than 20 are 34, 63, 45, 31, 56.

5. List the numbers that are less than 13.
1, 3, 6, 7, 11

The even number less than 13 is 6.

The odd numbers less than 13 are 1, 3, 7, 11.

List the numbers that are greater than 13.
14, 16, 18, 20, 21, 22, 23, 24, 25

The even numbers greater than 13 are 14, 16, 18, 20, 22, 24.

The odd numbers greater than 13 are 21, 23, 25.

Make a table to show the numbers.

	Even	Odd
< 13	6	1, 3, 7, 11
> 13	14, 16, 18, 20, 22, 24	21, 23, 25

7. List the numbers that are 16 and less.
2, 3, 4, 5, 6, 8, 9, 11, 12, 15, 16

The even numbers 16 and less are 2, 4, 6, 8, 12, 16.

The odd numbers 16 and less are 3, 5, 9, 11, 15.

List the numbers that are greater than 16.
17, 19, 21, 22, 26, 59

The even numbers greater than 16 are 22, 26.

The odd numbers greater than 16 are 17, 19, 21, 59.

Make a table.

	Even	Odd
16 and < 16	2, 4, 6, 8, 12, 16	3, 5, 9, 11, 15
> 16	22, 26	17, 19, 21, 59

9. The numbers in the top boxes are odd numbers. The numbers in bottom boxes are even numbers.

Odd	3, 5, 13, 15	17, 19, 21, 27, 29, 33, 41
Even	4, 6, 12, 14	18, 20, 22, 26, 28, 30, 36

The top left box and bottom left box numbers are less than 16.

The top right box and bottom right box numbers are greater than 16.

	< 16	> 16
Odd	3, 5, 13, 15	17, 19, 21, 27, 29, 33, 41
Even	4, 6, 12, 14	18, 20, 22, 26, 28, 30, 36

Lesson 2—Sorting Objects

🐝 TIME TO TRY 🐝
ANSWERS AND SOLUTIONS

1. The shapes can be sorted into two
    groups according to their sizes. Sort the
    shapes by drawing the three small
    shapes close to each other to show that
    they form one group. Then, draw the
    three large shapes close to each other to
    show they form another group.

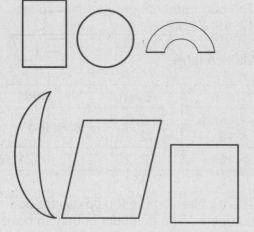

2. Look at the size of the shape, and count
    the number of sides the shape has.
    Draw the shape in the correct box.

    The triangle has 3 sides and is a small
    shape, so draw it in the box for 3 sides
    and small shape.

    The octagon has eight sides and is a
    large shape. Place It in the box for large
    shape and 4 or more sides.

    Continue to place the shapes in the
    correct boxes in the table.

This table shows all the shapes placed
correctly.

	Large Shape	Small Shape
3 sides		
4 or more sides		

3. Rule 1 is square or circle.
    Rule 2 is black or white.

    Start with the first row. Sort all the black
    shapes into black squares and black
    circles.

    Move to the second row. Sort all the
    white shapes into white squares and
    white circles.

	Squares	Circles
Black		
White		

4.

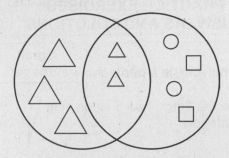

Triangles   Small Shapes

To sort the shapes into a Venn diagram, decide how the shapes are the same and how they are different. The shapes are big and small. Also, all the big shapes are triangles. The shapes can be sorted into big triangles in one circle and small circles and squares in the other circle. The small triangles go in the overlapping space because they are both triangles and small.

PRACTICE EXERCISES
ANSWERS AND SOLUTIONS

1. The small shapes are sorted into one group. The large shapes are sorted into another group.

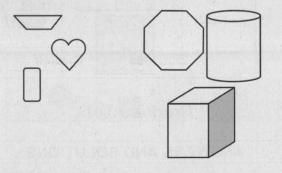

3. Sort the shapes according to size and number of sides.

	Large Shape	Small Shape
3 sides		
4 or more sides		

The triangle has three sides and is a small shape. Draw it in the box for 3 sides and small shape.

The square has four sides and is a large shape, so draw it in the box for 4 or more sides and large shape.

Continue to place the shapes in the correct boxes in the table.

	Large Shape	Small Shape
3 sides		△
4 or more sides	□ ◇ ▱	□ ⬠ ▱

5. David's first sorting rule is square or circle. His second sorting rule is black or white.

Start with the first row. Sort all the black shapes into black squares and black circles.

Move to the second row. Sort all the white shapes into white squares and white circles.

	Squares	Circles
Black	■	● ●
White	□ □	○

7. There are some white and some dark shapes. A Venn diagram must have at least one thing that is shared. The rule for the first circle is pentagons. The rule for the second circle is dark shapes. The dark pentagon goes in the overlapping space.

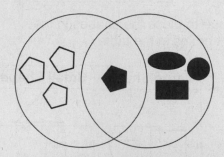

Lesson 3—Polygons

TIME TO TRY
ANSWERS AND SOLUTIONS

1. To answer this question, remember that a polygon is named by the number of sides it has. This figure has 6 sides.
The name for a 6-sided figure is a hexagon. The prefix *hex-* means 6.

2. The shape is an irregular polygon.
All of the sides of the shape are different lengths. They are not equal. Regular polygons have sides that are all the same length.

3. Shapes can be sorted by the number of sides they have. Although the shapes are both regular and irregular polygons, they have a different number of sides. Some have 3, some have 4, and some have 5 sides.

	3 Sides	4 Sides	5 Sides
Regular polygons	△	□	⬠
Irregular polygons	△	▱	⬠

PRACTICE EXERCISES
ANSWERS AND SOLUTIONS

1. The polygon is a pentagon.

Since the figure has 5 sides, it is a pentagon.

3. Since the figure has 3 sides, it is a triangle.

5. The sides of the polygon are not equal in length. Therefore, it is an irregular polygon.

7. Shapes can be sorted by the number of sides they have. Some of the shapes have 3 sides, some have 4 sides, and some have 5 sides.

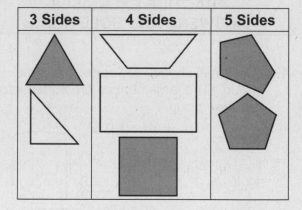

Practice Test

ANSWERS AND SOLUTIONS

1. List the numbers that are less than 23.
9, 11, 12, 16, 19, 21

The even numbers less than 23 are 12, 16.

The odd numbers less than 23 are 9, 11, 19, 21, 23.

List the numbers greater than 23.

28, 34, 37, 41, 43, 44, 45

The even numbers greater than 23 are 28, 34, 44.

The odd numbers greater than 23 are 37, 41, 43, 45.

Make a table to sort the numbers.

	Even	Odd
Less than 23	12, 16	9, 11, 19, 21, 23
Greater than 23	28, 34, 44	37, 41, 43, 45

3. List the numbers less than or equal to 27.
3, 6, 9, 12, 15, 18, 21, 24, 27

The even numbers less than or equal to 27 are 6, 12, 18, 24.

The odd numbers less than or equal to 27 are 3, 9, 15, 21, 27.

List the numbers greater than 27.
30, 33, 36, 39, 42, 45

The even numbers greater than 27 are 30, 36, 42.

The odd numbers greater than 27 are 33, 39, 45.

Make a table to sort the numbers.

	Even	Odd
27 or < 27	6, 12, 18, 24	3, 9, 15, 21, 27
> 27	30, 36, 42	33, 39, 45

5. The numbers in the top boxes are odd numbers. The numbers in bottom boxes are even numbers.

Odd	1, 3, 5, 7, 9, 11	13, 15, 17, 19, 21
Even	2, 4, 6, 8, 10	12, 14, 16, 18, 20

The top left box and bottom left box numbers are less than 12.

The top right box and bottom right box numbers are greater than or equal to 12.

	< 12	12 or > 12
Odd	1, 3, 5, 7, 9, 11	13, 15, 17, 19, 21
Even	2, 4, 6, 8, 10	12, 14, 16, 18, 20

7. The whole numbers are 1, 7, 2.
The fractions are $\frac{1}{6}, \frac{9}{11}, \frac{2}{3}, \frac{1}{9}$.

9. The small shapes are sorted into one group. The large shapes are sorted into another group.

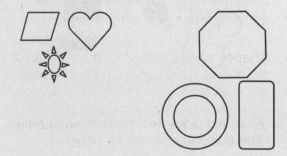

11. Jackson's first rule is triangles, trapezoids, or crosses. His second rule is grey or white.

Start with the first row. Sort all the grey shapes into grey triangles, grey trapezoids, and grey crosses.

Move to the second row. Sort all the white shapes into white triangles, white trapezoids, and white crosses.

	Triangles	**Trapezoids**	**Crosses**
Grey	▲	⬛	✚
White	△△	▽▽	✚

13. There are some white and some dark shapes. Venn diagrams must have at least one thing that is shared.

The rule for the first circle is circles. The rule for the second circle is dark shapes. The dark circle goes in the overlapping space.

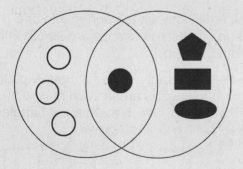

15. All of the sides are the same and equal. The polygon is a regular polygon.

17. Count the number of sides for each polygon.

The first polygon has 4 sides. This polygon is a quadrilateral.

The second polygon has 6 sides. This polygon is a hexagon.

19. Count the number of sides for the polygons.

The first polygon has 4 sides and is a quadrilateral.

The second polygon has 8 sides and is an octagon.

ESTIMATION

Lesson 1—Estimate, Count, and Compare

🐝 TIME TO TRY 🐝
ANSWERS AND SOLUTIONS

1. Count the number of stars in the first column. There are 11 stars. Since 11 is close to 10 and 10 is an easier number to count by, count by groups of ten.
To make an estimate, count how many columns there are. There are 19 columns. Estimate by counting by 10's, 19 times.
$10 + 10 + 10 + 10 + 10 + 10 + 10 + 10 + 10$
$+ 10 + 10 + 10 + 10 + 10 + 10 + 10 + 10$
$+ 10 + 10 + 10$
$= 190$

There are about 190 stars.

2. You know that there are 100 pieces of paper in the small stack. Look at the stack, and compare it to the number of pages in the textbook. Count about how many groups of 100 pages there are in the textbook. There are about 5 groups of 100 pages. Count by 100s, or add the 5 groups together.
$100 + 100 + 100 + 100 + 100 = 500$

The estimated number of pages in the textbook is 500.

PRACTICE EXERCISES
ANSWERS AND SOLUTIONS

1. To estimate the number of stars, count out 10 stars. Draw a circle around them. Use that circle as a referent. Count out other groups of stars that are about the same size. After you have circled all the groups, count how many groups you have. Count by tens for the number of groups. The total number is your estimate.

3. Count out a group of 10 squares. Draw a circle around it. Then, draw circles around other groups of squares that are about the same size. You have circled 6 groups.

Count by 10s to find your estimate.
$10 + 10 + 10 + 10 + 10 + 10 = 60$

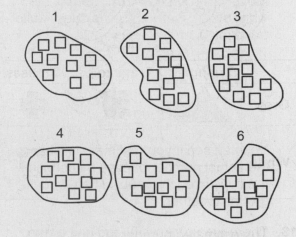

There are about 60 squares.

5. Start by estimating about how many beads there are in each bangle. There are about 10 beads in each bangle. Look at the 10 beads, and compare them to the number of bangles. There are 7 bangles. There are about 70 beads.
$10 + 10 + 10 + 10 + 10 + 10 + 10 = 70$

To find the exact number of beads, count how many beads are in each bangle. There are 12. Since there are 7 bangles, add the 12 bangles 7 times.
$12 + 12 + 12 + 12 + 12 + 12 + 12 = 84$

There are exactly 84 beads.

7. Look at the picture. There should be 10 cups in group one. Draw a circle around 10 cups. Now, draw circles around groups of cups that are about the same size. There are 10 groups altogether.
$10 + 10 + 10 + 10 + 10 + 10$
$+ 10 + 10 + 10 + 10 = 100$

You estimate that there are about 100 cups.

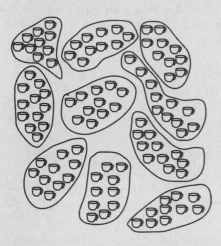

You can see if your estimate is close to the actual number of cups by counting the cups in each group. Then, add the groups together.

The estimated number of cups is 100.
The actual number of cups is 106.

```
  106
 −100
    6
```

The estimate was close to the actual number. So, the estimation is reasonable.

Lesson 2—Rounding Numbers

🐰 TIME TO TRY 🐰
ANSWERS AND SOLUTIONS

1. **a)** The digit 2 is less than 5. Therefore, the number 9 stays the same and the number to the right becomes zero. Rounded to the nearest ten, the number 92 becomes 90.

    b) The digit 5 is equal to 5. Therefore, the number 1 changes to 2 and the number to the right changes to zero. Rounded to the nearest ten, the number 15 becomes 20.

2. There is a 5 in the tens position, so the 4 in the hundreds position changes. The 4 becomes 1 greater, which is 5. All of the numbers to the right of the 5 become zeros. The number 455 is rounded up to 500. This is called rounding up because the rounded number is greater than the original.

PRACTICE EXERCISES
ANSWERS AND SOLUTIONS

1. Underline the digit 2 because it is in the tens place and the number is being rounded to the nearest ten. Circle the 4 in the ones position. Since 4 is less than 5, the 2 stays the same and the number to the right becomes a zero. The number 24 is rounded down to 20. This is called rounding down because the founded number is smaller than the original number.

3. The 1 in the tens position is less than 5, so it does not change the number in the hundreds position. The 4 in the hundreds position stays the same, and the numbers to the right become zeros. The number 419 is rounded down to 400. This is called rounding down because the rounded number is smaller than the original number.

5. To find about how many students play a sport, round all of the numbers to the tens position before finding the sum.

    ```
    105  →  110
     82  →   80
     65  →   70
     43  →   40
     36  →   40
            ───
            340
    ```

    About 340 students at Nigel's school play a sport.

7. B

To find the difference between the estimate and the exact number, subtract the lesser number from the greater number.

$$\begin{array}{r} 3\,\overset{3}{\cancel{4}}\,\overset{10}{\cancel{0}} \\ -\,3\,3\,1 \\ \hline 9 \end{array}$$

The estimate is only 9 away from the exact number. This means the estimate is reasonable.

Practice Test

ANSWERS AND SOLUTIONS

1. There are about 10 stars in each group, and there are 15 groups.
$$10 + 10 + 10 + 10 + 10 + 10 + 10 + 10$$
$$+10 + 10 + 10 + 10 + 10 + 10 + 10 = 150$$

There are about 150 stars in the picture.

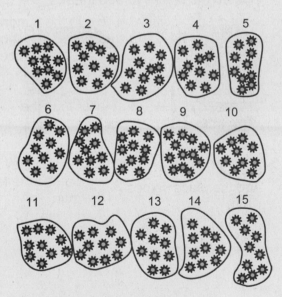

3. There are 13 blocks in each row. Use 10 for your estimate because it is easier to count by 10. There are a total of 9 rows. To make an estimate, count by 10 a total of 9 times.
10, 20, 30, 40, 50, 60, 70, 80, 90

There are about 90 blocks.

Since there are actually 13 blocks in each row, add 13 a total of 9 times.
$$13 + 13 + 13 + 13 + 13 + 13 + 13 + 13 + 13$$
$$= 117$$

There are exactly 117 blocks in total.

5. There are 10 candles in the small group. Compare the size of that group to the number of candles in the rows. It looks like there are about 10 groups of 10 candles in the figure.
$$10 + 10 + 10 + 10 + 10 + 10$$
$$+10 + 10 + 10 + 10 = 100$$

The estimated number of candles in the figure is about 100.

7. The digit 6 in the ones place is greater than 5. The number 8 changes to 9, and the number to the right changes to a zero.

Rounded to the nearest ten, the number 86 becomes 90.

9. The digit 7 is greater than 5, so the number 1 changes to 2 and the number to the right changes to zero.

Rounded to the nearest ten, the number 17 becomes 20.

11. There are 274 students in Grade 3. The digit 7 in the tens position is greater than 5, so the 2 in the hundreds position changes. The 2 becomes 1 greater, which is 3. All of the numbers to the right of the 3 become zero.

Rounded to the nearest hundred, the number 274 is 300.

There are about 300 students who study music in Grade 3.

ADDITION AND SUBTRACTION

Lesson 1—Addition with and without Regrouping

🦋 TIME TO TRY 🦋
ANSWERS AND SOLUTIONS

1. Start on the right, and work to the left.

Step 1
Add the ones column.
$7 + 2 = 9$

Write the answer under the line in the ones place.

Step 2
Add the tens column.
$8 + 1 = 9$

Write the answer under the line in the tens place.

Step 3
Add the hundreds column.
$4 + 1 = 5$

Write the answer in the hundreds place under the line.

$$\begin{array}{r} 482 \\ +117 \\ \hline 599 \end{array}$$

2. **Step 1**
Set up the addition problem.

The number 846 can be represented by 8 flats, 4 rods, and 6 units

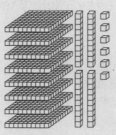

The number 143 can be represented by 1 flat, 4 rods, and 3 units.

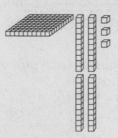

Line up the blocks to add them.

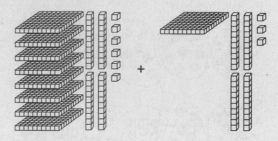

Step 2
Add the place values.

$$\begin{array}{r} 846 \\ +143 \\ \hline 989 \end{array}$$

3. **Step 1**
Set up the addition problem.

The number 615 can be represented by 6 flats, 1 rod, and 5 units. The number 369 can be represented by 3 flats, 6 rods, and 9 units.

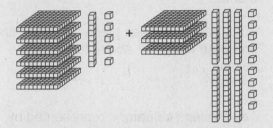

Add 615 + 369. Be sure to line up the numbers when you write them.

```
 615
+369
```

Step 2
Add the ones column.
5 + 9 = 14

Only 1 digit is allowed in a place value position, so you need to regroup the 14. The 14 ones are regrouped into 1 ten and 4 ones. Write a 4 in the ones place under the line. Write a small 1 above the tens column.

Step 3
Add the tens column.
1 + 6 + 1 = 8

It is important to remember to add the 1. Write an 8 in the tens place under the line.

Step 4
Add the hundreds column.
6 + 3 = 9

Write a 9 in the hundreds place under the line.

```
 615
+369
 984
```

1. **Step 1**
Add the ones column.
4 + 1 = 5

Write a 5 in the ones place under the line.

Step 2
Add the tens column.
4 + 3 = 7

Write a 7 in the tens place under the line.

Step 3
Add the hundreds column.
6 + 2 = 8

Write an 8 in the hundreds place under the line.

```
 644
+231
 875
```

3. **Step 1**
Add the ones column.
7 + 5 = 12

Only 1 digit is allowed in a place value position, so you need to regroup the 12. The 12 ones are regrouped into 1 ten and 2 ones. Write a 2 in the ones place under the line, and write a small 1 above the tens column.
4 + 3 = 7

Step 2
Add the tens column.
1 + 6 + 8 = 15

It is important to remember to add the 1. Only 1 digit is allowed in a place value position, so you need to regroup the 15. The 15 tens are regrouped into 1 hundred and 5 tens.

Write a 5 in the tens place under the line, and write a small 1 above the hundredths column.

ANSWERS AND SOLUTIONS

Step 3
Add the hundreds column
1 + 3 + 2 = 6

Write a 6 in the hundreds place under
the line.

_{1 1}
367
+285
652

5. **Step 1**
Add the ones column
9 + 6 = 15

Only 1 digit is allowed in a place value
position, so you need to regroup the 15.
The 15 ones are regrouped into 1 ten and
5 ones.

Write a 5 in the ones place under the line,
and write a small 1 above the tens
column.

Step 2
Add the tens column.
1 + 0 + 4 =5

It is important to remember to add the 1.
Write a 5 in the tens place under the line.

Step 3
Add the hundreds column.
6 + 2 = 8

Write an 8 in the hundreds place under
the line.

₁
609
+246
855

7. **Step 1**
Add the ones column.
7 + 6 = 13

Only 1 digit is allowed in a place value
position, so you need to regroup the 13.
The 13 ones are regrouped into 1 ten and
3 ones.

Write a 3 in the ones place under the line,
and write a small 1 above the tens
column.

Step 2
Add the tens column.
1 + 6 + 1 = 8

It is important to remember to add the 1.
Write an 8 in the tens place under
the line.

Step 3
Add the hundreds column.
4 + 2 = 6

Write a 6 in the hundreds place under
the line.

₁
467
+216
683

9. **Step 1**
Add the ones column.
9 + 7 = 16

Only 1 digit is allowed in a place value
position, so you need to regroup the 16.
The 16 ones are regrouped into 1 ten and
6 ones. Write a 6 in the ones place under
the line, and write a small 1 above the
tens column.

Step 2
Add the tens column.
1 + 2 + 9 = 12

It is important to remember to add the 1. Only 1 digit is allowed in a place value position, so you need to regroup the 12. The 12 tens are regrouped into 1 hundred and 2 tens.

Write a 2 in the place under the line, and write a small 1 above the hundreds column.

Step 3
Add the hundreds column.
1 + 2 + 5 = 8

It is important to remember to add the 1. Write an 8 in the hundreds place under the line.

```
  11
  229
 +597
  826
```

Lesson 2—Subtraction with and without Regrouping

🦋 TIME TO TRY 🦋
ANSWERS AND SOLUTIONS

1. **Step 1**
    Start on the right, and work to the left.

    Subtract the bottom number in the ones column from the top number.
    3 − 1 = 2

    Write the 2 under the line.

    Step 2
    Subtract the bottom number in the tens column from the top number.
    4 − 2 = 2

    Write the 2 under the line in the tens place.

Step 3
There is no bottom number in the hundreds column, so you can write the top number (7) under the line in the hundreds column.

```
  743
 − 21
  722
```

2. The number 687 can be represented by 6 flats, 8 rods, and 7 units. The number 254 can be represented by 2 flats, 5 rods, and 4 units.

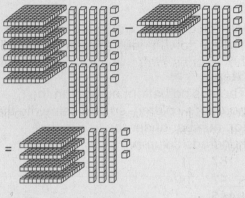

```
  687
 −254
  433
```

3. The number 578 can be represented by 5 flats, 7 rods, and 8 units. The number 49 can be represented by 4 rods and 9 units

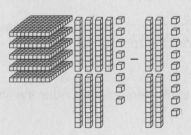

```
  578
 − 49
  529
```

PRACTICE EXERCISES
ANSWERS AND SOLUTIONS

1. Step 1
Subtract the bottom number in the ones column from the top number.
7 – 2 = 5

Write a 5 in the ones place under the line.

Step 2
Subtract the bottom number in the tens column from the top number.
8 – 4 = 4

Write a 4 in the tens place under the line.

Step 3
There is no bottom number in the hundreds column, so you can write the top number under the line in the hundreds column.

```
  187
– 42
  145
```

3. Step 1
Subtract the bottom number in the ones column from the top number.
7 – 4 = 3

Write a 3 in the ones place under the line

Step 2
Subtract the bottom number in the tens column from the top number.
2 – 1 = 1

Write a 1 in the tens place under the line.

Step 3
Subtract the bottom number in the hundreds column from the top number.
8 – 6 = 2

Write the 2 in the hundreds place under the line.

```
  827
–614
  213
```

5. The number 698 can be represented by 6 flats, 9 rods, and 8 units. The number 453 can be represented by 4 flats, 5 rods, and 3 units.

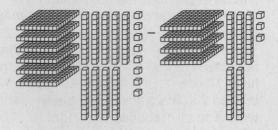

```
  698
–453
  245
```

The answer to the subtraction problem 698 – 453 is 245.

7. Step 1
Set up the subtraction problem.

The number 843 can be represented by 8 flats, 4 rods, and 3 units. The number 216 can be represented by 2 flats, 1 rod, and 6 units.

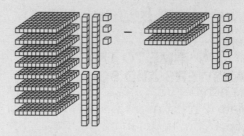

Subtract 843 – 216. Be sure to line up the numbers. Remember to subtract the bottom digit from the top digit.

```
  843
–216
```

Step 2
You have only 3 ones, so you cannot take 6 ones away. That means you need to borrow 1 ten and regroup. The 4 tens can be regrouped into 3 tens and 10 ones. Cross out the 4 tens, and write a small 3 above the 4.

Add the 10 ones to the 3 ones. You now have 13 ones. Cross out the 3, and write a small 13 above the 3. Now, subtract the ones.
13 – 6 = 7

Step 3
Subtract the tens.
3 – 1 = 2

Step 4
Subtract the hundreds.
8 – 2 = 6

      3 13
   843
  −216
   627

The answer to the subtraction problem 843 – 216 is 627.

9. **Step 1**
Set up the subtraction problem.

The number 321 can be represented by 3 flats, 2 rods, and 1 unit. The number 165 can be represented by 1 flat, 6 rods, and 5 units.

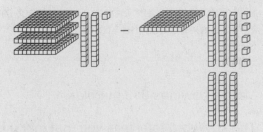

Subtract 321 – 165. Be sure to line up the numbers. Remember to subtract the bottom digit from the top digit.
   321
  −165

Step 2
You have only 1 one, so you cannot take 5 ones away. That means you need to borrow 1 ten and regroup. The 2 tens can be regrouped into 1 ten and 10 ones. Cross out the 2 tens, and write a small 1 above the 2.

Add the 10 ones to the 1 one. You now have 11 ones. Cross out the 1, and write a small 11 above the 1. Now, subtract the ones.
11 – 5 = 6

Step 3
You have only 1 ten left, so you cannot take 6 tens away. That means you have to borrow 1 hundred and regroup. The 3 hundreds can be regrouped into 2 hundreds and 10 tens. Cross out the 3 hundreds, and write a 2 above the 3. Add the 10 tens to the 1 ten. You now have 11 tens. Cross out the 1, and write a small 11 above the 1. Subtract the tens.
11 – 6 = 5

Step 4
Subtract the hundreds.
2 – 1 = 1

    2 11 11
   321
  −165
   156

The answer to the subtraction problem 321 – 165 is 156.

Lesson 3—Solving Problems with Addition, Subtraction, and Estimation

🦋 TIME TO TRY 🦋
ANSWERS AND SOLUTIONS

1. The key words *in all* tell you that this is an addition problem. You need to add the number of food items that Alaina's mom and grandpa gave her. The sum of these items is the answer to this problem.

$$
\begin{array}{r}
\overset{1}{3}4 \\
+16 \\
\hline
50
\end{array}
$$

Check your answer.

$$
\begin{array}{r}
50 \\
-16 \\
\hline
34
\end{array}
$$

Alaina collected 50 food items in all.

2. The key words *how many more* tell you that this problem is a subtraction problem. You are asked to figure out the difference in the number of hockey cards Matteo had when he got home compared to the number he took to school.

$$
\begin{array}{r}
\overset{4\ 13}{15\cancel{3}} \\
-138 \\
\hline
15
\end{array}
$$

Check your answer.

$$
\begin{array}{r}
\overset{1}{1}38 \\
+15 \\
\hline
153
\end{array}
$$

Matteo took 15 more cards to school than he brought home.

3. The key words *how many more* tell you that this problem is a subtraction problem. The word *about* tells you that you are looking for an estimated answer, not an exact answer. Use the first digit of the number and replace the digit in the ones place with a zero.

$$
\begin{array}{l}
\underline{8}6 \rightarrow 80 \\
\underline{3}1 \rightarrow 30
\end{array}
\qquad
\begin{array}{r}
80 \\
-30 \\
\hline
50
\end{array}
$$

Jonah has about 50 more hockey cards than baseball cards.

4. The word *approximately* lets you know that you are looking for an estimated answer, not an exact answer. Round the numbers to the nearest ten, and then find the sum.

$$
\begin{array}{l}
9\textcircled{6} \rightarrow 100 \\
2\textcircled{5} \rightarrow \underline{-30}
\end{array}
\qquad
\begin{array}{r}
70
\end{array}
$$

Treva has about 70 more rocks in her rock collection than she has stamps in her stamp collection.

PRACTICE EXERCISES
ANSWERS AND SOLUTIONS

1. The key words *in total* tell you that this is an addition problem. You need to add the number of marbles Marnie had to start with (621) to the number of marbles she won (192).

$$
\begin{array}{r}
\overset{1}{6}21 \\
+192 \\
\hline
813
\end{array}
$$

Marnie now has 813 marbles.

3. The key word *total* tells you that that this is an addition problem. To find the total amount Roggie donates to the charity, add all the amounts he collects.

$$5 + 7 + 10 + 15 + 8 + 3 = 48$$

Roggie collects $48 to donate to the charity.

5. The key words *how many more* tell you this is a subtraction problem. To find how many more acorns Bob has, subtract the number of acorns Sammy has from the number Bob has (916 – 784).

$$\begin{array}{r} \overset{8\ 11}{9\cancel{1}6} \\ -784 \\ \hline 132 \end{array}$$

Bob has 132 more acorns than Sammy.

7. The word *approximately* tells you that you are looking for an estimated answer, not an exact answer. To find the estimated answer, round both numbers to the nearest ten, and then add.

$$\underline{2}4 \rightarrow 20$$
$$3\underline{7} \rightarrow 40$$

$$\begin{array}{r} 20 \\ +40 \\ \hline 60 \end{array}$$

Altogether, Keith and Kelly have approximately 60 baseball cards.

9. **Step 1**
Find out how much Bonnie saved.

Add 157 and 343.

$$\begin{array}{r} \overset{1}{15}7 \\ +343 \\ \hline 500 \end{array}$$

Bonnie saved $500.

Step 2
Find out how much they saved altogether. Add Bonnie's savings to Morris's savings (157 + 500).

$$\begin{array}{r} 157 \\ +500 \\ \hline 657 \end{array}$$

Together, Morris and Bonnie save $657.

1.
$$\begin{array}{r} 240 \\ +255 \\ \hline 495 \end{array}$$

3.
$$\begin{array}{r} 699 \\ -527 \\ \hline 172 \end{array}$$

5.
$$\begin{array}{r} \overset{1}{2}39 \\ +109 \\ \hline 348 \end{array}$$

7.
$$\begin{array}{r} \overset{8\ 11}{3\cancel{8}1} \\ -224 \\ \hline 157 \end{array}$$

9. $\underline{7}2 \rightarrow 70$
$\underline{8}6 \rightarrow 90$

$$\begin{array}{r} \overset{1}{9}0 \\ +70 \\ \hline 160 \end{array}$$

11. $1\underline{9}4 \rightarrow 190$
$\underline{9}6 \rightarrow 100$

$$\begin{array}{r} 190 \\ -100 \\ \hline 90 \end{array}$$

13. The key word *sum* tells you this is an addition problem. To find the sum of the scores, add the three amounts together (127 + 94 138).

$$\begin{array}{r} \overset{1\ 1}{12}7 \\ 94 \\ +138 \\ \hline 359 \end{array}$$

The sum of their scores is 359.

15. The key words *how many more* tell you this is a subtraction problem. To find how many more points the Stampeders scored, subtract the Eskimos' points from the Stampeders' points (42 – 27).

$$\begin{array}{r} \overset{3\ 12}{42} \\ -27 \\ \hline 15 \end{array}$$

The Stampeders scored 15 points more than the Eskimos.

17. The word *about* tells you that you are looking for an estimated answer, not an exact answer. To find the estimated answer, round both numbers and subtract.

$$\begin{array}{l} \underline{7}3 \rightarrow 70 \\ \underline{2}8 \rightarrow 20 \end{array} \qquad \begin{array}{r} 70 \\ -20 \\ \hline 50 \end{array}$$

Christian needs to collect about 50 more stickers.

19. Step 1

Find the total cost of the drum and the doll (8 + 6).

$$\begin{array}{r} 8 \\ +6 \\ \hline 14 \end{array}$$

The drum and the doll cost $14.

Step 2

Find the amount of change ($20 – $14).

$$\begin{array}{r} \overset{0\ 10}{20} \\ -14 \\ \hline 6 \end{array}$$

You will receive $6 in change.

MENTAL MATH STRATEGIES

Lesson 1—Basic Facts

**TIME TO TRY
ANSWERS AND SOLUTIONS**

1. **a)** $6 - 3 = 3$

b) $2 + 2 = 4$

c) $10 - 5 = 5$

d) $8 + 8 = 16$

2.

Addition Problem	Double the Lesser Addend	Sum of the Double + 1	Answer to Problem
8 + 7	7 + 7	14 + 1	15
4 + 5	4 + 4	8 + 1	9
9 + 8	8 + 8	16 + 1	17
6 + 5	5 + 5	10 + 1	11
3 + 2	2 + 2	4 + 1	5

3.

Addition Problem	Double the Greater Addend	Sum of Double – 1	Answer to Problem
7 + 8	8 + 8	16 – 1	15
5 + 6	6 + 6	12 – 1	11
3 + 4	4 + 4	8 – 1	7

4. To find the answer using doubles plus two, double the lesser addend (7 + 7) and add 2.

$$7 + 9 = \underset{14}{\underline{7 + 7}} + 2$$
$$= 16$$
$$14 + 2 = 16$$

5. To find the answer using doubles take away two, double the greater addend (7 + 7) and take away 2.

$$5 + 7 = \underbrace{7 + 7}_{14} - 2$$
$$= 12$$
$$14 - 2 = 12$$

6. **a)** 6 + 9 = 15
To make the 9 a 10, take 1 away from the 6 and add it to the 9. The 6 becomes a 5 because 1 is taken away from 6. The 9 becomes a 10 because 1 is added to it.

5 + 10 = 15

b) 8 + 5 = 13
To make the 8 a 10, take 2 away from the 5 and add it to the 8. The 5 becomes a 3 because 2 is taken away from 5. The 8 becomes a 10 because 2 is added to 8.

10 + 3 = 13

c) 9 + 7 = 15
To make the 9 a 10, take 1 away from the 7 and add it to the 9. The 7 becomes a 6 because 1 has been taken away from 7. The 9 becomes a 10 because 1 has been added to 9.

10 + 6 = 16

7. **a)** $5 + 4 = 9$

b) $8 + 7 = 15$

c) $4 + 4 = 8$

d) $6 + 9 = 15$

8. **a)** 13 − 4 = 9

b) 14 − 7 = 7

c) 7 − 3 = 4

d) 11 − 9 = 2

PRACTICE EXERCISES
ANSWERS AND SOLUTIONS

1. 8 + 8 = 16

3. Double the lower number, 8.
$8 + 8 = 16$

Add 1 to the doubled number, 16.
$16 + 1 = 17$.

$9 + 8 = 17$

5. Double the greater number, 7.
$7 + 7 = 14$

Subtract 1 from the doubled number, 14.
$14 - 1 = 13$

$6 + 7 = 13$

7. Double the lower number, 7.
$7 + 7 = 14$

Add 2 to the doubled number, 14.
$14 + 2 = 16$

$7 + 9 = 16$

9. Double the greater number, 7.
$7 + 7 = 14$

Subtract 2 from the doubled number, 14.
$14 - 2 = 12$

$5 + 7 = 12$

11. To make the 8 a 10, take 2 away from the 5, and add it to the 8. The 5 becomes a 3.

$2 + 8 = 10$

$5 - 2 = 3$

$5 + 8 \rightarrow 3 + 10 = 13$

$5 + 8 = 13$

13. Find the 9 in the column on the left of the grid. Find the number 7 in the row at the top of the grid. Follow the column and the row to the point where they meet. The number is 16.

$9 + 7 = 16$

15. Find the 7 in the column to the left of the grid. Move your finger to the right until you find the 15. Slide your finger all the way to the top of the grid. You end up at 8. The difference between 15 and 7 is 8.

$15 - 7 = 8$

Lesson 2—Mental Math Addition Strategies

TIME TO TRY
ANSWERS AND SOLUTIONS

1. Think 23 = 20 + 3, and 36 = 30 + 6.

Add the tens.
20 + 30 = 50

Add the ones.
3 + 6 = 9

Add the tens and the ones.
50 + 9 = 59

2. Think 50 instead of 49 because it is easier to add 50 + 25 = 75. Next, take away the 1 that was added to the 49 to make 50.

$75 - 1 = 74$

3. You can see that 33 + 35 is the same as 34 + 34. Therefore, 34 + 34 = 68.

33 + 35 is 68

4. Think 22 + 23 is the same as doubling the lower number (22).
22 + 22 = 44

Then, add the 1 after.
44 + 1 = 45

22 + 23 = 45

PRACTICE EXERCISES
ANSWERS AND SOLUTIONS

1. **Step 1**
There are 2 tens in 27 (20) and 3 tens in 32. Add 20 and 30 $\rightarrow 20 + 30 = 50$.

Step 2
There are 7 ones in 27 and 2 ones in 32. Add 7 and 2 $\rightarrow 7 + 2 = 9$.

Step 3
Add the two sums together.
$50 + 9 = 59$

$27 + 32 = 59$

3. **Step 1**
There is 1 tens in 12 (10) and 5 tens in 56 (50). Add 10 and 50.
$10 + 50 = 60$

Step 2
There are 2 ones in 12 and 6 ones in 56. Add 2 and 6.
$2 + 6 = 8$

Step 3
Add the two sums together.
$60 + 8 = 68$

$12 + 56 = 68$

5. Method 1
Add 2 to 68 to make 70 (2 + 68 = 70).
Add 70 to 24.
$70 + 24 = 94$

Next, subtract the 2 that was added.
$94 - 2 = 92$

$68 + 24 = 92$

Method 2
Subtract 4 from 24 to make 20
$(24 - 4 = 20)$.
Add 20 to $68 \rightarrow 20 + 68 = 88$.

Next, add the 4 that was subtracted.
$88 + 4 = 92$

$68 + 24 = 92$

7. Add 2 to 28 to make $30 (2 + 28 = 30)$.
Add 1 to 39 to make $40 (1 + 39 = 40)$.
Add 30 to 40 to get 70 $(30 + 40 = 70)$.

You added $2 + 1 = 3$, so subtract 3 from 70 to get 67.
$70 - 3 = 67$

$28 + 39 = 67$

9. Subtract 4 from 54 to get 50
$54 - 4 = 50$

Subtract 3 from 23 to get 20
$23 - 3 = 20$

Add 50 to 20 to get 70
$(50 + 20 = 70)$

You subtracted 4 and 3 (7), so add 7 to 70 to get 77.
$70 + 7 = 77$

$54 + 23 = 77$

11. Step 1
Double the lesser addend.
$42 \rightarrow 42 + 42 = 84$

Step 2
Add $1 \rightarrow 84 + 1 = 85$.

$42 + 43 = 85$

Lesson 3—Mental Math Subtraction Strategies

TIME TO TRY
ANSWERS AND SOLUTIONS

1. To solve the problem 44 – 22 quickly in your head, think of the double
22 + 22 = 44. If 22 + 22 = 44, then
44 – 22 = 22.

2. To solve this problem, add 1 to 59 to get 60. Then, add 13 to 60 to get 73.
Add the 1 and the 13 $(1 + 13 = 14)$.

You had to add on 14 to 59 to get 73, so
$73 - 59 = 14$.

3. Start by making the number being subtracted end in a zero. The 19 becomes a 20 $(19 + 1 = 20)$.

Subtract 20 from 62.
$62 - 20 = 42$

Add back the 1 you subtracted.
$42 + 1 = 43$

$62 - 19 = 43$

4. Start by making the number being subtracted end in a zero. 22 is close to 20 so subtract 2 from 22 to make 20. $20 - 2 = 20$.

Subtract $70 - 20 = 50$
Subtract the 2 again to find the final answer.
$50 - 2 = 48$
$70 - 22 = 48$

PRACTICE EXERCISES
ANSWERS AND SOLUTIONS

1. To solve the problem $66 - 33$ quickly in your head, think of the double $33 + 33$.

$66 - 33 = 33$

3. Add 2 to 48 to get 50 $(48 + 2 = 50)$.
Add 14 to 50 to get 64 $(50 + 14 = 64)$.
Add the 2 and the 14 to get 16 $(2 + 14 = 16)$.

$64 - 48 = 16$

5. Add 3 to the 47 to get 50 $(47 + 3 = 50)$.
Add 9 to the 50 to get 59 $(50 + 9 = 59)$.
Add the 3 and the 9 to get 12 $(3 + 9 = 12)$.

$59 - 47 = 12$

7. The 21 becomes 20 $(21 - 1 = 20)$.
Subtract 20 from 64 $(64 - 20 = 44)$.
Subtract 1 $(44 - 1 = 43)$

$64 - 21 = 43$

ANSWERS AND SOLUTIONS

1. $7 + 7 = 14$

3. Double the greater number (35) and subtract 1.
$35 + 35 = 70$
$70 - 1 = 69$

$34 + 35 = 69$

5. Double the greater number (15) and subtract 2.
$15 + 15 = 30$
$30 - 2 = 28$

$13 + 15 = 28$

7. To make 9 a 10, subtract 1 from 6 and add it to 9. The 6 becomes 5 and 9 becomes 10.
$6 + 9 \rightarrow 5 + 10$
$5 + 10 = 15$

$6 + 9 = 15$

9. Find the 8 in the column on the left of the grid. Find the 9 in the row at the top of the grid. Follow along the row and down the column to the box where they meet. The number 15 is in the box.

$8 + 9 = 17$

11. The number 71 has 7 tens (70) and 1 ones (1). The number 18 has 1 ten (10) and 8 ones (8).
$71 + 18 = 70 + 1 + 10 + 8$
$71 + 18 = 70 + 10 + 1 + 8$
$71 + 18 = 80 + 9$
$71 + 18 = 89$

13. Make 32 a 30 by subtracting 2.
Add $\rightarrow 30 + 56 = 86$.

Add the 2 you subtracted $\rightarrow 86 + 2 = 88$.

$32 + 56 = 88$

15. Find the 7 in the column on the left side of the grid. Move right to the 16. Move up to the top of the grid. You end up at 9.

$16 - 7 = 9$

17. If you double 44 and get $\rightarrow 44 + 44 = 88$, you know that $88 - 44 = 44$.

19. Make 28 a 30 by adding 2.

Subtract $\rightarrow 68 - 30 = 38$
Subtract the 2 you added $\rightarrow 38 - 2 = 36$.

$64 - 28 = 36$

FRACTIONS

Lesson 1—Introduction to Fractions

TIME TO TRY
ANSWERS AND SOLUTIONS

1. The top number of a fraction is called the numerator. The bottom number of a fraction is called the denominator.

The denominator of the fraction $\dfrac{3}{5}$ is 5.

2. To sort the shapes into those that represent equal parts and those that do not, look carefully at the shapes in the circles. Put the circles that have equal parts in one group. Put the circles that do not have equal parts in another group.

Not Equal Parts	Equal Parts
◔ ⊕	⊘ ⊕ ✳

PRACTICE EXERCISES
ANSWERS AND SOLUTIONS

1. The top number of a fraction is called the numerator.

The numerator of the fraction $\dfrac{5}{10}$ is 5.

3. To draw a picture showing 2 equal parts, first draw a whole. You can use a circle for this problem. Since you are dividing it into 2, draw one line down the centre of the circle. There will be an equal part on either side of the line.

5. The pizza is divided into 4 parts, and 1 part is missing.

The fraction that shows the missing piece is $\frac{1}{4}$.

Lesson 2—Parts of a Whole

❦ TIME TO TRY ❦
ANSWERS AND SOLUTIONS

1. This picture shows $\frac{1}{5}$ of the star shaded.

2. a) The fraction $\frac{3}{5}$ can also be shown as

$\frac{1}{5} + \frac{1}{5} + \frac{1}{5} = \frac{3}{5}$. Colour in 3 of the

5 equal sections to show the

fraction $\frac{3}{5}$.

b) Count the number of sections of the star that are not shaded. Put this number as the numerator. The denominator is 5 because the whole is split into 5 equal parts. The fraction of the star that is not

shaded is $\frac{2}{5}$.

Check your answer. The fraction of the shaded part added to the fraction of the part that is not shaded equals a whole. A whole is shown when the numerator and the denominator are the same number.

$\frac{3}{5} + \frac{2}{5} = \frac{5}{5}$ $\frac{5}{5} = 1$ whole

3. The square is divided into 4 equal pieces, so the denominator is 4. The numerator is also 4, so you need to shade in all 4 sections of the square.

4. To represent $\frac{2}{5}$ as part of a whole, first draw a whole object, such as a circle. Divide the circle into 5 equal parts. Next, shade 2 parts. The shaded area represents the fraction $\frac{2}{5}$ as part of a whole.

PRACTICE EXERCISES
ANSWERS AND SOLUTIONS

1. Count the number of shaded sections. This number is the numerator.
The denominator is the number of pieces the whole is divided into. The shaded part shows the fraction $\frac{6}{10}$.

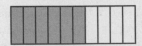

3. The rectangle is divided into 5 equal pieces, so the denominator is 5.
The numerator is 5, so you need to shade in 5 of the sections. This means that you will shade in the entire rectangle, which is one whole.

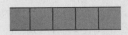

5. There are 10 pieces of pizza in total, so the denominator is 10. The numerator is the number of pieces left. There are 4 girls and each girl eats 2 pieces of pizza. There are 8 pieces ($4 \times 2 = 8$) of pizza eaten. To figure out how many pieces are left, subtract 8 pieces from 10 ($10 - 8 = 2$). Since there are 2 pieces left, the numerator is 2.

The fraction that shows how much pizza is left is $\frac{2}{10}$.

7. The number of shaded parts is 4.

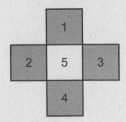

The total number of parts in the whole is 5.

$$\frac{\text{number of shaded parts}}{\text{total number of parts}} = \frac{4}{5}$$

The fraction of the figure that is shaded is $\frac{4}{5}$.

9. Start by dividing the circle into equal parts. To draw 4 equal parts, draw a line cutting the circle in half. Then, draw another line so the circle is in half again. The numerator tells you what part is shaded. Shade 3 of the 4 parts.

This picture represents the fraction $\frac{3}{4}$.

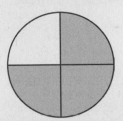

Lesson 3—Comparing Fractions

🐝 TIME TO TRY 🐝
ANSWERS AND SOLUTIONS

1. Because the fractions have the same denominator, the fraction with the greater numerator is greater. The first picture shows 5 parts with 1 of the 5 parts shaded. The second picture shows 5 parts with 4 parts shaded. The fraction that shows 4 shaded parts out of 5 is greater.

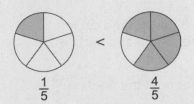

$$\frac{1}{5} \qquad < \qquad \frac{4}{5}$$

PRACTICE EXERCISES
ANSWERS AND SOLUTIONS

1. Since the denominators are the same, the fraction that has the greater numerator is the greater fraction. Since 7 is greater than 1, Mikka will most likely say $\frac{7}{8}$ is greater than $\frac{1}{8}$.

3. Both fractions have the same denominator, so look at the numerators.

The fraction $\frac{2}{4}$ has a 2 in the numerator.

The fraction $\frac{3}{4}$ has a 3 in the numerator.

Since 3 is greater than 2, the fraction $\frac{3}{4}$ is greater than $\frac{2}{4}$.

$$\frac{3}{4} > \frac{2}{4}$$

5. Both fractions have the same denominator, so look at the numerators. One fraction has a 5 in the numerator. The other fraction has a 3 in the numerator. Since 3 is less than 5, the fraction $\frac{3}{6}$ is less than the fraction $\frac{5}{6}$.

$$\frac{3}{6} < \frac{5}{6}$$

Practice Test

ANSWERS AND SOLUTIONS

1. There are 8 parts in the circle. The number of shaded parts is 3.

The numerator of the fraction $\frac{3}{8}$ is 3.

3. The rectangle is divided into 4 parts. There is 1 part that is shaded.

The fraction that tells what part is shaded is $\frac{1}{4}$.

5. The fraction $\frac{2}{4}$ can be represented by shading 2 parts out of 4 total. The picture shows the fraction $\frac{2}{4}$.

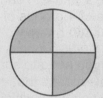

7. Both fractions have the same denominator, so look at the numerators. One fraction has a 6 in the numerator. The other fraction has a 5 in the numerator. Since 6 is greater than 5, the fraction $\frac{6}{10}$ is greater than $\frac{5}{10}$.

$$\frac{6}{10} > \frac{5}{10}$$

9. Both fractions have the same denominator, so look at the numerators.

The fraction $\frac{2}{5}$ has a 2 in the numerator.

The fraction $\frac{4}{5}$ has a 4 in the numerator.

Since 2 is less than 4, the fraction $\frac{2}{5}$ is less than the fraction $\frac{4}{5}$.

$$\frac{2}{5} < \frac{4}{5}$$

MULTIPLICATION AND DIVISION

Lesson 1—Multiplication

❧ TIME TO TRY ❧
ANSWERS AND SOLUTIONS

1. To show the equation $4 \times 4 = 16$ using equal groups, start with how many groups there are (4) and how many are in each group (4). Draw 4 groups with 4 in each group. Here is a picture of 4 groups of apples with 4 apples in each group.

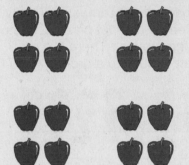

Altogether, there are 16 apples.

2. Written as repeated addition, the multiplication equation $3 \times 4 = 12$ is the same as adding 3 to itself 4 times.
$3 + 3 + 3 + 3 = 12$

It is also the same as $4 \times 3 = 12$ which is like adding 4 to itself 3 times.
$4 + 4 + 4 = 12$

3. To write the repeated addition equation as multiplication, count how many times 4 is added to itself. It is added 5 times, so you would write $4 \times 5 = 20$ or $5 \times 4 = 20$.

4. To solve this problem, draw 5 groups with 3 dollars in each group.

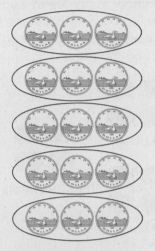

The equations that show and solve the problem are $5 + 5 + 5 = 15$ or $5 \times 3 = 15$.

Julie collected 15 dollars altogether.

To check your answer, count the dollars.

PRACTICE EXERCISES
ANSWERS AND SOLUTIONS

1. To show the multiplication equation $3 \times 5 = 15$ using equal groups, start with how many groups there are (3) and how many are in each group (5). Draw 3 groups with 5 in each group. Here is a picture of 3 groups with 5 footballs in each group.

1 group

1 group

1 group

Altogether, there are 15 footballs.

3. To show the equation $5 \times 4 = 20$ using equal groups, start with how many groups there are (5) and how many are in each group (4). Draw 5 groups with 4 in each group. Here is a picture of 5 groups with 4 hockey pucks in each group.

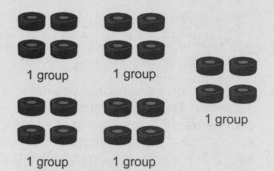

1 group   1 group

1 group

1 group   1 group

Altogether, there are 20 hockey pucks.

5. To write the repeated addition equation as multiplication, count how many times 2 is added to itself. It is added 3 times, so you would write $2 \times 3 = 6$ or $3 \times 2 = 6$.

7. To write the repeated addition equation as multiplication, count how many times 3 is added to itself. It is added 5 times, so you would write $3 \times 5 = 15$ or $5 \times 3 = 15$.

9. Draw 3 groups of 4 glasses

1 group

1 group

1 group

The equations that show and solve the problem are $4 \times 3 = 12$ or $3 \times 4 = 12$.

To check your answer, count all the glasses in the groups.

Roger can fill 12 glasses with soda.

Lesson 2—Division

🐝 TIME TO TRY 🐝
ANSWERS AND SOLUTIONS

1. The hiking leader can start by putting one camper in each of the 3 groups. That leaves 9 campers. Then, he can put another camper in each group leaving 6 campers. Then, put another camper in each group leaving 3 campers. Finally, the hiking leader can put one last camper in each of the groups. There are no campers left to put into a group.

The division equation $12 \div 3 = 4$ shows and solves the problem. The hiking leader should put four campers in each group.

2. The total number of flowers Chad has is 12. He bundles them into 2 groups.

Chad can start by giving one bundle of flowers to one friend. He will have one bundle left to give to another friend. The equation that shows the problem is $12 \div 6 = 2$.

Chad can give the flowers to two friends.

3. There are 20 pieces of chocolate. That number is the dividend. Jermain wants to share the chocolate with his three friends. There are 4 boys (Jermain plus his three friends). The divisor is 4.

The equation $20 \div 4 = 5$ shows and solves Jermain's problem.

Each boy gets five pieces of chocolate.

4. The division equation $20 \div 4 = 5$ is the same as subtracting 4 from 20 a total of 5 times.
$20 - 4 = 16$, $16 - 4 = 12$, $12 - 4 = 8$, $8 - 4 = 4$, $4 - 4 = 0$

It takes 5 groups of subtraction to get to 0.

5. Look at the first number in the repeated subtraction equation (15). It is the number that is that you are taking away from.

Next, look at the number being subtracted (5). That is the second number in the division sentence.

Finally, the number of times you subtract the 5 is the answer.

The repeated subtraction equation is shown by the division equation.
$15 \div 5 = 3$

PRACTICE EXERCISES
ANSWERS AND SOLUTIONS

1. The equation tells you that you have 12 items. To show the equation, you could draw 12 roses placing one rose in each of the 4 groups. There are 8 roses left. Place a second rose in each group. There are 4 roses left. Place a third rose in each group. There are no roses left. This picture shows the division equation using equal sharing.

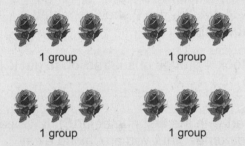

1 group   1 group

1 group   1 group

3. Savin starts with 25 oranges and separates the oranges into groups of 5.

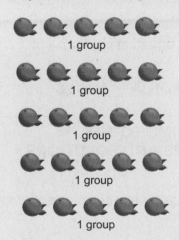

1 group

1 group

1 group

1 group

1 group

The equation that shows the problem is $25 \div 5 = 5$.

Savin can make 5 groups of 5 from the bag of oranges.

5. Divide the 9 dollars into 3 groups. There will be 3 equal groups with 3 dollars in each group.

1 group   1 group   1 group

The equation that shows and solves the problem is $9 \div 3 = 3$.

Each child will get three dollars.

7. The equation $16 \div 4 = 4$ means the same as subtracting 4 from 16 a total of 4 times.

The equations $16 - 4 = 12$, $12 - 4 = 8$, $8 - 4 = 4$, $4 - 4 = 0$ show repeated subtraction.

It took 4 groups of subtraction to get to 0, so $16 \div 4 = 4$.

9. Start with the first number (15). It will be the number that you are taking away from. Next, look at the number that is being subtracted (3). The number of times you subtract the is the answer (5).

The division equation is $15 \div 3 = 5$.

Lesson 3—Arrays

🐛 TIME TO TRY 🐛
ANSWERS AND SOLUTIONS

1. There are 7 groups with 1 piece of pizza in each group.

The equation that describes the array is $7 \times 1 = 7$.

There are seven pieces of pizza altogether.

2. To create the array, count how many rows you need and how many are in each row. In the multiplication equation 3×4, there are 3 rows with 4 in each row.

The equation $3 \times 4 = 12$ describes the array.

3. There are 3 rows with 5 soccer balls in each row. There are 15 soccer balls in total. The multiplication and division equations that represent the array of soccer balls are:

$3 \times 5 = 15$
$5 \times 3 = 15$
$15 \div 5 = 3$
$15 \div 3 = 5$

PRACTICE EXERCISES
ANSWERS AND SOLUTIONS

1. There are 4 rows with 4 balls in each row $(4 \times 4 = 16)$, or there are 4 columns with 4 balls in each column.
$4 \times 4 = 16$

3. There are 5 rows with 1 ball in each row or there is 1 column of 5 balls.
$5 \times 1 = 5$, $1 \times 5 = 5$

5. You can create an array by counting how many rows you need and how many are in each row. The first number in the equation is a 3, so you need 3 rows. The second number in the equation is a 2, so there should be 2 in each row.

This array of dogs shows the equation $3 \times 2 = 6$.

7. To write the multiplication equations for the array, count how many rows of stop signs (3).

Next, count how many stop signs are in each row (4). The total number of stop signs is the product. Remember that it does not matter in which order you write the factors. The answer is the same either way.

These are the multiplication equations for the array.
$3 \times 4 = 12$
$4 \times 3 = 12$

To write the division equations for the array, start with the total number of stop signs (12).

Next, you can either use the number of rows (3) or the number of stop signs in each row (4). Whichever number you use, the other number will be the quotient.

These are the division equations for the array.
$12 \div 3 = 4$
$12 \div 4 = 3$

9.

This is the array Fonda made. There are 3 groups with 3 pennies in each group. The equation that represents the array is $3 \times 3 = 9$.

Fonda has nine pennies altogether.

Practice Test

ANSWERS AND SOLUTIONS

1. To show the multiplication equation $2 \times 5 = 10$ using equal groups, start with how many groups there are (2) and how many are in each group (5). Draw 2 groups with 5 in each group. The picture shows 2 groups of bananas with 5 bananas in each group.

1 group

1 group

Altogether, there are 10 bananas.

3. To write the repeated addition as multiplication, count how many times 1 is added to itself. It is added 4 times, so you would write $1 \times 4 = 4$ or $4 \times 1 = 4$.

5. Draw 4 groups with 4 cars in each group.

1 group   1 group

1 group   1 group

To determine the answer, count all the cars.

The equations that show how many cars Rijiv has are $4 + 4 + 4 + 4 = 16$ and $4 \times 4 = 16$.

Rijiv has 16 toy cars.

7. Lulu gives 1 cookie to each friend. She has 0 cookies left.
$5 \div 5 = 1$

1 group   1 group   1 group   1 group   1 group

Lulu can give each friend one cookie.

9. The total number of students is 20. The number of microscopes is 5. To solve the problem, draw 5 microscopes. Now, divide the students into equal groups until all the students are assigned to a microscope.

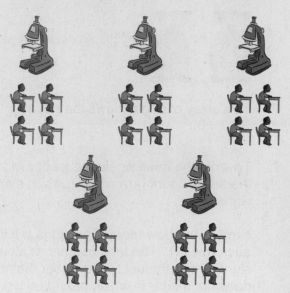

The equation that shows and solves Daniel's problem is $20 \div 5 = 4$.

Four students have to share each microscope.

11. The first number in the division sentence is 25. The number being subtracted is 5. The amount of times 5 can be taken away from 25 is the answer.

The division equation is $25 \div 5 = 5$.

13. There are 12 carrots. There are 4 rabbits, so the carrots must be divided into 4 groups. The equation that shows the problem is $12 \div 4 = 3$.

The rabbits will get three carrots each.

15. There are 3 rows of baseballs. Each row has 2 balls. The multiplication equation is $3 \times 2 = 6$.

There are six baseballs altogether.

17. To write the multiplication equations for the array, count how many rows of cars (5).

Next, count how many cars are in each row (3). The amount total number of cars is the product. Remember that it does not matter in what order you write the factors. The answer is the same.

The multiplication equations are $5 \times 3 = 15$ and $3 \times 5 = 15$.

To write the division equations for the array, start with the total number of cars (15).

Next, you can either use the number of rows or the number of cars in each row as the number dividing 15 into groups. The number you do not choose is the answer.

The division equations are $15 \div 5 = 3$ and $15 \div 3 = 5$.

19. 10
The array has 2 rows with 5 curling rocks in each row. The equations that represent the array are $2 \times 5 = 10$ or $5 \times 2 = 10$.

There are 10 curling rocks altogether.

SOLVING EQUATIONS

Lesson 1—Understanding Equations and Symbols

🦋 TIME TO TRY 🦋
ANSWERS AND SOLUTIONS

1. The ■ represents the unknown number in the equation. It represents the number that 4 must be added to for the sum to be 10.

2. Choose two different shapes, signs, or letters to represent the unknown. The unknown is the number that 8 must be subtracted from to get a difference of 14.

   Here are two different ways you can represent the same unknown. You may have used different symbols to represent the unknown.
   □ – 8 = 14
   ? – 8 = 14

3. The unknown is the total number of balloons that were tied together before 5 floated away. Choose a symbol to represent the unknown.

   Some balloons floating away from the others is a clue to subtract.

   One equation that expresses the picture problem is ▲ – 5 = 7.

   Another equation that can express the picture problem is 7 + 5 = ▲.

4. The unknown (N) is the number of toy cars the two boys have altogether.

   The word *altogether* is a clue to add.

   An equation that expresses the problem is 13 + 11 = N.

PRACTICE EXERCISES
ANSWERS AND SOLUTIONS

1. The symbol □ represents the unknown number in the equation. It represents the number that is added to 8 to get the sum of 11.

3. Here are two examples of the same equation with the unknown expressed by different symbols. Your answer may be different.
   ▲ + 12 = 24
   h + 12 = 24

5. The unknown is the total number of apples. Let the letter *A* represent the unknown. The operation to use is addition.

   The equation you can write to express the problem is 6 + 2 = A.

7. The unknown is the number of carrots Caleb picked from the garden. The word *left* tells you the operation is subtraction.

   The equation you can write to express the problem is □ – 15 = 12.

Lesson 2—Solving Equations that Contain an Unknown

🦋 TIME TO TRY 🦋
ANSWERS AND SOLUTIONS

1. Count up from 27 to 31.
   28, 29, 30, 31

   There are 4 counts from 27 to 31, so the unknown number is 4.
   27 + 4 = 31
   31 = 31

2. Count down from 17 to 13.
16, 15, 14, 13

There are 4 counts from 17 to 13, so the unknown number is 4.
$17 - \square = 13$
$17 - 4 = 13$

3. **Step 1**
Start with 4 ten rods and 5 units to represent the number 45.

Step 2
Take away the 1 ten rod and 3 units that represent the number 13.

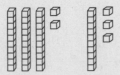

Step 3
You are left with 3 ten rods and 2 units representing the number 32.

The solution is $45 - 13 = 32$.

4. If you know that ▲ $- 19 = 6$, then you know that $6 + 19 = $ ▲.

Since $6 + 19 = 25$, then ▲ $= 25$.

Check your work by substituting 25 for ▲ in the equation.
$25 - 19 = 6$
$6 = 6$

Since both sides of the equation are equal, your solution is correct.

PRACTICE EXERCISES
ANSWERS AND SOLUTIONS

1. Count up from 22 to 27.
23, 24, 25, 26, 27

You need 5 counts to get from 22 to 27. So, the unknown is the number 5.

$22 + 5 = 27$

3. Count down from 50 to 47.
49, 48, 47

You need 3 counts to get from 50 to 47. So, the unknown is the number 3.

$50 - 3 = 47$

5. **Step 1**
Start with 5 ten rods and 2 units to represent the number 52.

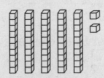

Step 2
Add the 3 ten rods and 5 units that represent the number 35.

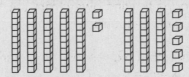

Step 3
You now have 8 ten rods and 5 units representing the number 87.

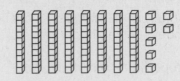

$52 + 35 = 87$

ANSWERS AND SOLUTIONS

7. If $N + 12 = 36$, then $36 - 12 = N$.

Since $36 - 12 = N$, then $N = 24$.

Check your work by substituting 24 for N in the equation.
$24 + 12 = 36$
$36 = 36$

Since both sides of the equation are equal, your solution is correct.

Practice Test

ANSWERS AND SOLUTIONS

1. The symbol ☐ represents the unknown number in the equation. The unknown number is the number that must be added to 12 to get 33.

3. The unknown is the number of erasers Shaylah has now.

The equation you can write to express the problem is $5 + 6 = ☐$.

5. If $☐ + 15 = 45$, then $45 - 15 = ☐$.
Since $45 - 15 = 30$, then $☐ = 30$.

Check your work by substituting 30 for ☐ in the equation.
$30 + 15 = 45$
$45 = 45$

Since both sides of the equation are equal, your solution is correct.

7. **Step 1**
Start with 4 ten rods and 5 units to represent the number 45.

Step 2
Take away the 2 ten rods and 2 units that represent the number 22.

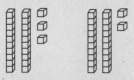

Step 3
You are left with 2 ten rods and 3 units representing the number 23.

The solution is $45 - 22 = 23$.

9. The symbol ▲ represents the unknown number in the equation. It represents the number that is subtracted from 93 to get 15.

11. The unknown is the number of cards Hudson had to begin with.

The equation you can write to express the problem is $☐ - 22 = 29$.

PATTERNS

Lesson 1—Introduction to Patterns

🐛 TIME TO TRY 🐛
ANSWERS AND SOLUTIONS

1. The numbers in the pattern are becoming less. The pattern starts at 320 and decreases by 10 for each term.

   The pattern is decreasing.

2. To compare the counting patterns, look at how each pattern decreases. The first pattern is decreasing by 5. The second pattern is decreasing by 10.

3. To find the number the pattern is changing by, you can count backward from 71 to 62. You can also subtract the lesser number from the greater number.

   To count backward, start at 71 and find how many counts it takes to get to 62.
   71, 70, 69, 68, 67, 66, 65, 64, 63, 62

   It takes 9 counts.

   Starting with 71, when you subtract the next term, you get 9.
   $71-62=9$, $62-53=9$, $53-44=9$

   The pattern is that the numbers get smaller by 9 for each term.

PRACTICE EXERCISES
ANSWERS AND SOLUTIONS

1. The numbers in the pattern are becoming less. The pattern starts at 12 and decreases by 2 for each term.

   The pattern is decreasing.

3. To compare the counting patterns, find out what numbers the patterns are increasing by.

   The first pattern is increasing by 5. The second pattern is also increasing by 5.

5. The pattern is growing by 1. Ray uses 1 more stick each time he makes a new figure. The fourth figure has 4 sticks, so Ray will use 5 sticks to make the fifth figure.

Lesson 2—Patterns Using Pattern Rules

🐛 TIME TO TRY 🐛
ANSWERS AND SOLUTIONS

1. To find the pattern rule, look for the difference between the numbers.

   You can subtract the lesser number from the greater number ($31-21=10$), or you can count up from 21 to 31. The pattern rule is to add 10 each time. The next 3 numbers in the pattern are 51, 61, 71.

   $41+10=51$, $51+10=61$, $61+10=71$

2. To find the pattern rule, look for the difference between the numbers.

   You can subtract the lesser number from the greater number ($143-136=7$), or you can count down from 143 to 136.

   The pattern rule is to subtract 7.

   The next three numbers in the pattern are 122, 115, 108.

   $129-7=122$, $122-7=115$, $115-7=108$

3. To figure out the pattern rule, look at the number of balls used for the first and second figures. There are 4 more balls in figure 2 than in figure 1. Move on to the third figure. There are 4 more balls in figure 3 than there are in figure 2. You have found the pattern rule. The pattern rule is to add 4.

Use the information to predict how many balls are in figure 5. Add 4 balls to the number of balls in figure 4 ($16 + 4 = 20$).

There are 20 balls needed in figure 5.

4. To figure out the pattern rule for the picture, look at the number of hearts in shape 1 and shape 2. There are 2 fewer hearts in shape 2 than in shape 1 ($11 - 9 = 2$). Move on to shape 3. There are 2 fewer hearts in shape 3 than there are in shape 2 ($9 - 7 = 2$). You have found the pattern rule. Two hearts are taken away for each new shape.

Use the information to predict how many hearts are in shape 4 and shape 5. Since each shape goes down by 2 hearts, subtract 2 hearts from shape 3 to get shape 4 ($7 - 2 = 5$).

Then, subtract 2 hearts from shape 4 to get shape 5 ($5 - 2 = 3$).

There are 5 hearts in shape 4 and 3 hearts in shape 5.

5. To describe the pattern rule, determine how the pattern is changing.

The numbers are becoming less, so it is a decreasing or shrinking pattern. You can count down 4 counts (94, 93, 92, 91, 90), or you can subtract the numbers. $94 - 90 = 4$

The pattern rule is to start at 94 and subtract 4 each time.

6. To find the pattern rule, look for the difference between the numbers.

Start with the first number in the pattern. Find the difference between it and the second number. The difference is 5. Since the pattern is decreasing by 5, the pattern rule is to subtract 5. Take away 5 from the number before the blank ($610 - 5 = 605$). The missing number is 605.

You can check your answer by subtracting 5 from 605. If you get 600, then 605 is the missing number.

7. Start at 35. Add 9 to 35 ($35 + 9 = 44$). The second number in the pattern is 44. Add 9 to 44 ($44 + 9 = 53$). The third number in the pattern is 53. Add 9 to 53 ($53 + 9 = 62$). The fourth number in the pattern is 62. Add 9 to 62 ($62 + 9 = 71$). The fifth number in the pattern is 71.

The pattern is 35, 44, 53, 62, 71.

PRACTICE EXERCISES
ANSWERS AND SOLUTIONS

1. The pattern rule is to add 7. The next three numbers in the pattern will be 35, 42, 49.

$28 + 7 = 35$, $35 + 7 = 42$, $42 + 7 = 49$

3. To describe the pattern rule, determine how the pattern is decreasing.

The pattern is decreasing by 100. The pattern rule is to start at 842 and subtract 100 each time.

5. To find the pattern rule, look for the difference between the numbers.

Starting with the first number in the pattern, find the difference between it and the second number. The difference is 100. The difference between the second and third numbers is also 100. The pattern rule is to add 100. Add 100 to the number before the blank.
$250 + 100 = 350$

The missing number is 350.

You can check your answer by adding 100 to 350 to get 450, the next number in the pattern.

7. $639 - 9 = 630$, $630 - 9 = 621$, $621 - 9 = 612$, $612 - 9 = 603$, $603 - 9 = 594$

The number pattern is 639, 630, 621, 612, 603, 594.

9. To find the pattern rule, look for the difference between the numbers.

Starting with the first number in the pattern, find the difference between it and the second number. The difference is 5. The difference between the second and third numbers is also 5. The pattern rule is to add 5. Add 5 to the number before the blank ($17 + 5 = 22$).

②₊₅ ⑦₊₅ ⑫₊₅ ⑰₊₅ ㉒₊₅

The missing number is 22.

11. Start at 250. Subtract 20 from 250 to get 230 ($250 - 20 = 230$). Subtract 20 from 230 to get 210. Subtract 20 from 210 to get 190. Subtract 20 from 190 to get 170.

The number pattern is 250, 230, 210, 190, 170.

13. To find the pattern rule, look for the difference between numbers.

Starting with the first number in the pattern, find the difference between it and the second number. The difference is 15. The difference between the second and third numbers is also 15. Since the pattern is decreasing by 15, the pattern rule is to subtract 15. Subtract 15 from the number before the blank ($295 - 15 = 280$). The missing number is 280.

Check your answer by subtracting 15 from 280 ($280 - 15 = 265$). If you get 265, then 280 is the missing number.

Practice Test

ANSWERS AND SOLUTIONS

1. The numbers in the pattern are becoming greater. They start at 622 and increase by 2 for each term.

The pattern is increasing.

3. To compare the skip counting patterns, find what number the pattern is increasing or decreasing by.

The first pattern is increasing by skip counting in 10s. The second pattern is decreasing by skip counting in 10s.

5. Starting at 95, the numbers in the pattern are becoming less by 10 each time. The pattern is to subtract 10. You can count backward from 95 to 5, or you can subtract the smaller number from the bigger number.

7. To complete the pattern, you must find the pattern rule.

To find the difference between the numbers, subtract the lesser number from the greater number. The difference between the first two numbers is 2 because $94 - 92 = 2$. Check the difference between the next two numbers to see if the difference is also 2 ($96 - 94 = 2$).

The pattern rule is to add 2 each time. The completed pattern is 92, 94, 96, 98, 100, 102, 104.

9. To complete the pattern, find the pattern rule. Subtract the lesser number from the greater number. The difference between the first two numbers is 5 because $234 - 229 = 5$. Check the difference between the next two numbers to see if the difference is also 5 ($229 - 224 = 5$).

Since each number goes down by 5, the pattern rule is to subtract 5. The pattern is 234, 229, 224, 219, 214, 209.

11. To figure out the pattern rule, look at the number of blocks used for the first and second figures. There are 3 more blocks in the second figure than the first. Move on to the third figure. There are 3 more blocks in the third figure than the second. The pattern rule is to add 3.

Use the rule to predict how many blocks are in the fourth figure. Add 3 blocks to the number of blocks in figure 3 ($7 + 3 = 10$).

There will be 10 blocks in the fourth figure.

13. To describe the pattern rule, determine how the pattern is changing.

The numbers are becoming greater, so the pattern is increasing or growing. To find by how much, you can count up starting from 64 (64, 65, 66, 67). That is 3 counts. Or, you can subtract numbers to find the difference ($67 - 64 = 3$).

The pattern rule is to start at 64 and add 3 to each term to get the next term.

15. To find the missing number, look for the difference between the numbers.

Starting with the first number in the pattern, find the difference between it and the second number. The difference is 25. Since the pattern is shrinking by 25, the pattern rule is to subtract 25. Subtract 25 from the number before the blank ($275 - 25 = 250$). The missing number is 250.

You can check your answer by subtracting 25 from 250. If you get 225, then 250 is the missing number.

17. Start at 26. Add 7 to 26 ($26 + 7 = 33$). The second number in the pattern is 33. Add 7 to 33 ($33 + 7 = 40$). The third number in the pattern is 40. Add 7 to 40 ($40 + 7 = 47$). The fourth number in the pattern is 47. Add 7 to 47 ($47 + 7 = 54$). The fifth number is 54.

The pattern is 26, 33, 40, 47, 54.

19. The numbers in the pattern become greater by 9 each time. The pattern rule for the shaded numbers is to add 9 to each term to get the next term.

TIME

Lesson 1—Time Measurement

✿ TIME TO TRY ✿
ANSWERS AND SOLUTIONS

1. Minutes could be used to measure the length of time it would take to clean your room. If your room is an absolute mess, it might take hours.

2. Most movies are between one and a half hours long to two and a half hours long. Your favourite movie would most likely be measured in hours.

3. Yes, it is likely that washing your car would take more than a minute but not a long time, such as a full day.

4. To find out how long Jill was gone for, count up from the hour she left to the hour she returned.
10:15, 11:15, 12:15, 1:15, 2:15, 3:15, 4:15, 5:15, 6:15

   Next, count up the minutes. You can count by 15 minutes.
6:15, 6:30, 6:45

   She was gone for 8 hours and 30 minutes.

5. You would begin counting on the Friday, Saturday, Sunday, Monday, Tuesday, Wednesday, and Thursday.

   Sally was gone for 7 days.

6. Calculate the number of days she was gone in March $(31 - 22 = 9)$

   Add the number of days in April (30), May (31), June (30), July (31) and the number of days in August (8).
$9 + 30 + 31 + 30 + 31 + 8 = 139$ days

   Mimi's world cruise took 139 days.

PRACTICE EXERCISE
ANSWERS AND SOLUTIONS

1. Most grade 3 classes last between 20 and 40 minutes. The time your Math class lasts would likely be measured in minutes.

3. A 16 team tournament would take about 15 games to complete. Hours would be too short of a time period, and weeks too long of a time period.

   The time would most likely be measured in days.

5. To find out how long Iman spent doing his homework, count up by 5 minute blocks.
7:20, 7:25, 7:30, 7:35, 7:40, 7:45, 7:50.
→ 7 blocks.

   Add 5 to itself 7 times.
$5 + 5 + 5 + 5 + 5 + 5 + 5 = 35$ minutes.

   It took Iman 35 minutes to complete his homework.

7. Count the number of months from November to March, including both November and March, because he attended dance class in those months. November, December, January, February, March.

   Jesse attends hip hop dance classes for 5 months.

9. Ice Hockey Season usually take most of the winter.
Ice Hockey—5 months

Watching a movies usually take part of an evening.
Watching a movie—hours

Snapping your fingers takes about 1 second.
Snap your fingers—1 second

It usually takes a small length of time to tie your shoes.
Tie your shoes—1 minute

It is common for holidays to last weeks.
Go on a holiday—2 weeks

Lesson 2—Units of Time

 **TIME TO TRY**
ANSWERS AND SOLUTIONS

1. To solve this problem, remember that there are 60 seconds in a minute. To find out how many minutes, subtract.
540 − 60 = 480
480 − 60 = 420
420 − 60 = 360
360 − 60 = 300
300 − 60 = 240
240 − 60 = 180
180 − 60 = 120
120 − 60 = 60
60 − 60 = 0

It took Kyle 9 minutes to walk his dog.

2. To find out how many minutes Ariel was at the concert, count up to determine how many hours long it was.
1:00, 2:00, 3:00, 4:00, 5:00. 4 hours

An hour has 60 minutes, so to find out how many minutes 4 hours has, add 60 4 times.
60 + 60 + 60 + 60 = 240

There are 240 minutes in 4 hours.

3.

Month	Holiday/Celebration
January	New Years
February	Valentine's Day
March	St. Patrick's Day
April	Easter
May	Mother's Day
June	Father's Day
July	Canada Day
August	Civic Holiday
September	Back to School
October	Thanksgiving/Halloween
November	Remembrance Day
December	Christmas

4. Answers will vary.
Calendars should have a label, the correct number of days for that month, and the correct order of days.

PRACTICE EXERCISE
ANSWERS AND SOLUTIONS

1. Remember there are 60 seconds in each minute. To find out how many minutes are in 480 seconds, subtract.
    $480 - 60 = 420$
    $420 - 60 = 360$
    $360 - 60 = 300$
    $300 - 60 = 240$
    $240 - 60 = 180$
    $180 - 60 = 120$
    $120 - 60 = 60$
    $60 - 60 = 0$

    480 seconds is equal to 8 minutes.

3. Each day has 24 hours. 3 days has
    $24 + 24 + 24 = 72$ hours.

    3 days is equal to 72 hours.

5. Each day is 24 hours
    $24 + 24 + 24 = 72$ hours
    3 days = 72 hours

    Each week is 7 days
    $7 + 7 + 7 + 7 + 7 + 7 = 42$ days
    6 weeks = 42 days

    Each minute has 60 seconds
    $60 + 60 + 60 = 180$ seconds
    3 minutes = 180 seconds

    60 seconds make up a minute
    $600 - 60 = 540, 540 - 60 = 480,$
    $480 - 60 = 420, 420 - 60 = 360,$
    $360 - 60 = 300, 300 - 60 = 240,$
    $240 - 60 = 180, 180 - 60 = 120,$
    $120 - 60 = 60, 60 - 60 = 0$
    600 seconds = 10 minutes

    Each hour has 60 minutes
    $60 + 60 = 120$ minutes
    2 hours = 120 minutes

7. Each minute has 60 seconds. Add 60 to itself 8 times.
    $60 + 60 + 60 + 60 + 60 + 60 + 60 + 60$
    $= 480$ seconds

    It took Paul 480 seconds to run 3 laps of the track.

9. Calculate the number of days left in January $(31 - 17 = 14)$. Add the number of days in February (28) and the number of days in March (2).
    $14 + 28 + 2 = 44$ days

    Alton's exercise program lasted 44 days

11.

April 2112

SUN	MON	TUES	WED	THU	FRI	SAT
1	2	3 Greg	4	5	6	7
8	9	10	11	12	13 Good Fri	14
15 Easter	16	17	18	19	20	21
22	23	24	25 Ted	26	27	28
29	30	28				

Practice Test

ANSWERS AND SOLUTIONS

1. It takes a very short period of time to pour a glass of milk. The most likely measure is seconds.

3. No, a marathon is 42 kilometres and quite a long distance. Experienced marathoners take 2 to 3 hours to complete one.

5. Count up from 4:30 in 15 minute blocks. 4:45, 5:00, 5:15. There are 3 blocks of 15 minutes.

Add 15 to itself 3 times.
$15 + 15 + 15 = 45$ minutes

Sheila took 45 minutes to write her book report.

7. Count up from 10:00 in the morning to 3:00 in the afternoon. 11:00, 12:00, 1:00, 2:00, 3:00. There are 5 blocks.

Dean spent 5 hours snowmobiling with his father.

9. From 9:15 to 11:15 is 2 hours. From 11:15 to 11:45 is 30 minutes or $\frac{1}{2}$ hour. They spent a total of
$2 + \frac{1}{2} = 2\frac{1}{2}$ hours baking cookies.

They spent $2\frac{1}{2}$ hours baking cookies.

11. 1 minute is 60 seconds. Subtract 60 until you reach 0.
$120 - 60 = 60,\ 60 - 60 = 0$

You subtracted 60 twice, so Chloe brushed her teeth for 2 minutes.

13. From 1:15 to 2:15 is 1 hour or 60 minutes.

Count up from 2:15 in 15 minute blocks, 2:30, 2:45, 3:00.
3 blocks $\rightarrow 15 + 15 + 15 = 45$ minutes.

From 3:00 to 3:10 is 10 minutes.

To find the total number of minutes Basil watched television add
$60 + 45 + 10 = 115$ minutes.

Basil watched television for 115 minutes.

15. Count the number of days. Be sure to include Wednesday and Monday as she was at camp both of those days.

Wednesday, Thursday, Friday, Saturday, Sunday, Monday

Gillian spent 6 days at camp.

17. From 10:30 to 12:30 is 2 hours. Each hour is 60 minutes.
60 + 60 = 120

12:30 to 1:00 is $\frac{1}{2}$ hour or 30 minutes.

1:00 to 1:05 is 5 minutes.

To find the length of time Archie was away add $120 + 30 + 5 = 155$ minutes.

Archie was away 155 minutes.

19.

September 2114

SUN	MON	TUES	WED	THU	FRI	SAT
	1	2	3	4	5	Read a 6 Book Day
7	8	Teddy Bear 9	10	11	12	Peanut 13 Day
14	Elephant 15 Day	16	17	18	19	20
21	22	23	24	25	26	27
28	29	30				

LENGTH AND PERIMETER

Lesson 1—Estimating Length

🐝 TIME TO TRY 🐝
ANSWERS AND SOLUTIONS

1. How many finger widths would fit along length of the glue stick? It might take about 6 finger widths. You could estimate that the length of the glue stick would be about 6 cm.

2. To estimate how long a car is, remember one metre is approximately the length from the fingertips on your left hand to the fingertips on your right hand when your arms are open wide. Would a car be one arm length? Not likely—it would be closer to 3.5 m.

PRACTICE EXERCISES
ANSWERS AND SOLUTIONS

1. Since about 9 finger widths would fit along the length of a pen, the length of the pen would be about 9 cm.

3. Since about 25 finger widths would fit along the length of a hammer, the length of the hammer would be about 25 cm.

5. A metre is approximately the length from a doorknob on a door to the floor.

    Since the height of a small girl would be close to the length from the doorknob on a door to the floor, her height would be about 95 cm.

7. One metre is approximately the length from the fingertips on your left hand to the fingertips on your right hand when your arms are open wide. The length of the bus might take about 13 arm lengths.

    A good estimate would be about 13 m.

9. No, one metre is about the measurement of the height from the floor to a doorknob on a door. It would be more reasonable if a marker were estimated in centimetres.

Lesson 2—Measuring Length

🐝 TIME TO TRY 🐝
ANSWERS AND SOLUTIONS

1. Line up your ruler with the beginning of the line, and follow the line until it ends. Look at the number it has stopped at (4). That is how long the line is. Write 4 cm on the line.

2. Since the given shape is an octagon, all the sides are equal.

    Line up a ruler with the end of the side of the shape.

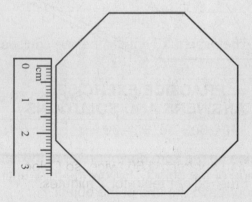

The length of each side of the octagon is 2 cm.

3. To find the length of the shape, line a ruler up with the edge of the shape, and measure the length of the shape.

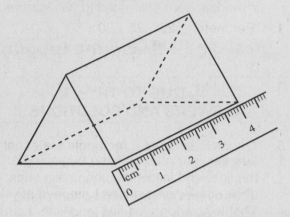

The length of the shape is 4 cm.

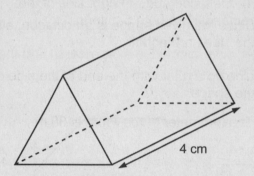

4 cm

PRACTICE EXERCISES
ANSWERS AND SOLUTIONS

1. Line up the zero on your ruler at the left side of the object. Follow the ruler until you reach the end of the object. Read the number where the object stops.

   The crayon is 7 cm long.

3. Line up the zero on your ruler at the left side of the object. Follow the ruler until you reach the end of the object. Read the number where the object stops.

   The scissors are 9 cm long.

5. Line up a ruler with the end of the side of the shape.

   The bottom of the pentagon is 2.7 cm.

7. Line up a ruler with one end of the matchstick.

   The length of the matchstick is 4 cm.

Lesson 3—Drawing Lines

🐝 TIME TO TRY 🐝
ANSWERS AND SOLUTIONS

1. Begin by placing your ruler on the paper and marking where the zero is. Draw a line along the ruler's edge until you reach the number 18. Stop at the tick for the number 18.

2. Draw a tick on the paper. Using your finger, measure 11 finger widths, and draw a tick after the 11th finger width. Connect the ticks with a line.

PRACTICE EXERCISES
ANSWERS AND SOLUTIONS

1. Begin by placing your ruler on the paper and marking where the zero is. Draw a line along the ruler's edge until you reach the number 10. Stop at the tick for the number 10.

3. Place a ruler in a vertical position on the paper, and mark where the zero is. Draw a line along the ruler's edge until you reach the number 7. Stop at the tick for the number 7.

5. Draw a tick on the paper.

   Using your finger, measure 15 finger widths, and draw a tick after the 15th finger width.

   Connect the ticks with a line.

Lesson 4—Perimeter

🦋 TIME TO TRY 🦋
ANSWERS AND SOLUTIONS

1. The perimeter is the distance around the outside of an object. Add the length of all sides to find the perimeter of the object.

    Perimeter $= 30+30+30+30$
    $\qquad\quad\; =120$ cm

2. The dimensions of the letter H are given below.

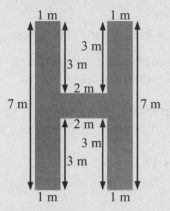

    The perimeter of H
    $= 7+7+1+1+1+1+3+3+3+3+2+2$
    $= 34$ m

3. One side of the square is broken into two parts. Each part looks to be about the same size and width as your finger. Since you know that one finger width is 1 cm, the whole side would be about 2 cm long $(1+1=2)$.

    All four sides of the square look to be the same length.
    2 cm $+2$ cm $+2$ cm $+2$ cm $= 8$ cm
    or $2 \times 4 = 8$ cm

    A good estimate for the perimeter of the square is about 8 cm.

PRACTICE EXERCISES
ANSWERS AND SOLUTIONS

1. Perimeter $= 25 + 25 + 20 + 60$
    $\qquad\quad\; = 130$ cm

3. Perimeter $= 35 + 35 + 35$
    $\qquad\quad\; = 105$ cm

5. Opposite sides of a rectangle are equal in length.

    That means the top and bottom of the rectangle are both 10 m long.

    The left side and the right side of the rectangle are both 5 m long.

    Add the four lengths together to find the perimeter.
    $10 + 10 + 5 + 5 = 30$

    The perimeter of the room is 30 m.

7. Perimeter $= 3 + 2 + 6 + 2 + 3 + 4 + 12 + 4$
    $\qquad\quad\; = 36$ cm

9. One side of the octagon is broken into two parts. Each part looks to be about the same size and width as your finger. Since one finger width is about 1 cm, the side length would be about 2 cm $(1 + 1 = 2)$.

    All eight sides of the octagon look to be the same length.
    $2 + 2 + 2 + 2 + 2 + 2 + 2 + 2 = 16$
    or $2 \times 8 = 16$

    A good estimate is that the perimeter of the octagon is about 16 cm.

Lesson 5—Constructing Shapes for a Given Perimeter

🐝 TIME TO TRY 🐝
ANSWERS AND SOLUTIONS

1. Find all the possible combinations for a rectangle with a perimeter of 12 cm.

    Divide the perimeter by 2: $12 \div 2 = 6$.
    Find all the combinations of numbers that total 6.
    5 + 1: 5 + 5 + 1 + 1 = 12 cm
    4 + 2: 4 + 4 + 2 + 2 = 12 cm
    3 + 3: 3 + 3 + 3 + 3 = 12 cm

    Draw the rectangles using centimetre grid paper. Be sure to label each side.

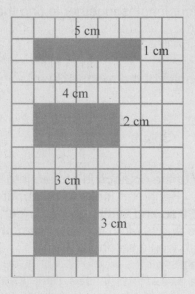

PRACTICE EXERCISES
ANSWERS AND SOLUTIONS

1. To draw a square with a perimeter of 20 cm, divide 20 by 4 because a square has four side lengths that are equal.
    $20 \div 4 = 5$

    Each side length should be 5 cm long.

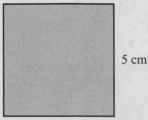

5 cm

5 cm

    Find all the possible combinations for a rectangle with a perimeter of 36 cm.

    Divide the perimeter by 2: $36 \div 2 = 18$.
    Find all the combinations of numbers that total 18.
    17 + 1: 17 + 17 + 1 + 1 = 36 cm
    16 + 2: 16 + 16 + 2 + 2 = 36 cm
    15 + 3: 15 + 15 + 3 + 3 = 36 cm
    14 + 4: 14 + 14 + 4 + 4 = 36 cm
    13 + 5: 13 + 13 + 5 + 5 = 36 cm
    12 + 6: 12 + 12 + 6 + 6 = 36 cm
    11 + 7: 11 + 11 + 7 + 7 = 36 cm
    10 + 8: 10 + 10 + 8 + 8 = 36 cm
    9 + 9:   9 + 9 + 9 + 9 = 36 cm

Your rectangle should look like one of the following. Be sure to label each side.

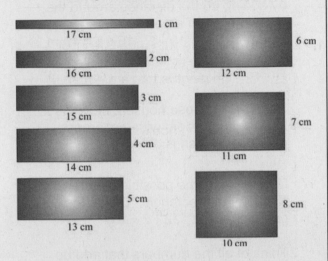

3. Find all the possible combinations for a rectangle with a perimeter of 18 cm.

Divide the perimeter by 2: $18 \div 2 = 9$.
Find all the combinations of numbers that total 9.
$8 + 1$: $\quad 8 + 8 + 1 + 1 = 18$ cm
$7 + 2$: $\quad 7 + 7 + 2 + 2 = 18$ cm
$6 + 3$: $\quad 6 + 6 + 3 + 3 = 18$ cm
$5 + 4$: $\quad 5 + 5 + 4 + 4 = 18$ cm

Draw the rectangles using centimetre grid paper. Be sure to label each side.

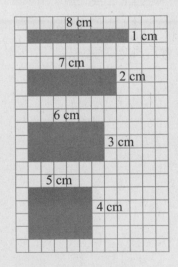

5. Find all the possible combinations for a rectangle with a perimeter of 14 cm.

Divide the perimeter by 2: $14 \div 2 = 7$.
Find all the combinations of numbers that total 7.
$6 + 1$: $\quad 6 + 6 + 1 + 1 = 14$ cm
$5 + 2$: $\quad 5 + 5 + 2 + 2 = 14$ cm
$4 + 3$: $\quad 4 + 4 + 3 + 3 = 14$ cm

Draw the rectangles using centimetre grid paper. Be sure to label each side.

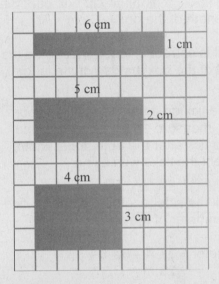

Practice Test

ANSWERS AND SOLUTIONS

1. Since 4 finger widths would fit along the length of a pair of sunglasses, their length would be about 4 cm.

3. One metre is approximately the length between the fingertips on your left hand and the fingertips on your right hand when your arms are open wide.

The length of the lamppost takes about 5 arm lengths.

Thus, the length would be about 5 m.

5. The length of a laptop can be estimated in centimetres since its length can be found by counting the number of finger widths that would fit along the laptop.

Since 30 cm is the length of your ruler and a laptop is about that same length, a good estimate for the length of a laptop would be about 30 cm.

7. Line up your ruler with the end of the side of the box.

The length of the box is 5 cm.

Daniel is correct. Robert measured the height of the box instead of the length.

9. Draw a tick on the paper. Using your finger, measure 16 finger widths, and draw a tick after the 16th finger width. Connect the ticks with a line.

11. Add all the side lengths together to find the perimeter of the shape.

Perimeter $= 3 + 4 + 6 + 8 + 3 + 4$
$\qquad\quad = 28$ m

13. One side of the heptagon is broken into three parts. Each part looks to be about the same size and width as a finger. Since one finger width is about 1 cm, the side length would be about 3 cm.
$(1 + 1 + 1 = 3)$

All seven sides of the heptagon look to be the same length.
$3 + 3 + 3 + 3 + 3 + 3 + 3 = 21$ cm
or $3 \times 7 = 21$

A good estimate of the perimeter of the heptagon is about 21 cm.

15. To find the house that Sergio should choose, find the perimeter of each room by adding up the distance around the outside of each room.
Room 1: $\qquad 15 + 5 + 15 + 5 = 40$ m
Room 2: $\qquad 12 + 12 + 12 + 12 = 48$ m
Room 3: $10 + 9 + 8 + 7 + 2 + 2 = 38$ m

Sergio will choose house 2 because it has the living room with the largest perimeter, which is 48 m.

17. Determine all the possible lengths and widths of the rectangle. Divide the perimeter by 2: $32 \div 2 = 16$.

Think of all the numbers that add up to 16.
$1 + 15 = 16$
$2 + 14 = 16$
$3 + 13 = 16$
$4 + 12 = 16$
$5 + 11 = 16$
$6 + 10 = 16$
$7 + 9 = 16$
$8 + 8 = 16$

MASS

Lesson 1—Estimating Weight

🦋 TIME TO TRY 🦋
ANSWERS AND SOLUTIONS

1. Think of how much 50 jellybeans would weigh. Does a soccer ball weigh more or less than this? It would weigh more.

   The best estimate is 500 g.

2. Two computer disks weigh about 6 g, so one computer disk would weigh about one-half of that. Since half of 6 is 3, one computer disk would weigh about 3 g. One jellybean weighs about 1 g.

   It would take three jellybeans to balance a scale with only one computer disk.

3. The question is asking how much the groups of jellybeans would weigh in total. Since each group has 25 jellybeans, and there are 4 groups, there must be 100 jellybeans.
   100 jellybeans = 100 grams

   The groups of jellybeans would weigh 100 grams.

PRACTICE EXERCISES
ANSWERS AND SOLUTIONS

1. Pretend to hold a DVD in one hand and 2 jellybeans (2 g) in the other hand. Do you think they would weigh about the same? If you are not sure, think of holding a DVD in one hand and 200 jellybeans in the other hand. Which hand would feel heavier? The one with 200 jellybeans would.

   The best estimate is 2 g.

3. Since you know that 1 paperclip = 1 gram and 1 000 grams = 1 kilogram, then 1 000 paperclips = 1 kilogram.

5. Pretend to hold a cabbage in one hand and 3 jellybeans (3 g) in the other hand. The weights are not same. Now, pretend to hold the cabbage in one hand and 300 jellybeans in the other hand. These weights will be about the same.

   The best estimate is 300 g.

7. The scale is balanced, so the weight of the jellybeans is the same as the weight of the two cherries. To find out approximately how much the two cherries weigh, count the number of jellybeans on the one side of the scale. One jellybean weighs approximately 1 g. Since there are 14 jellybeans, they must weigh about 14 g.

   This means that the two cherries also weigh about 14 g.

9. The weight of a textbook is about 1 kilogram.
   1 textbook = 1 kilogram
   2 textbooks = 2 kilograms

   The 2 books would weigh approximately 2 000 grams.

Lesson 2—Measuring and Recording Weight

🦋 TIME TO TRY 🦋
ANSWERS AND SOLUTIONS

1. Read the scale. The weight that the scale shows is the weight of the object on the scale.

   300 grams (300 g)

2. When the two sides of a balance scale are even with each other (balanced), the two sides have equal masses. There are five 1-kilogram weights on one side of the scale so the chair weighs 5 kg.

3. The connecting blocks will weigh the same. Each block still has the same mass, so the weight is the same even if the blocks are arranged in a different shape.

PRACTICE EXERCISES
ANSWERS AND SOLUTIONS

1. To find the weight of the boxes on the weigh scale, add 500 g + 500 g or multiply 500 g × 2.

   There is a total weight of 1 000 g (1 kg) on the weigh scale.

3. Add the weight of the objects on the scale to find the total weight on the scale. Add 1 kg + 1 kg + 1 kg + 1 kg + 1 kg + 1 kg + 1 kg = 7 kg or multiply 1 kg × 7.

   The total weight of the books on the scale is 7 kg.

5. Read the scale from the given figure. The weight that the scale shows is the weight of the tomatoes on the scale. The weight is 2 kilograms.
   2 kilograms = 2 000 grams.

   The tomatoes weigh 2 000 grams.

7. The two sides have equal masses, which means that the 1 kg mass and the mass of the rabbit are equal to 5 kg.

   The rabbit weighs 4 kg.

9. Read the weight of the objects scale. There are 4 weights that are 500 grams each.
   500 g + 500 g + 500 g + 500 g = 2 000 g
   2 000 grams = 2 kg.

   The total weight on the scale is 2 kilograms.

Practice Test

ANSWERS AND SOLUTIONS

1. Pretend to hold a pumpkin in one hand and 6 jellybeans (6 g) in the other hand. The weights are not same. The weight of 6 000 jellybeans is about 6 kg. Now, pretend to hold the pumpkin in one hand and 6 000 jellybeans in the other hand. These weights are about the same.

   The best estimate is 6 kg.

3. Pretend to hold a pineapple in one hand and 1 jellybean (1 g) in the other hand. The weights are not same. The weight of 1 000 jellybeans is about 1 kg. Now, pretend to hold the pineapple in one hand and 1 000 jellybeans in the other hand. These weights are about the same.

   The best estimate is 1 kg.

5. The weight of an average textbook is about 1 kilogram.

   Since 1 textbook = 1 kilogram,
   3 textbooks would be 3 kilograms.

   Three textbooks would weigh around 3 000 grams.

7. Since 1 vitamin = 1 gram and
   1 000 grams = 1 kilogram,
   1 000 capsules = 1 kilogram.

9. When the two sides of a balance scale are even with each other (balanced), the two sides have equal masses. This means that the 2 kg mass and the mass of the puppy equal 5 kg.

    The puppy has a mass of 3 kg.

11. Each egg weighs 50 g. There are 7 eggs.
    50 + 50 + 50 + 50 + 50 + 50 + 50 = 350

    The eggs weigh 350 grams.

13. Read the scale. The weight that the scale shows is the weight of the baby on the scale.

    The baby weighs 3 kg.
    3 kilograms = 3 000 grams.

    The weight of the baby is 3 000 grams.

15. Each box weighs 100 g.

    Count the number of boxes.
    There are 5 boxes.

    100 + 100 + 100 + 100 + 100 = 500

    The weight of 5 boxes is 500 g.

3-D OBJECTS

Lesson 1—3-D Objects

**🦋 TIME TO TRY 🦋
ANSWERS AND SOLUTIONS**

1. a) This solid is called a square pyramid. This pyramid is named by the shape of its base, which is a square. The arrow is pointing to where the edges meet, called a vertex.

    b) This solid is called a cone. The base or face is always a circle. The arrow is pointing to the flat surface on the bottom, which is called a face.

    c) This is another square-based pyramid. The arrow is pointing to where two sides meet up, which is called an edge.

2. There are 4 faces on a triangular prism. All of the shapes of the faces are triangles.

3. Count the faces (the flat sides of the object). There are 5; 2 on the ends and 3 on the sides. Now, count the edges (where the faces meet). There are 9. Finally, count the vertices (where the edges meet at a corner). There are 6.

4. a)

Name of 3-D Object	Number of Faces	Shape of Face(s) (2-D)	Number of Straight Edges	Number of Vertices
Cone	1	circle	0	1
Cylinder	2	circle	0	0
Cube	6	square	12	8
Rectangular prism	6	rectangle	12	8

b) To sort the objects by number of edges, look at the chart to see how many edges each object has. The cone and the cylinder have 0 straight edges. The cube and rectangular prism have 12 edges each.

0 Straight Edges	12 Straight Edges
Cone	Cube
Cylinder	Rectangular prism

PRACTICE EXERCISES ANSWERS AND SOLUTIONS

1. There are five faces on a square-based pyramid. The shape of the face on the bottom is a square. The faces on the sides are triangles.

3. 9 edges: triangular prism

5. 4 vertices: triangular-based pyramid

7. octagonal prism

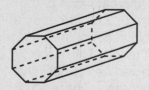

9. square-based pyramid

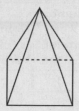

11. rectangular prism

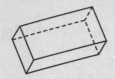

13.

Name of 3-D Object	Number of Faces	Number of Edges	Number of Vertices
Triangular prism	5	9	6
Cube	6	12	8
Rectangle prism	6	12	8
Triangular-based pyramid	4	6	4

15. This object is called a pentagonal prism. The prism is named for its base, which is the shape of a pentagon. The arrow is pointing to where the edges meet to form a corner called a vertex.

17. Count the faces (the flat sides of the object). There are 8 faces. Count the edges (where the faces meet). There are 18 edges. Count the vertices (where the edges meet at a corner).

   There are 12 vertices.

19. cube

21. pentagonal-based pyramid

23. triangular-based pyramid

Lesson 2—Constructing 3-D Objects

🐝 TIME TO TRY 🐝 ANSWERS AND SOLUTIONS

1. **Step 1**
    You will need 9 straws: 3 should have the length of the triangle; 6 should have the length of the rectangle.

    A triangular prism has 6 vertices. Thus, you will need 6 marshmallows.

    Step 2
    Make a triangle-shaped base by connecting three straws and three marshmallows. Connect one straw to stand vertically from each marshmallow. These will form the side edges of the triangular prism. Place a marshmallow on top of each vertical straw. Then, make the triangular-shaped top by connecting three straws to the marshmallows, as shown in the diagram.

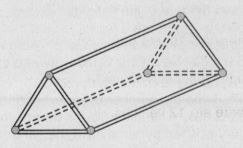

PRACTICE EXERCISES ANSWERS AND SOLUTIONS

1. **Step 1**
    You will need 12 straws: 4 should have the length of the rectangle; 4 should have the width of the rectangle; and 4 should have the length of the side edges.

    A rectangular prism has 8 vertices. Thus, eight marshmallows are needed.

    Step 2
    Next, make a rectangle-shaped base by connecting two straws that have the length of the rectangular face and two straws that form the width of the rectangular face using four marshmallows.

    Connect one straw to stand vertically from each marshmallow. These will form the side edges of the rectangular prism.

    Place a marshmallow on top of each vertical straw. Then, make the rectangular-shaped top by connecting four straws to the marshmallows, as shown in the diagram.

3. First, count the edges and vertices on the square-based pyramid.

A square-based pyramid has 8 edges. Four sides of the square base are the same length and four side edges of the pyramid are the same length.

Therefore, you will need 8 straws—4 should have the side length of the square and 4 should have the length of the side edges.

A square-based pyramid has 5 vertices. Thus, you will need five marshmallows.

Next, make a square base by connecting four straws and four marshmallows. Connect one straw to stand from each marshmallow. All these sides will meet at one vertex. Place a marshmallow on top of the vertex, as shown in the diagram.

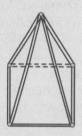

Practice Test

ANSWERS AND SOLUTIONS

1. This 3-D object is a rectangular prism. The prism is named by its base, which is the shape of a rectangle. The arrow is pointing to where the edges meet to form a corner called a vertex.

3. This object is called a triangular-based pyramid. The pyramid is named by its base, which is the shape of a triangle. The arrow is pointing to where the two faces meet, which is called an edge.

5. This solid is called a cone. There is one face on a cone. The base or face is always a circle.

7. Count the faces (the flat sides of the object). There are 6 faces. Count the edges (where the faces meet). There are 12 edges. Count the vertices (where the edges meet at a corner).

There are 8 vertices.

9. Count the faces (the flat sides of the object). There are 4 faces, one on the base and 3 on the sides. Count the edges (where the faces meet). There are 6 edges. Count the vertices (where the edges meet at a corner).

There are 4 vertices.

11. Count the faces (the flat sides of the object). There are 7 faces, 2 on the base and 5 on the sides. Count the edges (where the faces meet). There are 15 edges. Count the vertices (where the edges meet at a corner).

There are 10 vertices.

13. The shapes from the chart can be sorted into the number of faces each object has. The triangular prism and the square-based pyramid have the same number of faces (5). The cube and the pentagonal pyramid have the same number of faces (6).

5 Faces	6 Faces
Triangular prism	Cube
Square-based pyramid	Pentagonal pyramid

15. A hexagonal prism has 18 edges (made by the straws), 12 vertices (made by the marshmallows), and 8 faces (made when the straws are connected to the marshmallows).

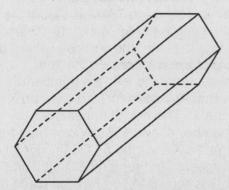

Mark made a hexagonal prism.

STATISTICS AND PROBABILITY

Lesson 1—Collecting and Organizing Information

TIME TO TRY
ANSWERS AND SOLUTIONS

1.

Pets of Students in Grade 3B Class	
Pet	**Tally of Students**
Dog	ΗΗΙ
Cat	ΗΗΙ ΙΙ
Fish	ΙΙΙΙ
Rabbit	ΙΙΙ
Hamster	ΙΙ
Snake	Ι
No Pet	ΙΙΙΙ

2.

Name of Student	Doctor Dodge Ball	Capture the Flag	Obstacle Baseball
Trent		√	
Sherri			√
Abigail			√
Lane	√		
Dana			√
Michael		√	
Josh	√		
Julia	√		
Trevor	√		
Alysha		√	
Helen			√
Alden		√	
Carlos		√	
Teresa			√
Sutton		√	
Hayden	√		
Luke	√		
Geneiva			√
Tessa		√	
Jen	√		
Randy		√	

3. Begin by drawing a horizontal line. Place the numbers that fall within the range of the data (0–10) on the line. Make sure the ticks (numbers) are spread out evenly on the line.

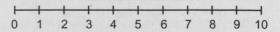

Next, plot the numbers on the line. The first number is a 4 (the number of hours that Allie read for), so draw an X over the 4. The next number is a 5 (the number of hours that Victor read for), so draw an X over the 5. Do this for all of the numbers, and remember that if one number is repeated you have to place the second X above the first X.

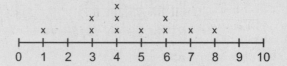

PRACTICE EXERCISES
ANSWERS AND SOLUTIONS

1. To find out which type of dog is the smartest, you should survey people who own or have owned dogs (B).

3. To find out what instrument is the most fun to play, you should survey students who play an instrument (D).

5. They could create a chart to keep track of the information. They could keep a tally of their results using tally marks.

7.

Favourite Type of Sandwich	Tally
Ham and Cheese	卌 卌 卌 l
Turkey	卌 卌 lll
Tuna	卌 ll
Egg Salad	llll
Roast Beef	卌 卌

9.

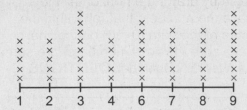

11.

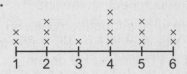

13.

Day	Tally of Tickets
0–10	‖‖ ‖‖ ‖‖ ‖‖ ‖‖ ‖‖ ‖‖
11–20	‖‖ ‖‖ ‖‖ ‖‖ ‖‖
21–30	‖‖ ‖‖ ‖‖ ‖‖ ‖‖ ‖‖ ‖‖ ‖‖	
31–40	‖‖ ‖‖ ‖‖ ‖‖ |||

Lesson 2—Understanding Data Presented

🐝 TIME TO TRY 🐝
ANSWERS AND SOLUTIONS

1. a) Each tally mark (|) represents one student. Each group (‖‖) represents five students.

Look at the marks across from the word walk. Count them.
5 + 4 = 9

9 students walk to school.

b) Yes, skateboarding has 5 students (‖‖), and bike riding has 4 students (||||). The number 5 is more than 4, so more students skateboard to school than ride a bike.

c) There are 4 students (||||) who take the bus and 4 students (||||) who ride their bikes. The same number of students take the bus and ride their bikes.

2. a) To find out which ice cream choice is most popular, count all of the students who chose chocolate (5), vanilla (4), and strawberry (3).

The most popular ice cream was chocolate.

b) To find out who chose strawberry look in the column marked strawberry. Once you see a check mark, you can follow it across to see whose name is in that row.

Andrea, Dina, and Hunter all chose strawberry ice cream.

c) To find out how many more students chose vanilla than chose strawberry, look at the numbers. You can see that 4 students chose vanilla and 3 students chose strawberry.
4 − 3 = 1

One more student chose vanilla than chose strawberry.

PRACTICE EXERCISES
ANSWERS AND SOLUTIONS

1. Add the total number of votes by adding the values of each of the bars of data.
20 + 16 + 24 + 28 + 6 + 8 = 102

In total, 102 students took part in the survey.

3. The least popular flavour is tiger.

5. Subtract the students who chose bubblegum from the students who chose strawberry to find out how many more students voted strawberry than bubblegum.
$24 - 8 = 16$

Therefore, 16 more students chose strawberry than chose bubblegum.

7. To find out how many more students chose math than chose science, look at the checklist. 5 students chose math as their favourite subject. 3 students chose science. Subtract these two numbers to find the answer.
$5 - 3 = 2$

Two more students chose math than chose science.

9. Count the number of tally marks beside the word bicycle. There are 13 tally marks.

13 bicycles went by Justin's house.

11. Count the number of tally marks beside all the vehicles. There are 7 tally marks beside the word car, there are 5 tally marks beside the word bus, and there are 13 tally marks beside the word bicycle. Add the total number of tally marks together.
$7 + 5 + 13 = 25$

A total of 25 vehicles went by Justin's house.

13. Look at the tally marks beside students who have 2, 3, or 4 pets and add them together.

Six students have 2 pets, 1 student has 3 pets, and 2 students have 4 pets.
$6 + 1 + 2 = 9$

In total, 9 students have 2 or more pets.

Lesson 3—Creating Bar Graphs

🐝 TIME TO TRY 🐝
ANSWERS AND SOLUTIONS

1. First, write a title for your graph. A good title would be "Growth of a Bean Sprout."

Next, decide what information goes on each axis. Number of days will go on the x-axis, and the height will go on the y-axis. For the y-axis, decide on a scale. A good scale for this question is 0–16.

Write the number of days along the x-axis (1, 3, 5, and 7).

Finally, draw in your bars so that they show the data.

Growth of a Bean Sprout

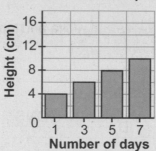

2. To draw a conclusion from the bar graph, look at the information presented. Reading books was chosen by 5 of the students as their favourite activity, and watching cartoons was chosen by 20 as their favourite activity.

One conclusion could be that reading books is the least popular favourite activity and cartoon watching is the most popular favourite activity.

PRACTICE EXERCISES
ANSWERS AND SOLUTIONS

1. The title of the bar graph is located at the top of the graph. It tells you what the data represents. The title for this graph is "Sports Played by 3rd Graders."

3. The *y*-axis is the line on the left side of the graph. The label of the *y*-axis is "Number of 3rd Graders."

5. The title of the bar graph is located at the top of the graph. It tells you what the data represents. The title for this graph is "Grade 3 Ice Cream Choices."

7. The *y*-axis is the line on the left side of the graph. The label of the *y*-axis is "Number of Students."

9. The bar graph is missing a title and labels on the *x*- and *y*-axes.

Practice Test

ANSWERS AND SOLUTIONS

1. Dayton should make a tally mark for each vehicle that drives by. If he uses a tally mark for each vehicle that passes by, he can count the bundles by fives and the singles by ones to get the total number. This method would take the least time. It would be the best for Dayton to use.

3. Begin by drawing a horizontal line. Place the numbers that fall within the range of the data (0–20) on the line. Make sure the ticks (numbers) are spread out evenly on the line.

Next, plot the numbers on the line.

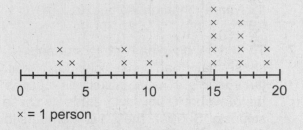

× = 1 person

5. There are two bars with a height of 80 on the graph. Courtney scored 80 on tests 2 and 6.

7. Count and add all of the tally marks on the chart.

Basketball—25
Hockey—23
Baseball—19
Tennis—12

$25 + 23 + 19 + 12 = 79$

There were 79 student responses recorded in the chart.

9. Count the tally marks beside the word "Friday" to find how many hours of sleep Sarah got on Friday night. There are 8 tally marks, so Sarah got 8 hours of sleep on Friday night.

11.

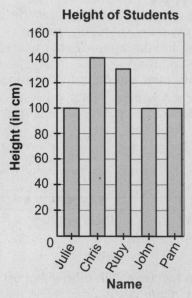

Height of Students

13.

Activity	Tally
Ball Thrown	|||||
Wagon Pull	|||
3-Legged Race	||||
Tug of War	||||||||

15. Begin by drawing a horizontal line. Place the numbers that fall within the range of the data (129–141) on the line. Make sure the ticks (numbers) are spread out evenly on the line.

Next, plot the numbers on the line.

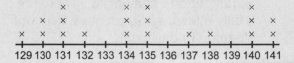

ORDERING INFORMATION

SCHOOL ORDERS

Please contact the Learning Resource Centre (LRC) for school discount and order information.

THE KEY **Study Guides** are specifically designed to assist students in preparing for unit tests, final exams, and provincial examinations.

THE KEY **Study Guides** – $29.95 each plus G.S.T.

SENIOR HIGH		JUNIOR HIGH	ELEMENTARY
Biology 30	Biology 20	English Language Arts 9	English Language Arts 6
Chemistry 30	Chemistry 20	Math 9	Math 6
English 30-1	English 20-1	Science 9	Science 6
English 30-2	Mathematics 20-1	Social Studies 9	Social Studies 6
Applied Math 30	Physics 20	Math 8	Math 4
Pure Math 30	Social Studies 20-1		
Physics 30		Math 7	English Language Arts 3
Social Studies 30-1	English 10-1		Math 3
Social Studies 30-2	Math 10 Combined		
	Science 10		
	Social Studies 10-1		

Student Notes and Problems (SNAP) Workbooks contain complete explanations of curriculum concepts, examples, and exercise questions.

SNAP Workbooks – $29.95 each plus G.S.T.

SENIOR HIGH		JUNIOR HIGH	ELEMENTARY
Biology 30	Biology 20	Math 9	Math 6
Chemistry 30	Chemistry 20	Science 9	Math 5
Applied Math 30	Mathematics 20-1	Math 8	
Pure Math 30	Physics 20	Science 8	Math 4
Math 31			
Physics 30	Math 10 Combined	Math 7	Math 3
	Science 10	Science 7	

Visit our website for a tour of resource content and features or order resources online at
www.castlerockresearch.com

#2340, 10180 – 101 Street   **Phone:** 780.448.9619
Edmonton, AB Canada T5J 3S4   **Toll-free:** 1.800.840.6224
e-mail: learn@castlerockresearch.com   **Fax:** 780.426.3917

CASTLE ROCK
RESEARCH CORP

ORDER FORM

Learning Resources Centre

Castle Rock Research is pleased to announce an exclusive distribution arrangement with the Learning Resources Centre (LRC). Under this agreement, schools can now place all their orders with LRC for order fulfillment. As well, these resources are eligible for applying the Learning Resource Credit Allocation (LRCA), which gives schools a 25% discount off LRC's selling price. Call LRC for details.

Orders may be placed with LRC by
Telephone: 780.427.2767
Fax: 780.422.9750
Internet: www.lrc.education.gov.ab.ca
Or mail: 12360 – 142 Street NW
Edmonton, AB T5L 4X9

Learning Resources Centre

THE KEY	QUANTITY
Biology 30	
Chemistry 30	
English 30-1	
English 30-2	
Applied Math 30	
Pure Math 30	
Physics 30	
Biology 20	
Chemistry 20	
Mathematics 20-1	
Physics 20	
Social Studies 20-1	
English 10-1	
Math 10 Combined	
Science 10	
Social Studies 10-1	
English Language Arts 9	
Math 9	
Science 9	
Social Studies 9	
Math 8	
Math 7	
English Language Arts 6	
Math 6	
Science 6	
Social Studies 6	
Math 4	
English Language Arts 3	
Math 3	

Student Notes and Problems Workbooks	QUANTITY	
	SNAP Workbooks	Solution Manuals
Math 31		
Biology 30		
Chemistry 30		
Applied Math 30		
Pure Math 30		
Physics 30		
Biology 20		
Chemistry 20		
Mathematics 20-1		
Physics 20		
Math 10 Combined		
Science 10		
Math 9		
Science 9		
Math 8		
Science 8		
Math 7		
Science 7		
Math 6		
Math 5		
Math 4		
Math 3		

TOTALS
KEYS
SNAP WORKBOOKS
SOLUTION MANUALS
SOLUTION MANUALS

PAYMENT AND SHIPPING INFORMATION

Name: _____
School Telephone: _____

SHIP TO
School: _____
Address: _____
City: _____ Postal Code: _____

PAYMENT
☐ by credit card
VISA/MC Number: _____
Expiry Date: _____
Name on card: _____
☐ enclosed cheque
☐ invoice school   P.O. number: _____

CASTLE ROCK
RESEARCH CORP

#2340, 10180 – 101 Street, Edmonton, AB T5J 3S4   **Phone:** 780.448.9619 **Fax:** 780.426.3917
Email: learn@castlerockresearch.com **Toll-free:** 1.800.840.6224
www.castlerockresearch.com